Core Chemistry

Core Chemistry

Dennis Garvie Principal Chemistry Teacher Portobello High School Edinburgh
John Reid Principal Chemistry Teacher Holy Rood High School Edinburgh
Anne Robertson Formerly Assistant Adviser in Science Lothian Region

Oxford University Press

Oxford University Press, Walton Street, Oxford OX2 6DP
Oxford London Glasgow New York Toronto Melbourne
Wellington Cape Town Ibadan Nairobi Dar es Salaam Lusaka
Delhi Bombay Calcutta Madras Karachi
Kuala Lumpur Singapore Jakarta Hong Kong Tokyo

First published 1976
Reprinted 1976, 1977 (twice)

Filmset on 'Monophoto' 600 by Fyldetype Limited, Kirkham PR4 3BJ
Printed by Lowe & Brydone Printers Limited, Thetford, Norfolk

Contents

Preface

In this book we have attempted to provide for the needs of pupils preparing for the Scottish Certificate of Education Examination Board's Ordinary Grade Examination in chemistry. The book will also be of use to those studying chemistry to GCE O-level.

The book is divided into two sections; the first contains twenty-one chapters of text and the second contains experiments. This structure will allow the teacher to use both sections of the book in class and it will enable pupils to read the text uninterrupted by experimental details. Each chapter of the text contains a summary to emphasize the main points covered, and a large selection of questions, including examination questions. Some of these questions are difficult, but they should encourage a careful reading of the text as well as supplying useful discussion points. The experiments in the second section are all linked back to the text, and it is important not only that pupils perform the experiments for themselves, but also that they understand, from the text, the chemistry underlying them. For, although learning by discovery is important as a teaching method, we feel it is equally important for pupils to have a textbook containing the basic information.

The approach to some topics might appear unfamiliar. For example, bonding is presented in such a way that pupils will realize that electrovalent bonding and pure covalent bonding are extremes in a spectrum of bonding and that all bonding is the resultant of forces of attraction and repulsion. The electron cloud pictures are intended to give some idea of the three-dimensional shape of the reacting species and, although this method has several shortcomings with regard to electrovalent bonds and sp^2 bonds, it is a small price to pay for the elimination of 'target diagrams'. Chemical formulae and equations are usually presented in the molecular form rather than the ionic form because there are fewer variables to handle at the outset, and we feel that there is no reason for not using the term 'valency' at this level. Also, since calculations from equations tend to be based on moles of compounds rather than on moles of ions, the ratio of moles of reacting species is more readily identified from the molecular equation. The treatment of selective discharge of ions in electrolysis is intended to reflect the reactivity series and, although there may be justifiable criticism of the mechanism in some cases, particularly the discharge of OH^- (aq) in the case of dilute sulphuric acid, the simplicity of the mechanism commends itself at this level.

We would like to acknowledge the help we have received in preparing this book from British Petroleum Ltd, the National Sulphuric Acid Association, Scottish Agricultural Industries, and Shell International Petroleum

Ltd. We also wish to thank the following for permission to use questions from their papers: the Scottish Certificate of Education Examination Board (marked *SCEEB*) and Pillans and Wilson Ltd (marked *P & W*).

DG
JR
AMR

1 The nature of matter

1.1 States of matter

All materials about us consist of **matter.** Matter is defined as anything which occupies space and has mass. All types of matter can be classified under the three headings: **solids, liquids** or **gases.** These three headings are known as the three **states** of matter.

Table 1.1 The three states of matter

Solid	*Liquid*	*Gas*
Wood	Water	Oxygen
Metal	Oil	Nitrogen
Plastic	Vinegar	Carbon dioxide

We may consider the properties of a material to help us to decide in which state of matter the material is.

Table 1.2

	Solid	*Liquid*	*Gas*
Volume	Fixed	Fixed	Not fixed
Shape	Fixed	Not fixed	Not fixed

Solids are denoted by (s): Ice $H_2O(s)$.
Liquids are denoted by (l): Water $H_2O(l)$.
Gases are denoted by (g): Steam $H_2O(g)$.

1.2 Physical and chemical changes

It is possible to change matter from one state into another.
A block of ice **melts** to form water: solid → liquid.
Water **boils** to form steam: liquid → gas.
Such changes are called **physical** changes, and they are usually easy to reverse.

There are other changes which involve the formation of new substances.
Paraffin oil **burns** to produce carbon dioxide and water: liquid → gases.
Iron metal **rusts** to form iron oxide: solid → solid.

Such changes are called **chemical** changes, and they are usually difficult to reverse.

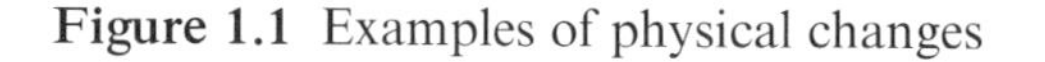
Figure 1.1 Examples of physical changes

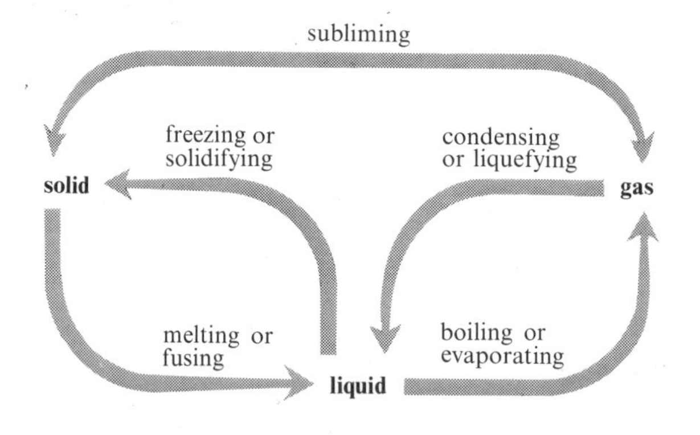

1.3 Particulate nature of matter

Scientists believe that all matter is made up of tiny **particles.** By considering the properties and reactions of solids, liquids, and gases, we can offer evidence for this particulate nature of matter.

Diffusion of gases

If someone with a strong smelling perfume enters a room, the perfume can soon be smelt in the furthest corner of the room, even if there are no draughts. To explain this, it is suggested that perfume is made up of particles which spread among the small particles of air in the room.

Figure 1.2

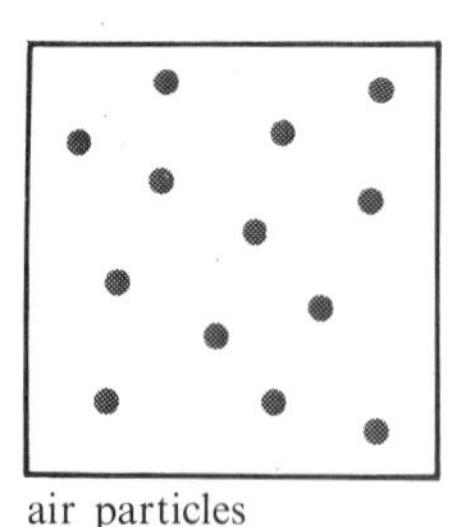
air particles

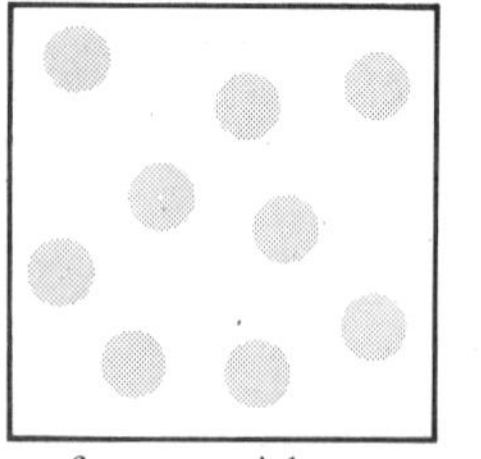
perfume particles

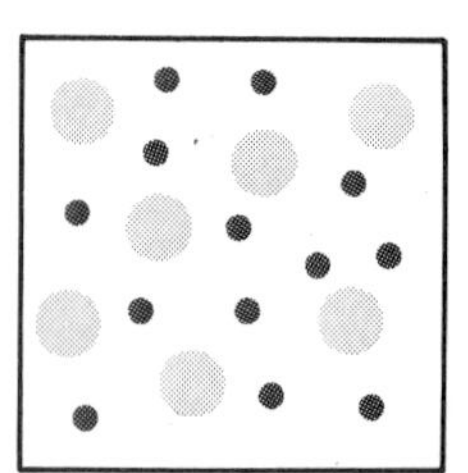
perfume particles have diffused through the air particles

Mixing of coloured liquids

If a test-tube is set up containing a layer of water and a layer of ink, the colour of the liquid in the test-tube becomes uniform within a few days when the test-tube is left undisturbed. To explain this, it is suggested that the particles of the two liquids mix together and distribute themselves evenly throughout the test-tube.

Figure 1.3

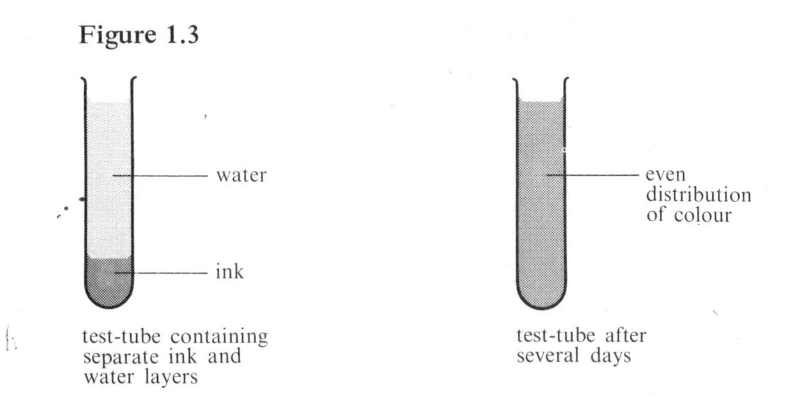

test-tube containing separate ink and water layers

test-tube after several days

Dissolving a solid

When a crystal of purple potassium manganate(VII) is dropped into a beaker of water, the purple colour spreads through the water as the crystal dissolves (Figure 1.4). The solubility of a solid is explained by proposing that the particles of the solid are distributed among the particles of the liquid. When the solution is diluted many times, the colour becomes fainter and fainter before it eventually disappears. We can account for this by assuming that the particles must be very small and very numerous.

Figure 1.4

adding a potassium manganate(VII) crystal to water

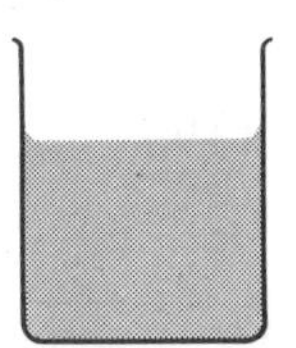

potassium manganate(VII) solution

A solid will also 'dissolve' in another solid. If a test-tube is set up containing a colourless gel (a jelly-like solid) and a blue crystal of copper(II) sulphate, as shown in Figure 1.5, and left for several weeks, the copper(II) sulphate crystal dissolves and its colour spreads throughout the gel.

Figure 1.5

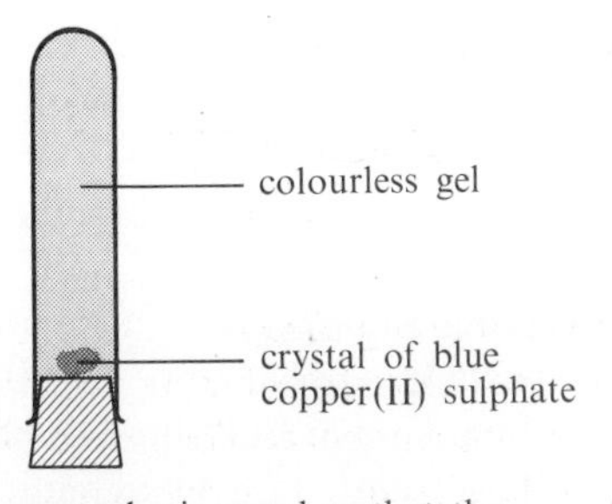

test-tube inverted so that the heavy crystal is at bottom

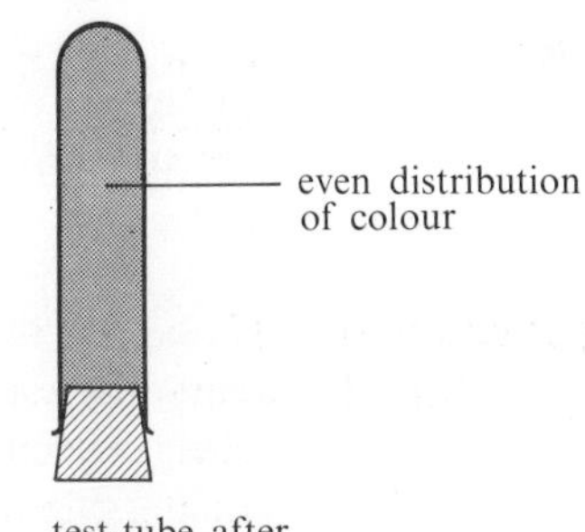

test-tube after several weeks

It is interesting to note the different rates at which substances mix. The smell of perfume travels through the air in minutes, whereas it takes days for the water and ink to become thoroughly mixed, and weeks before the colour of the crystal has completely spread through the gel. In other words, gases mix more quickly than liquids, which in turn mix more quickly than solids. Can we account for these facts?

We know that liquids have more energy than solids, because solids have to be supplied with heat energy to change them into liquids:

Ice + heat → water

We also know that gases have more energy than liquids, because liquids have to be supplied with heat energy to change them into gases:

Water + heat → steam

It is reasonable to suppose, then, that gas particles are moving faster than liquid particles because thay have more energy. In the same way, liquid particles are moving faster than solid particles. This explains why gases mix more quickly than liquids, and why liquids mix more quickly than solids.

The relative speeds at which the particles of solids, liquids, and gases move must also determine how closely the particles are packed within these substances. The particles of a gas move most quickly, so they will occupy the most space. The particles of a solid move least quickly, so they will occupy the least space. A diagrammatic representation of the relative spacing of the particles in solids, liquids, and gases is shown in Figure 1.6.

Figure 1.6

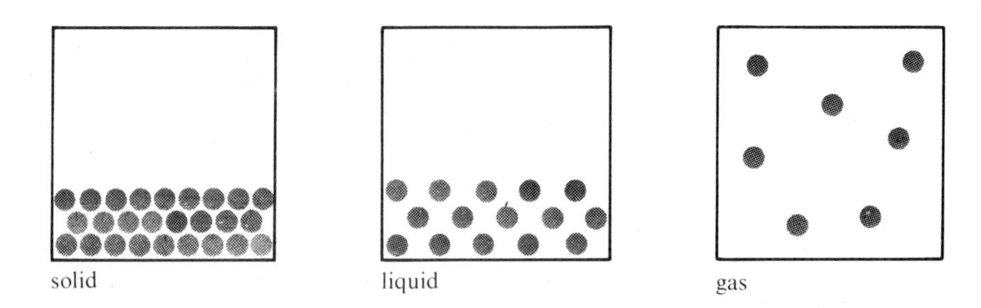

For a given substance the solid is usually more dense than the liquid, and the liquid is usually more dense than the gas.

We have assumed that particles always possess some kinetic energy, that is, they are always 'on the move'. Can we offer any evidence for this?

If some smoke is introduced into a small box or 'smoke cell', illuminated with a very strong light, and examined using a powerful microscope, we see a rather unusual sight. The small particles of soot, which comprise the smoke, are lit up like stars, and are seen to jostle about in a random movement. The dark smoke particles appear to be bright because we are in fact seeing reflections of the light source from the smoke particles. The random jostling movement can be accounted for by assuming that the smoke cell contains a great number of fast-moving air particles which are continually bumping into the smoke particles from all directions. This random jostling movement of the smoke particles is referred to as Brownian movement, after Robert Brown who was the first to observe it over a hundred years ago. A suitable set-up for viewing Brownian movement is shown in Figure 1.7.

Figure 1.7 Microscope and smoke cell arrangement for viewing Brownian movement

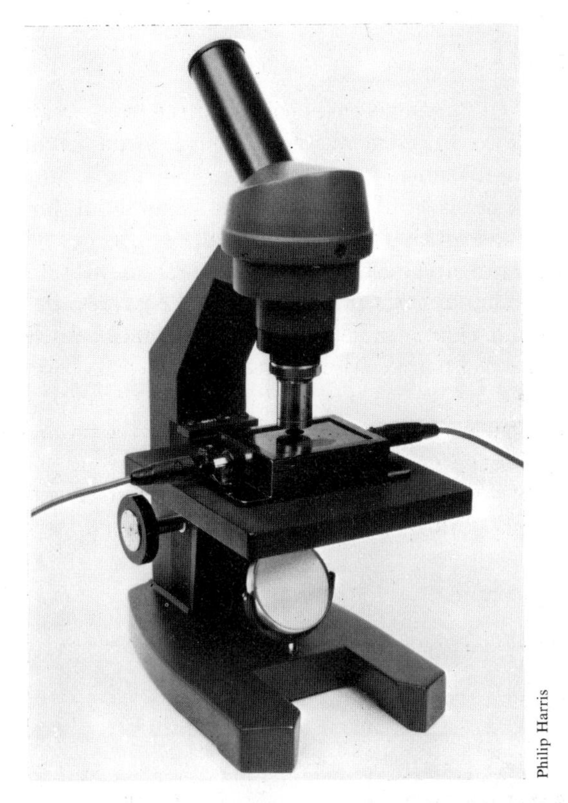

Philip Harris

1.4 Elements, compounds, and mixtures

As there are many different kinds of matter, it seems sensible to divide them up into groups on the basis of their properties. The most convenient division is shown below.

Elements Elements are substances which cannot be decomposed into anything simpler by chemical means—we assume that they contain just one type of particle.

Compounds Compounds are substances which can be decomposed into simpler substances by chemical means—we assume they contain more than one type of particle, and that the particles are chemically joined together.

Mixtures Mixtures are composed of two or more substances each of which retains its own characteristic properties—we assume that they contain different types of particles which are physically mixed rather than chemically joined.

Table 1.3 Examples of elements, compounds, and mixtures

Elements	*Compounds*	*Mixtures*
Iron Sulphur	Iron(II) sulphide	Iron/sulphur powder mixture
Nitrogen Oxygen	Nitrogen dioxide	Nitrogen/oxygen mixture (air)

Elements

There are 105 elements of which eighty-four occur naturally on the earth. One of the most fascinating facts of science is that most of the materials which we work with are made up from about thirty of these elements. The elements which do not occur naturally have all been made by man. It is interesting to note that many of these man-made elements have been named after famous scientists: curium after Marie Curie; einsteinium after Albert Einstein; and mendelevium after Dimitri Mendeleev.

Figure 1.8 Marie Curie, Albert Einstein, and Dimitri Mendeleev

Other elements have been named after places, for example:berkelium after Berkeley in America; neptunium after the planet Neptune; and californium after California.

The relative distribution by mass of the ten most abundant elements in the earth's crust, atmosphere, and oceans is given in Table 1.4.

Table 1.4

Element	*Percentage abundance*	*Element*	*Percentage abundance*
Oxygen	49.5	Potassium	2.4
Silicon	25.8	Magnesium	1.9
Aluminium	7.5	Hydrogen	0.9
Iron	4.7	Titanium	0.6
Calcium	3.4	All other elements	0.7
Sodium	2.6		

Compounds and mixtures

Sometimes it is difficult to decide whether a substance is a compound or a mixture. Consideration of the characteristic differences between compounds and mixtures may help us to do this. Table 1.5 summarizes these differences.

Table 1.5

Compounds	*Mixtures*
Constituents require a chemical reaction to separate them	Constituents can be separated by physical means
Properties are different to properties of constituents	Properties are intermediate to those of constituents
Formation and separation involve chemical change	Formation and separation do not involve chemical change
Constituents are present in fixed proportions	Constituents are present in any proportions

To show how this works, let us consider the examples which have already been shown in Table 1.3. First we shall look at iron and sulphur.

1 Iron(II) sulphide is difficult to change back into iron and sulphur, whereas an iron filings/sulphur mixture can easily be separated using a magnet.
2 Iron(II) sulphide looks nothing like iron and sulphur, whereas the mixture retains the looks of both constituents.
3 When iron combines with sulphur, a new substance, iron(II) sulphide, is formed.
4 In the formation of iron(II) sulphide, fixed amounts of iron and sulphur are required, whereas the mixture can be prepared with varying amounts of iron and sulphur.

Now consider nitrogen and oxygen.

1 Nitrogen dioxide is difficult to separate into nitrogen and oxygen, whereas a nitrogen/oxygen mixture can be easily separated by fractional distillation of the liquefied mixture. (This method is used in the industrial preparation of both nitrogen and oxygen from air; see chapter 13).
2 Nitrogen dioxide is a brown gas which bears no resemblance to the colourless nitrogen or oxygen, whereas a nitrogen/oxygen mixture will show the properties of one or other, or both, of the constituents depending on their relative concentrations.
3 When nitrogen combines with oxygen a new substance, nitrogen dioxide, is formed.
4 Nitrogen dioxide contains a fixed proportion of nitrogen and oxygen, whereas the nitrogen/oxygen mixture can be obtained in varying concentrations.

1.5 Metals and non-metals

The elements are often divided into groups on the basis of their properties. The most convenient division is that of **metals** and **non-metals.** Some characteristic differences are shown in Table 1.6.

Table 1.6

Metals	*Non-metals*
Lustrous (shiny)	Not lustrous (except for graphite and iodine)
Malleable (can be hammered into shape)	Brittle
Ductile (can be drawn out into wires)	Non-ductile
Good conductors of heat and electricity	Poor conductors (except for graphite)

There are, of course, borderline elements which do not fit clearly into one or other of these categories, such as germanium, arsenic, gallium, and antimony. These elements are often referred to as **metalloids.**

The most complete 'classification' of the elements that we have at the moment is the division into groups in the Periodic Table. The Periodic Table will be considered at greater length in chapter 2.

1.6 The use of symbols

Prehistoric man painted hunting scenes on the walls of caves.

Figure 1.9 Paintings by bushmen in Southern Africa

Radio Times Hulton Picture Library

The Pharaohs of Egypt decorated the interior of their tombs with descriptions of their lives using paintings and hieroglyphics.

Figure 1.10 These hieroglyphics are 3500 years old

Radio Times Hulton Picture Library

In the Middle Ages, the alchemists attempted to produce gold from base metals. They used symbols for their substances to keep their work secret.

Figure 1.11 Symbols used by alchemists

John Dalton (1766–1844) was the first chemist who really distinguished elements from compounds. He represented elements by symbols and the compounds as combinations of these symbols (Figure 1.12).

Figure 1.12

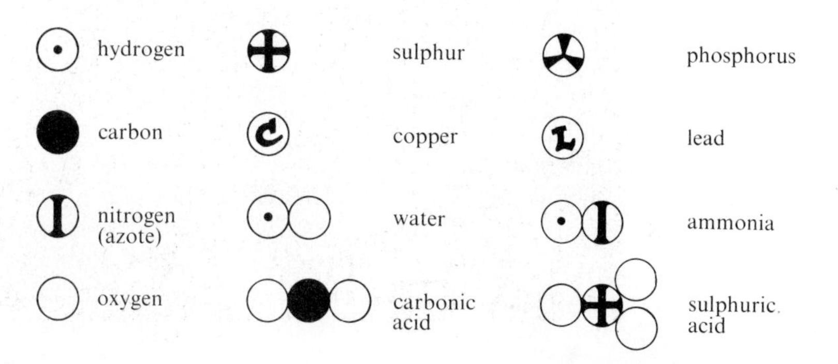

Jons Jacob Berzelius (1779–1848) was the first person to use letters as symbols for elements. This replaced the crude picture systems used previously, and is now universal. The element is represented by the first letter of its name. Where two elements would have the same symbol, two letters are used, or sometimes one or two letters of the Latin name of the element. Table 1.7 gives the symbols of some common elements. The words in brackets give the Latin names for various elements.

Table 1.7

Element	*Symbol*	*Element*	*Symbol*
Aluminium	Al	Lead (Plumbum)	Pb
Argon	Ar	Lithium	Li
Barium	Ba	Magnesium	Mg
Beryllium	Be	Manganese	Mn
Boron	B	Mercury (Hydrargyrum)	Hg
Bromine	Br	Neon	Ne
Calcium	Ca	Nickel	Ni
Carbon	C	Nitrogen	N
Chlorine	Cl	Oxygen	O
Chromium	Cr	Phosphorus	P
Cobalt	Co	Potassium (Kalium)	K
Copper (Cuprum)	Cu	Silicon	Si
Fluorine	F	Silver (Argentum)	Ag
Gold (Aurum)	Au	Sodium (Natrium)	Na
Helium	He	Sulphur	S
Hydrogen	H	Tin (Stannum)	Sn
Iodine	I	Xenon	Xe
Iron (Ferrum)	Fe	Zinc	Zn
Krypton	Kr		

Chemists are not always very careful in using their symbols. So if you come across 'H', ask yourself carefully does it mean just hydrogen or 1 atom of hydrogen.

1.7 Solutions, suspensions, and colloids

It is very easy, in terms of everyday life, to talk of solutions, for example, salt solutions, or sugar solutions. What do we actually mean by the term **solution?**

A solution is defined as a 'homogeneous mixture of two or more substances'. A homogenous mixture means that the mixture is the same all the way through. The substance which dissolves is called the **solute.** The dissolving substance is called the **solvent.** Most solutions to which we refer are ones in which the solvent is water. Such solutions are more correctly called **aqueous** solutions. However, water need not be the solvent. There are many substances which are not soluble in water—such substances require non-aqueous solvents to dissolve them. Table 1.8 gives some examples of various solutes and the solvent which will dissolve them.

Table 1.8

Solute	*Suitable solvent*
Salt	Water
Sugar	Water
Iodine	Ethanol
Naphthalene	Benzene
Grease	Tetrachloromethane (Carbon tetrachloride)
Nail varnish	Propanone (Acetone)

We often tend to think of solutions as being solid solutes dissolved in liquid solvents, but this is not always the case. Solutions can be made by dissolving: gases in liquids, gases in gases, solids in liquids, solids in solids, or liquids in liquids. As long as the mixture is homogeneous, then the term 'solution' applies. In a true solution the particles of the solute break up to such an extent that they disappear into the spaces between the solvent particles and become quite invisible to the human eye, even with the help of a microscope.

However, in some liquids the solute particles do not break up to this extent, and can be seen by the naked eye. These liquids should not be called solutions, and a more correct term is **suspension.** Suspensions are the result of solutes which do not dissolve, or perhaps only partially dissolve in the solvent. For example, chalk forms a suspension in water, as does magnesium hydroxide (Milk of Magnesia), and sulphur. A suspension is defined as a 'heterogeneous mixture of two or more substances'. A heterogenous mixture means that the mixture is not the same all the way through. Given sufficient time, the solid particles in a suspension will settle to the bottom of the container, a process often referred to as sedimentation. When this happens, the pure liquid can be decanted (poured off). An alternative method of separating the constituents of a suspension is to filter off the suspended solid (see page 232).

There are solutions in which the size of the solute particles is intermediate between those in true solutions and those in suspensions. We call these **colloidal solutions.** Colloidal particles are too small to be caught by filter papers, unlike suspended particles, and they are also too small to be seen by the naked eye. Yet, unlike the dissolved particles in true solutions, they are large enough to reflect a beam of light which falls on them, so they can be 'seen' under these conditions. Figure 1.13 illustrates what can be seen when a beam of light is directed into a colloidal solution. This is called the Tyndall effect after John Tyndall, who was the first person to observe it. In colloidal solutions the dispersed particles need not necessarily be solids and the dispersal medium need not necessarily be a liquid.

Figure 1.13

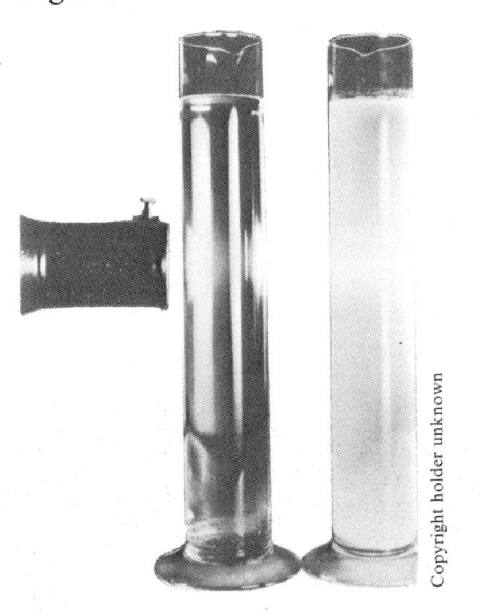

Table 1.9 Examples of colloidal solutions

Colloidal solution	*Dispersed medium (i.e. colloidal particles)*	*Dispersal medium*
Indian ink	Carbon	Water
Smoke	Carbon	Air
Milk	Fat	Water
Foam	Air	Water
Salad dressing	Vinegar	Oil

The last example in Table 1.9, where both media are liquids, is called an **emulsion.**

Bearing in mind that colloidal particles are too small to be caught by filter paper, how can we remove these particles from a colloidal solution?

If we look at the formation of deltas where muddy rivers flow into the sea, we find a possible explanation. Muddy river water contains colloidal particles of mud which do not settle under normal conditions. We assume that they do not settle because they are very small and they are also electrostatically charged. Particles which are electrostatically charged with the same charge resist settling because there is a mutual repulsion between like charges (Figure 1.14a). When the weakly charged colloidal particles in river water meet the oppositely charged particles in sea-water, the colloidal particles are drawn towards the particles in the sea-water, and so become drawn together themselves (Figure 1.14b). They form larger, heavier clusters of mud particles, and so sink to the sea-bed and form a delta (Figure 1.15).

Figure 1.14

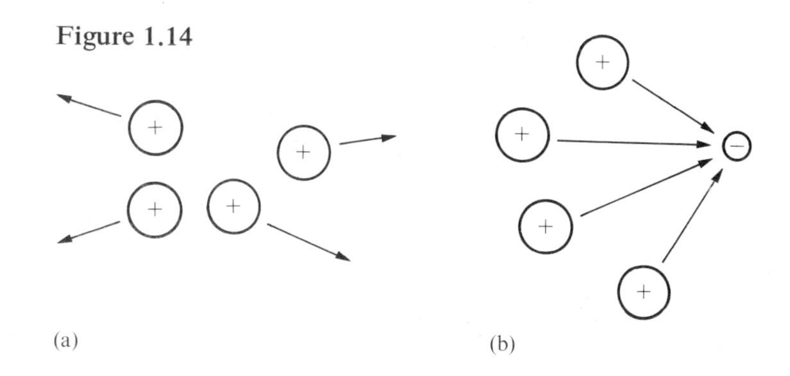

Figure 1.15 A well-formed river delta

Many industrial firms avoid polluting the atmosphere by removing smoke particles using a similar technique to delta formation. An electricity supply is used to maintain a high electrical potential across a chimney (Figure 1.16).

Figure 1.16

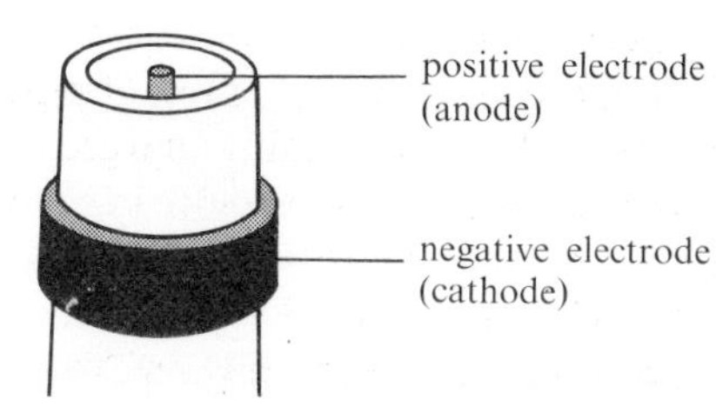

As the colloidal smoke particles travel up the chimney, they are attracted to the charged electrodes in just the same way as the colloidal mud particles in the river water were attracted to the oppositely charged particles in the sea-water. So the smoke particles cluster together to form soot which is deposited in the chimney (Figure 1.17), and can be removed by sweeping.

Figure 1.17

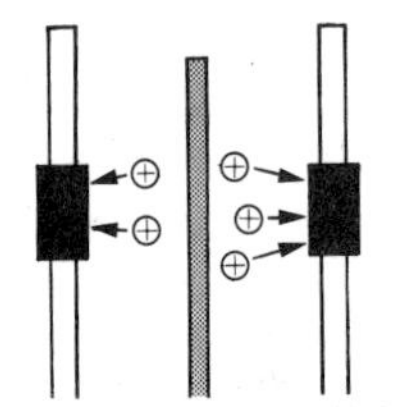

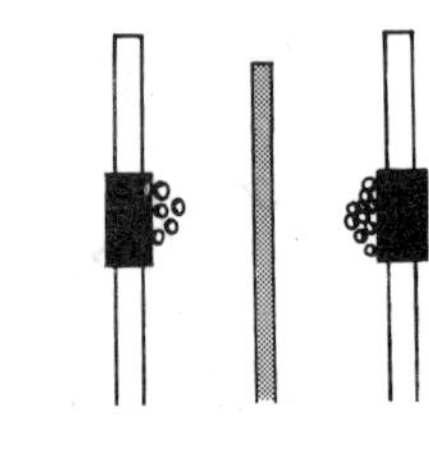

positively charged particles attracted to cathode

neutral soot particles

Summary

From this chapter you should know:

1. There are three states of matter—solid, liquid, and gas.
2. Physical changes are changes of state and are easily reversed.
3. Chemical changes involve the formation of new substances and are not easily reversed.
4. Matter is made up of small particles which are most closely packed in solids and least closely packed in gases.
5. The simplest types of matter are called elements, of which there are 105 known today.
6. The more complex types of matter, which are made up of more than one element are called:
   Compounds, which are difficult to split up.
   Mixtures, which are relatively easy to split up.
7. Elements are often classified as metals or non-metals.
8. Solutions are homogeneous mixtures of two or more substances (the dissolved substance is called the solute, the dissolving substance is called the solvent).
9. Suspensions are heterogeneous mixtures of two or more substances.
10. Colloidal solutions are ones which contain particles which are too small to be seen by the naked eye, but large enough to reflect light (Tyndall effect).

Experiments for this chapter can be found on pages 252–4.

Questions

1 How would you show whether a brown solution was colloidal or not? *P & W*

2 'All matter is made up of small moving particles.' Describe briefly two experiments which you could carry out in order to illustrate the above statements. *P & W*

3 If a few crystals of copper(II) sulphate are placed at the bottom of a tube filled with water, the blue colour of the salt very slowly reaches the top of the tube without heating or stirring. Explain this observation.

4 In a cinema, the projector beam becomes much more obvious when people in the audience begin to smoke. Why should this be so? *SCEEB*

5 What is an emulsion?
Explain the following observations: 'When greasy dishes are being washed, soap must be added to help an emulsion form. The use of hot water alone does not wash the dishes properly and a greasy ring is left in the wash-basin.' *SCEEB*

6 When a heap of orange ammonium dichromate(VI) powder is touched with a hot wire, a large quantity of a green powder is formed, the mass glows red-hot and steam is given off. What evidence is there that a chemical reaction has taken place? *SCEEB*

7 Why is it likely to be more economical to obtain oxygen from air than from water? *SCEEB*

8 Explain why car headlights are less effective in fog.

9 A balloon filled with hydrogen gas deflates faster than a balloon filled with carbon dioxide gas.
1 Explain why the balloons deflate at all.
2 Explain why the hydrogen balloon deflates faster.

10 A pupil looking at floating pollen grains through a microscope noticed that the pollen grains appeared to dance about in a random fashion. Explain this random motion.

2 Atomic theory

2.1 Atomic theory of matter

All the examples we considered in chapter 1 would indicate that matter is made up of small particles. John Dalton (1766–1844) called these particles **atoms.** The word 'atom' means something which cannot be cut. In 1808 Dalton put forward his atomic theory in which he suggested that:

1. Matter consisted of small, indivisible, indestructible particles called atoms.
2. Atoms of the same element were identical, but were different from atoms of other elements.
3. Chemical compounds were made by the union of small whole numbers of atoms to give 'compound atoms'.

One of the shortcomings of this particulate theory was that the atoms were thought to be indivisible. Later experiments, however, have indicated that atoms are divisible. It is now generally accepted that atoms are composed of a number of smaller particles called **electrons, protons,** and **neutrons.**

The existence of the electron and proton was first demonstrated by J. J. Thomson (1846–1940) in 1897. When he passed electricity at high voltage through a gas at low pressure, he found that two coloured glows were produced in the tube (Figure 2.1).

Figure 2.1

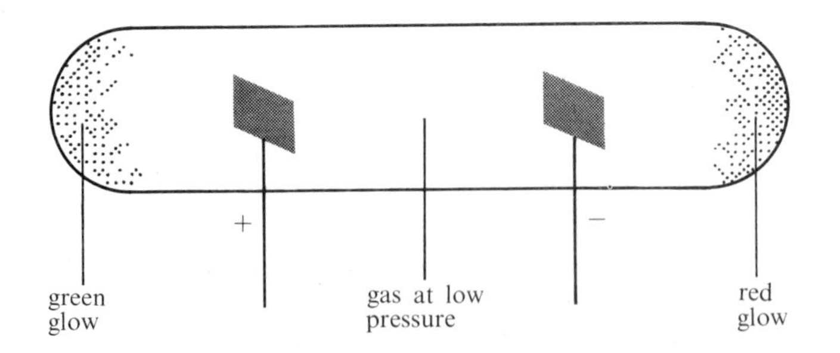

When he brought a magnet near the tube, Thomson was able to change the position of the glowing regions. A much stronger magnet was required to deflect the red glow compared with that needed to deflect the green glow.

Thomson explained these observations by suggesting that the high electrical voltage split the gas particles into two streams of oppositely charged particles. These streams travelled to opposite ends of the tube and caused the two regions to glow. Gas particles must therefore be composed of oppositely charged particles. He attributed the green glow to the very light, negative particles called electrons, and the red glow to much heavier, positively charged particles called protons.

There was much speculation about the way in which the electrons and protons were arranged in the atom. A popular idea was the 'plum pudding' model in which the protons and electrons were thought to be in a random arrangement in the atom, like plums and raisins in a plum pudding.

A solution to the problem of arrangement was provided by an experiment devised by H. Geiger and E. Marsden in 1911. They fired the newly discovered alpha particles (which are positively charged) at a thin piece of gold foil and found that most of the alpha particles passed straight through, but that about 1 in 20 000 was deflected (Figure 2.2).

Figure 2.2

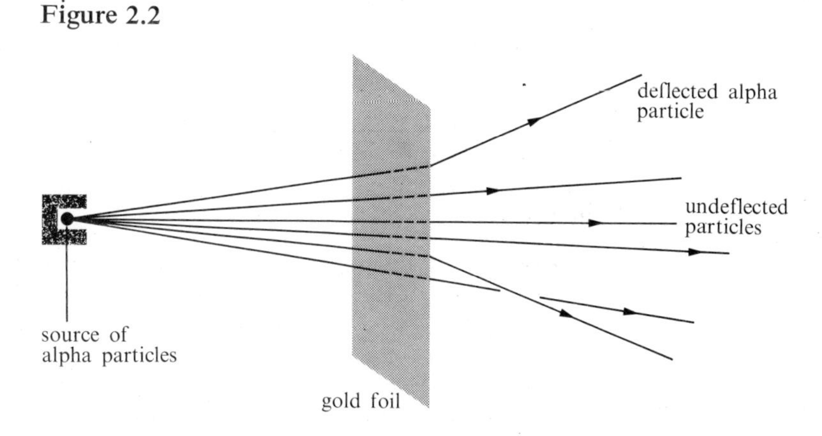

The observations of Geiger and Marsden were explained by Lord Rutherford. He suggested that most of the mass of the atom was concentrated in a positively charged nucleus at the centre of the atom, and that the electrons surrounded the nucleus. This theory accounted for the experimental observations. The positively charged alpha particles approached the positive nuclei, but as like charges repel each other, the alpha particles were deflected (Figure 2.3).

Figure 2.3

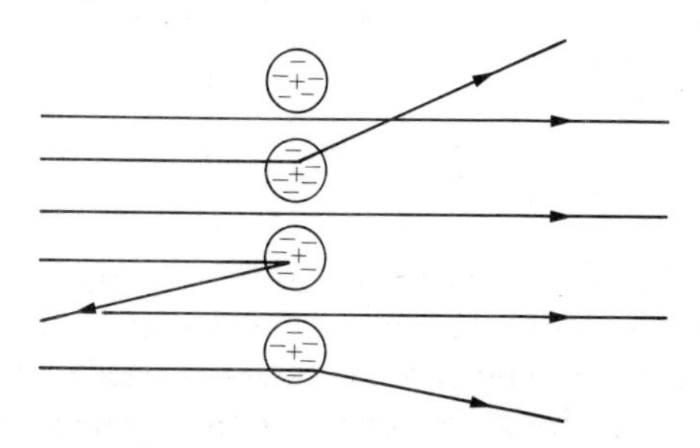

Because most of the alpha particles passed straight through the gold foil, there must be considerable spaces between nuclei. Ocassionally an alpha particle was reflected back towards the source. In Rutherford's words:

'It was almost as incredible as if you had fired a fifteen-inch shell at a piece of tissue paper and it came back and hit you. On consideration I realized that this scattering backwards must be the result of a single collision, and when I made calculations, it was impossible to get anything of that order of magnitude unless you took a system in which the greater part of the mass of the atom was concentrated in a minute nucleus.'

From measurements of the masses of atoms it was found that the mass of the nucleus could not be accounted for by protons alone. In 1920 Rutherford suggested that some nuclei also contained neutral particles which had about the same mass as the proton. He called these neutral particles neutrons. The presence of neutrons in atoms was experimentally verified by J. Chadwick in 1932, while studying radioactivity.

2.2 Modern atomic theory

Atoms are made up of small, sub-atomic particles called protons, neutrons, and electrons. The protons and neutrons together make up the dense core of the atom called the nucleus. The electrons are very light, small particles which are situated around the nucleus. The probability of finding the electrons is greatest within a certain volume about the nucleus. This volume is represented as an **electron cloud** (Figure 2.4).

Figure 2.4

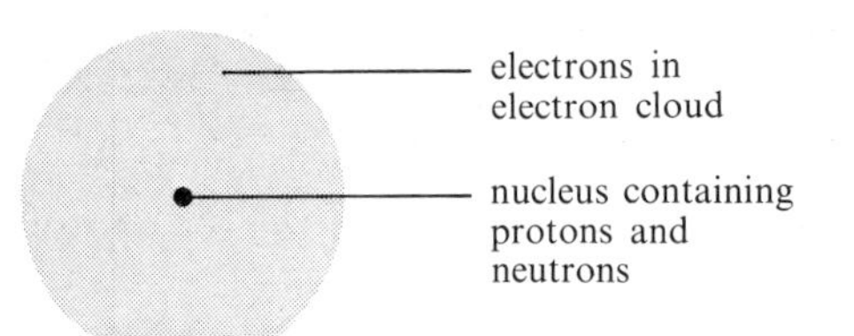

Because the masses of atoms and the particles of which they are composed are so small, it is inconvenient to express them in the conventional units of mass (kilogram). Instead these small masses are expressed in atomic mass units (a.m.u.): 1 a.m.u. = 1.66×10^{-27} kg. The relative masses of the sub-atomic particles are given in Table 2.1. Since atoms are electrically neutral, there must be an equal number of protons and electrons in an atom. The proton is assigned a charge of 1+ and therefore the electron must have a charge of 1−.

Table 2.1 Summary of charge and mass of sub-atomic particles

Particle	*Relative mass (a.m.u.)*	*Charge*	*Approximate relative mass (a.m.u.)*
Proton	1.007 254	1+	1
Electron	0.000 5484	1−	0
Neutron	1.008 613	0	1

2.3 Atomic number

The **atomic number** of an atom is the number of protons in the nucleus of that atom. This is one aspect of the structure of an atom which definitely identifies an element.

Example 1 Hydrogen has one proton in the nucleus, and therefore the atomic number of hydrogen is 1.
Any atom whose atomic number is 1 contains one proton and is therefore a hydrogen atom.

Example 2 Sodium has eleven protons in the nucleus, and therefore the atomic number of sodium is 11.
Any atom whose atomic number is 11 contains eleven protons and is therefore a sodium atom.

The atomic number is the number of protons in the atom. Because atoms are electrically neutral, the atomic number will also be equal to the number of electrons. For example:
Atomic number of sodium = 11
Number of protons = 11
Number of electrons = 11

2.4 Mass number

The **mass number,** as the term suggests, is the mass of the atom. Since the electron mass is virtually zero in comparison with the other sub-atomic particles, the mass number is the sum of the number of protons and neutrons:

Mass number = number of protons + number of neutrons.

From this:

Number of neutrons = mass number − number of protons.

The information about an atom is often given in the way shown below:

Mass number →
Z ← Symbol of the element
Atomic number →

For example, an atom of chlorine, whose mass number is 35 and atomic number is 17, may be written as $^{35}_{17}Cl$. From this we can conclude the following:

1 Mass number = 35
2 Atomic number = 17
3 Number of protons = 17
4 Number of electrons = 17
5 Number of neutrons = 18

Determination of the mass of the atom The instrument used to determine mass numbers is called the **mass spectrometer** and one is shown in Figure 2.5.

Figure 2.5

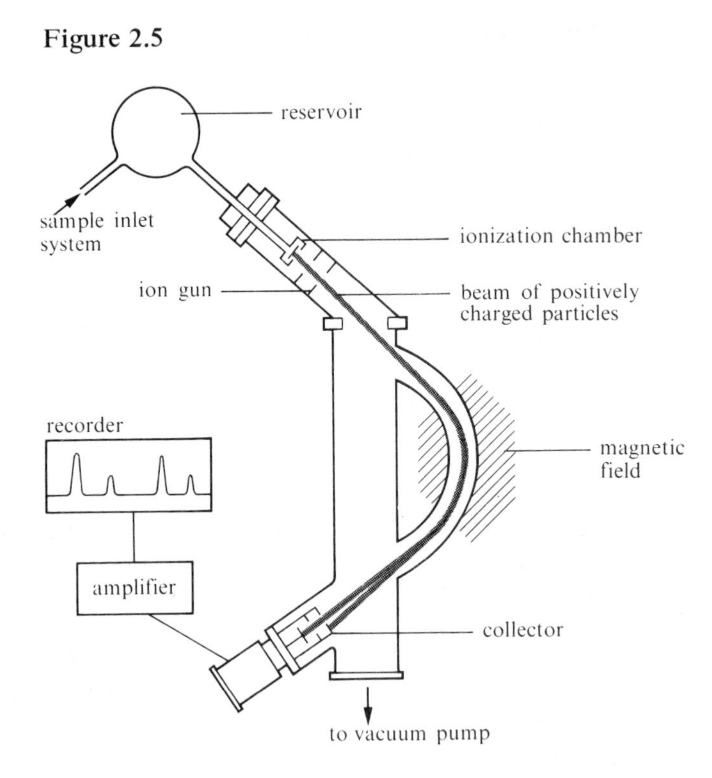

There are many different types of mass spectrometer, but they all operate on similar principles.

1 The element is vaporized.
2 The gas is bombarded by high energy electrons, which remove electrons from the atoms. The atoms then become positively charged particles.
3 These charged particles are projected into the magnetic field, where they are deflected according to their mass. The heavier particles will not be deflected as much as the lighter particles.
4 By varying the strength of the magnetic field, different masses can be made to pass through the slit. Each beam, on passing through the slit, strikes a collector plate where it acquires an electron to 'neutralize' each positive charge it contains. This produces a flow of current in the collector circuit which is amplified and recorded as a peak on a moving chart. The more electrons needed, the more current is produced, and the higher the peak on the recorder.

For example, chlorine gas, when analysed in the mass spectrometer, gives the trace shown in Figure 2.6. The trace shows that there are two different chlorine atoms present. One has a mass/charge ratio of 35 and the other a mass/charge ratio of 37. The bombarding electrons are most likely to remove one electron. Therefore we can assume that the charge of the deflected particle is 1+. Thus we can say that chlorine gas contains atoms which have mass numbers of 35 and 37, and that the atoms present are $^{35}_{17}Cl$ and $^{37}_{17}Cl$.

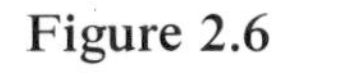

Figure 2.6

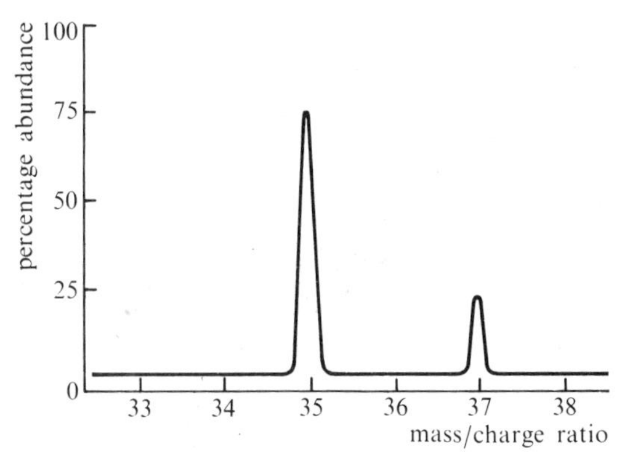

2.5 Isotopes

One of Dalton's suggestions was that all atoms of an element were identical. However, the information obtained from the mass spectrometer for chlorine (Figure 2.6), showed that there were two different atoms present, each with a different atomic mass.

It has been shown that most elements do not contain atoms which are all identical. Atoms which have the same atomic number but different mass numbers are known as **isotopes.** The different masses are due to the atoms having different numbers of neutrons. For example:

Chlorine has two isotopes: $^{35}_{17}Cl$ and $^{37}_{17}Cl$.
Neon has three isotopes: $^{20}_{10}Ne$, $^{21}_{10}Ne$, and $^{22}_{10}Ne$.

The mass spectrometer is very important because it indicates:

1 The presence of isotopes.
2 The mass number(s) of the isotope(s) present.
3 The abundance of the isotope(s).

2.6 Relative atomic mass

The **relative atomic mass** of an element is the average mass of one atom of an element, on a scale where the carbon 12 isotope, $^{12}_{6}C$, has a mass of 12.00000 a.m.u. The value of the relative atomic mass is determined from information obtained from mass spectrometer data.

Example 1 Chlorine gas has two isotopes, $^{35}_{17}Cl$ and $^{37}_{17}Cl$, with abundances of 75 per cent and 25 per cent respectively.

$$
\begin{aligned}
\text{Relative atomic mass} &= \text{mass due to } ^{35}_{17}Cl + \text{mass due to } ^{37}_{17}Cl \\
&= \frac{35 \times 75}{100} + \frac{37 \times 25}{100} \\
&= 26.25 + 9.25 \\
&= 35.5
\end{aligned}
$$

The relative atomic mass of chlorine is 35.5, i.e. the average mass of one atom of chlorine is 35.5.

Example 2 Copper has two isotopes, $^{63}_{29}Cu$ and $^{65}_{29}Cu$, with abundances of 69 per cent and 31 per cent respectively.

Relative atomic mass = mass due to $^{63}_{29}Cu$ + mass due to $^{65}_{29}Cu$

$$= \frac{63 \times 69}{100} + \frac{65 \times 31}{100}$$

$$= 43.47 + 20.15$$

$$= 63.62$$

The relative atomic mass of copper is 63.62, i.e. the average mass of one atom of copper is 63.62.

2.7 Standards of relative atomic mass

It has always been of great importance to chemists to know the relative atomic masses of atoms, so that they could predict the quantities of materials required for chemical reactions. At one time, the relative masses were calculated by measuring the quantities of elements which would combine with each other.

The first standard used was hydrogen, as it was the lightest of all elements. By taking the mass of the hydrogen atom to be one unit, all the other atoms therefore had positive relative atomic masses. Later the hydrogen standard was replaced by oxygen.

Oxygen was favoured for several reasons:

1 It was easier to handle than hydrogen.
2 It was more readily available.
3 Most elements combined with oxygen.

The new standard involved taking the mass of the oxygen atom as sixteen units. On this scale many of the other elements had relative atomic masses which were whole numbers and, as this was very useful for chemists' calculations, the scale was used for a number of years.

With the invention of the mass spectrometer came the discovery of isotopes, and the realization that the oxygen standard was inadequate. Naturally occurring oxygen was shown to consist of a mixture of three isotopes, $^{16}_{8}O$, $^{17}_{8}O$, and $^{18}_{8}O$, the relative abundances of which were 99.76 per cent, 0.04 per cent, and 0.20 per cent respectively Chemists took the average value for the relative atomic mass as sixteen units, whereas physicists took the mass of the isotope $^{16}_{8}O$ as sixteen units. Obviously some compromise had to be reached as it was undesirable to have two 'standard' scales, even if they only differed to a very small degree. Following an international agreement in 1960, the modern practice is to use carbon as the standard. This scale, which takes the mass of the most commonly occurring isotope of carbon, $^{12}_{6}C$, to be twelve units exactly, has not altered the relative atomic masses of the elements by very much, but it means that there is now a scale which is accepted throughout the world. It is important to note two points at this stage. Firstly, the relative atomic mass scale is purely arbitrary. There is no reason why the present scale should not be superseded, sometime in the future, by a more convenient scale. Secondly, relative atomic masses have no units. This is because they are not actual masses of atoms, but rather that they are masses relative to the arbitrary standard.

2.8 Electron arrangement

We have considered the protons and neutrons in the atom, and it is now necessary to look at the electrons. We must ask two questions about the electrons:

1 Is the energy of every electron identical?
2 Do all the electrons occupy the same electron cloud?

Identical energies? Each electron must possess a certain energy to maintain its distance from the nucleus, since, without this energy, it would collapse into the nucleus.

In 1913 Niels Bohr suggested that the electrons of a particular atom were to be found in definite **energy levels.** A very simple representation of the energy levels of an atom is shown in Figure 2.7. The electrons with the lowest energy will be nearest the nucleus, and will occupy the level where $n = 1$. As the energies of the electrons increase, the levels $n = 2$, $n = 3$, and $n = 4$ will be occupied. Figure 2.7b shows the cross section from A to B of the atom in Figure 2.7a.

Figure 2.7

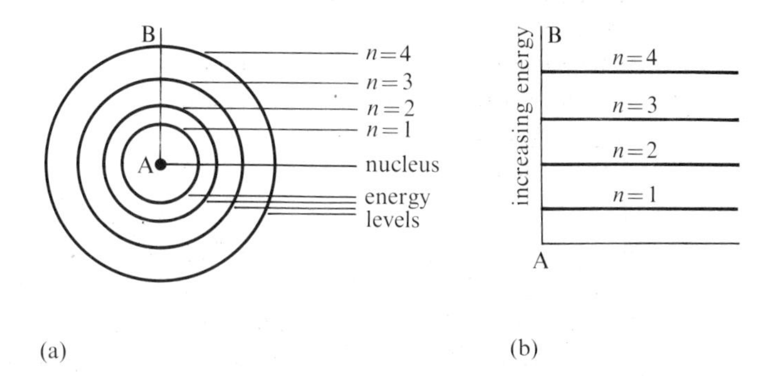

The whereabouts of electrons in energy levels has been determined, and it was found that the maximum number of electrons in each energy level is given by the expression $2n^2$, where n is the number of the energy level. Hence the total number of electrons possible is:

2 in the first level
8 in the second level
18 in the third level
32 in the fourth level

Table 2.2 gives the number of electrons present in each level, and the electron arrangements of the first twenty elements in the Periodic Table.
The lower energy levels usually fill up before the higher ones. However, there is a discrepancy in the electron arrangements of potassium and calcium. The fourth level has started to fill up before the third level is complete with eighteen electrons. As the size of the atom increases the energy levels get closer together, and eventually the fourth energy level overlaps the third energy level. The third level can contain a maximum of eighteen electrons but, when the level contains eight electrons, overlapping occurs and a maxi-

mum of two electrons is added to the fourth level before the third level continues to fill up.

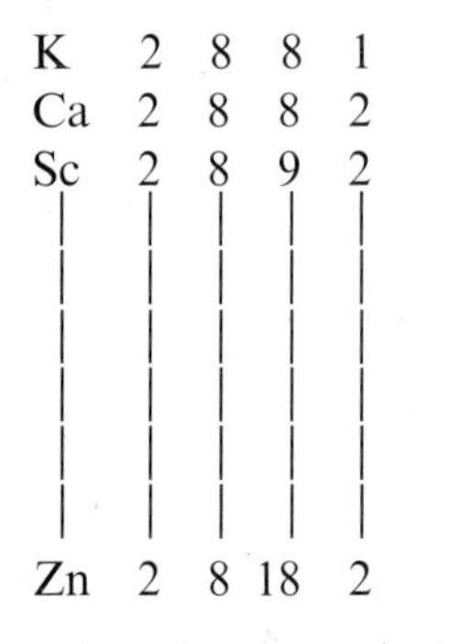

When the element zinc is reached the first three levels are completely full.

Table 2.2

	Number of electrons in				
Atom	*1st level*	*2nd level*	*3rd level*	*4th level*	*Electron configuration*
H	1				1
He	2				2
Li	2	1			2.1
Be	2	2			2.2
B	2	3			2.3
C	2	4			2.4
N	2	5			2.5
O	2	6			2.6
F	2	7			2.7
Ne	2	8			2.8
Na	2	8	1		2.8.1
Mg	2	8	2		2.8.2
Al	2	8	3		2.8.3
Si	2	8	4		2.8.4
P	2	8	5		2.8.5
S	2	8	6		2.8.6
Cl	2	8	7		2.8.7
Ar	2	8	8		2.8.8
K	2	8	8	1	2.8.8.1
Ca	2	8	8	2	2.8.8.2

The same electron cloud?

Although the electron cloud is represented by a sphere in Figure 2.4, the shape of the electron cloud is thought to be more complex. We shall consider the electron clouds for atoms with one or two electrons in the highest energy level to be spherical (Figure 2.8a). Atoms with three or more electrons in the highest level we shall represent as shown in Figure 2.8b.

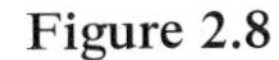

Figure 2.8

These clouds are actually arranged in three dimensions, although here they are represented two-dimensionally. This is done to make the diagrams easier to understand.

The maximum number of electrons that a cloud can contain is two. Hence spherical clouds can hold two electrons. Atoms which have three or more electrons in the highest energy level have four electron clouds. Each cloud can contain two electrons. Hence the maximum number would be eight electrons. Let us consider how atoms would appear using this system. We only need to consider the electrons in the highest energy level (the outer electrons), as all other levels will be complete.

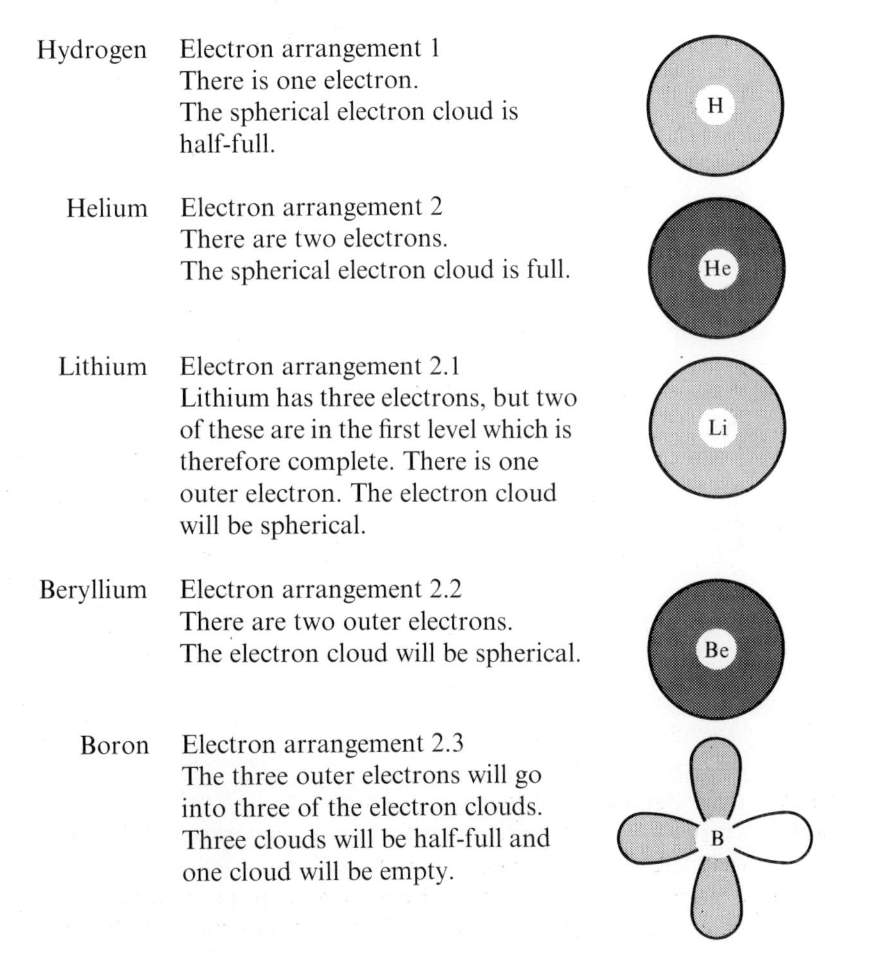

Hydrogen — Electron arrangement 1
There is one electron.
The spherical electron cloud is half-full.

Helium — Electron arrangement 2
There are two electrons.
The spherical electron cloud is full.

Lithium — Electron arrangement 2.1
Lithium has three electrons, but two of these are in the first level which is therefore complete. There is one outer electron. The electron cloud will be spherical.

Beryllium — Electron arrangement 2.2
There are two outer electrons.
The electron cloud will be spherical.

Boron — Electron arrangement 2.3
The three outer electrons will go into three of the electron clouds. Three clouds will be half-full and one cloud will be empty.

Carbon — Electron arrangement 2.4
The four outer electrons will each occupy a separate electron cloud.

Nitrogen — Electron arrangement 2.5
There are five outer electrons. One of the electron clouds will be full and three of the clouds will be half-full.

Oxygen — Electron arrangement 2.6
There are six outer electrons. Two of the electron clouds will be full and two will be half-full.

Fluorine — Electron arrangement 2.7
There are seven outer electrons. Three of the electron clouds will be full and one will be half-full.

Neon — Electron arrangement 2.8
There are eight outer electrons. Each of the electron clouds will be full.

Calcium — Electron arrangement 2.8.8.2
There are two outer electrons. Therefore the electron cloud will be spherical and full.

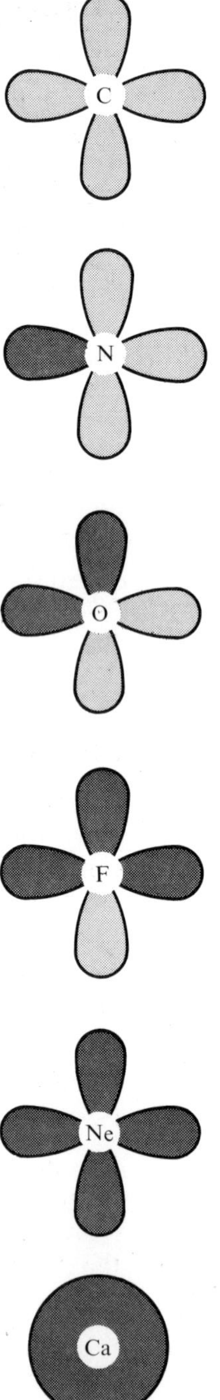

Krypton — Electron arrangement 2.8.18.8
There are eight outer electrons. Like neon all the electron clouds will be full.

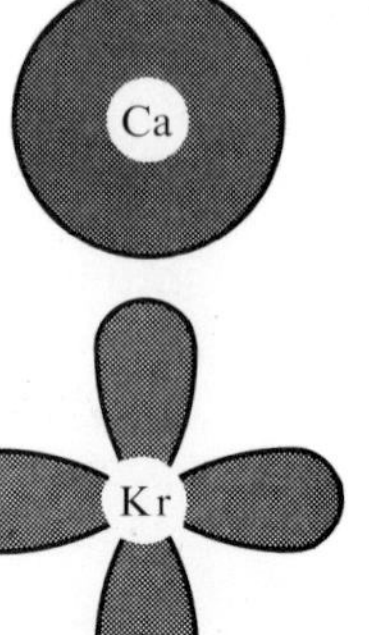

2.9 The tetrahedral shape

We have said that electron clouds are three-dimensional rather than two-dimensional. Let us consider an atom of neon. It has eight outer electrons and is illustrated on page 34. Each electron cloud contains two electrons. We know that electrons are negatively charged so each electron cloud will repel the other three in exactly the same way. There is a mutual repulsion between each of the clouds, and they will try to get as far from each other as possible. When they do this, the result is a tetrahedral arrangement (Figure 2.9).

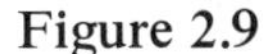
Figure 2.9

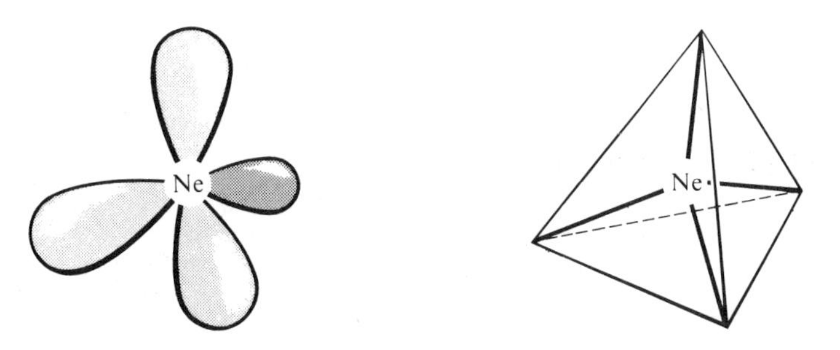

2.10 Arrangement of the elements

Up to the year 1800 only thirty-four elements were known. By 1870 this number had almost doubled, and by 1974 the figure was 105. The belief that all systems had a certain degree of order led to the idea that these elements could be arranged in a definite way.

In 1817, J. W. Döbereiner (1780–1849) observed that certain elements had similar chemical properties and he found that he could group them in threes:

Lithium	Calcium	Chlorine
Sodium	Strontium	Bromine
Potassium	Barium	Iodine

He called these groups 'triads', and this was the first attempt to arrange the elements in some kind of order.

By 1863 many more elements had been discovered. J. Newlands arranged the elements in order of their relative atomic masses. He divided the elements into groups of seven, as he found that every eighth element had properties similar to the first element of the preceding series.

Li	Be	B	C	N	O	F
Na	Mg	Al	Si	P	S	Cl
K	Ca	Cr	Ti	Mn	Fe	

Newlands called these groups 'octaves'. This method did produce a degree of regularity, but the great disadvantage of this system was that, as new elements were discovered, they could not be fitted into the octave structure.

In 1864 Lothar Meyer (1830–95) plotted a graph of atomic volume against relative atomic mass (Figure 2.10). The atomic volume of an element is the relative atomic mass divided by the density of the element.

Figure 2.10 Meyer's graph of atomic volume against relative atomic mass

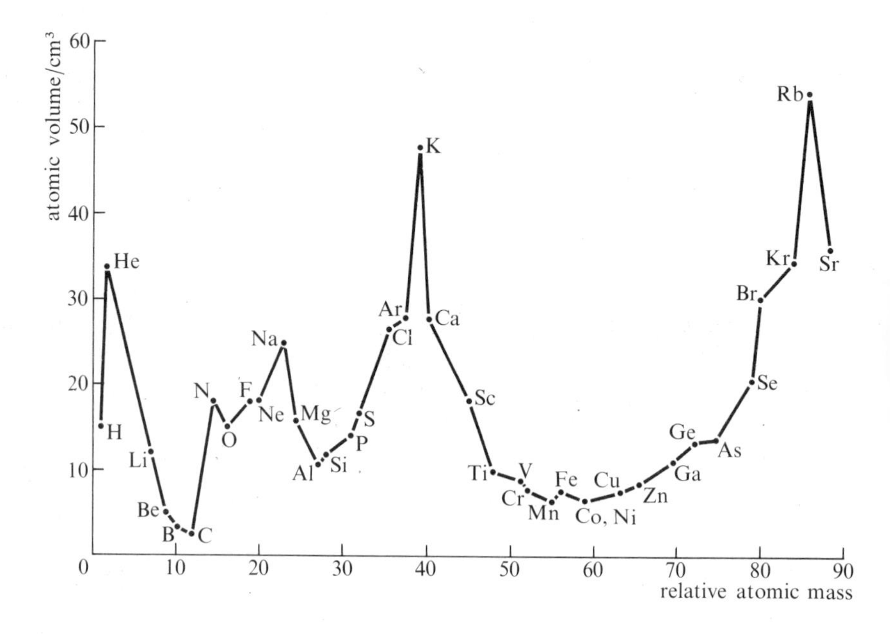

You can see from the graph, as Meyer did, that the elements with similar properties recur at approximately the same point in each part of the graph. The noble gases neon, argon, and krypton are all at similar positions on the graph, which would indicate that there is a relation between the properties of the elements and their relative atomic mass.

Dimitri Mendeleev (1839–1907) used increasing relative atomic mass, in conjunction with similar chemical properties, as the basis for arranging the elements. His table was constructed in such a way that gaps were left where the pattern would otherwise be destroyed. He predicted the properties of these elements, as then undiscovered, quite accurately.

Mendeleev's table is similar to the one in use today, but it was H. Moseley who put the table into the present form. Moseley worked with X-rays and found that the energy of the X-rays produced by an element increased as the relative atomic mass increased. He could not, however, obtain an exact relation between the relative atomic mass and the energy of the X-rays, so he assigned a number to each element according to its position in the Periodic Table. This number, which he called the **atomic number,** is the number of protons (or the number of electrons) in a neutral atom. Using the atomic number, Moseley was able to obtain an exact relation with the energy of the X-rays produced.

The Periodic Table as we know it today is shown in Figure 2.11. The **periods** run from left to right horizontally, and each element has an atomic number one unit greater than the preceeding element. For example, Period 2 contains the following elements.

3 Li	4 Be		5 B	6 C	7 N	8 O	9 F	10 Ne

The **groups** run from top to bottom and contain elements with the same number of electrons in their highest energy levels. Members of Group 1, Li, Na, and K have one electron in the highest energy level. Members of Group 2, Be, Mg, and Ca have two electrons in the highest energy level.

Group 1 Li (2.1) Na (2.8.1) K (2.8.8.1).
Group 2 Be (2.2) Mg (2.8.2) Ca (2.8.8.2)

Figure 2.11 The modern form of the Periodic Table

	group 1	group 2	transition series	group 3	group 4	group 5	group 6	group 7	group 8
number of electrons in the highest energy level	1	2		3	4	5	6	7	8
period 1	1 H								2 He
period 2	3 Li	4 Be		5 B	6 C	7 N	8 O	9 F	10 Ne
period 3	11 Na	12 Mg		13 Al	14 Si	15 P	16 S	17 Cl	18 Ar
period 4	19 K	20 Ca	21 Sc 22 Ti 23 V 24 Cr 25 Mn 26 Fe 27 Co 28 Ni 29 Cu 30 Zn	31 Ga	32 Ge	33 As	34 Se	35 Br	36 Kr

It can be shown that elements in the same group have similar properties. For example, the elements in Group 1 are all reactive metals. The Group 8 elements all have eight electrons in the highest energy level, with the exception of helium, which has two. The Group 8 elements were called 'inert gases', meaning that they were completely unreactive. It has been discovered that they do react under certain special circumstances, and they are now called the **noble gases.** The lack of reactivity of these elements is normally attributed to the fact that there are eight electrons in the highest energy level. These eight electrons are often referred to as a **stable octet.** When other elements react, they usually do so in such a way as to obtain this stable octet. It is very important to remember this when we consider the bonding of elements in the next chapter.

The graph in Figure 2.12 shows the atomic number of elements plotted against the number of electrons in the highest energy level. You will see that all members of Group 8 are on the peaks of the graph, and that all the members of the other groups occur at exactly the same position on the graph. All elements with three electrons in the highest energy level belong to Group 3. By reading across the graph you can obtain the other groups in the

Periodic Table, and by reading from the bottom to the top of each peak, you will obtain the periods in the Periodic Table.

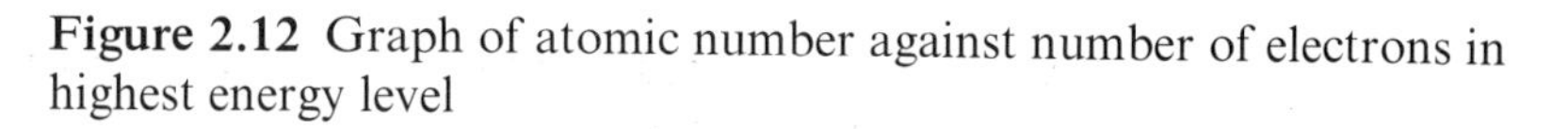

Figure 2.12 Graph of atomic number against number of electrons in highest energy level

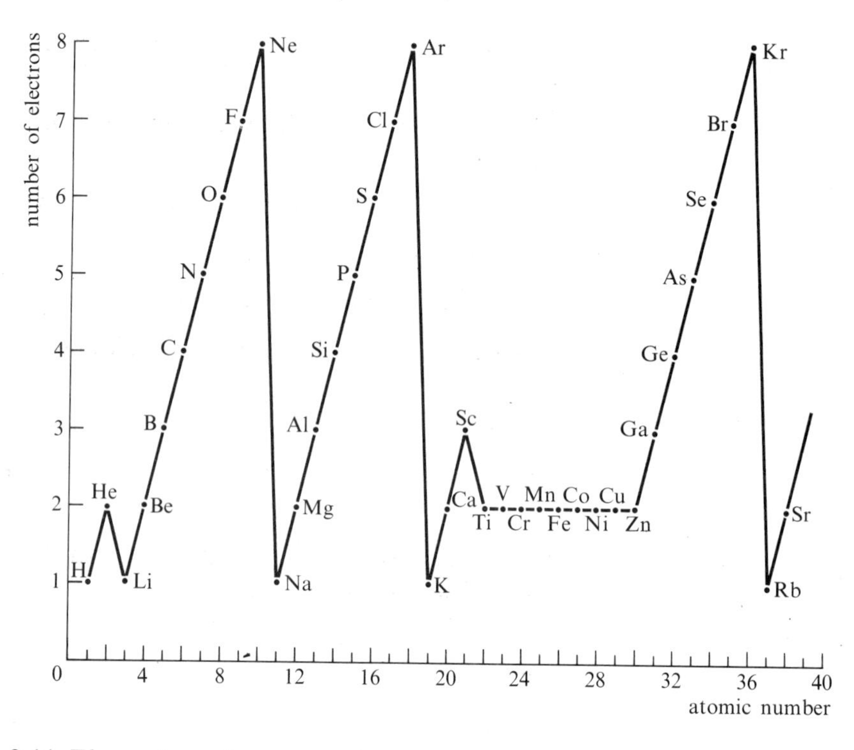

2.11 Elements and compounds

In terms of modern atomic theory we can now define elements and compounds more accurately than we did in chapter 1.

Elements Elements are substances whose atoms all contain the same number of protons in the nucleus.

Compounds Compounds are substances which contain two or more elements combined chemically.

Summary

From this chapter you should know:

1 Atoms are composed of protons and neutrons in a nucleus, which is surrounded by electrons.

2 The nucleus of an atom is very small and dense, so the atom is mostly empty space.

3 The electrons are most likely to be found in electron clouds about the nucleus.

4 The atomic number = number of protons = number of electrons.

5 The mass number = number of protons + number of neutrons.

6 How the mass number is determined.

7 Isotopes are atoms with the same atomic numbers but different mass numbers.

8 The relative atomic mass is the average mass of one atom of an element.

9 Elements are arranged in the Periodic Table according to their atomic number and number of outer electrons.

10 The noble gases have eight electrons in their highest energy levels, and because of this they are very stable.

Questions

1 1 How many (a) protons and (b) neutrons are there in one atom of each of the following: ^{37}Cl and ^{108}Ag?
2 In each case, give two characteristics which you would expect to associate with elements having:
2.1 One outer electron.
2.2 Seven outer electrons.
2.3 Eight outer electrons. *P & W*

2 $^{3}_{1}H$ and $^{3}_{2}He$ are not considered to be isotopes. Using named examples, explain what isotopes are.

3

Element	*Atomic number*	*Mass number*	*Number of* *Protons*	*Electrons*	*Neutrons*
Al	13	(a)	(b)	(c)	14
(d)	(e)	50	(f)	(g)	26

Write down the letters (a) to (g) and opposite each write the corresponding piece of information which is missing from the above table. *SCEEB*

4 How did Lord Rutherford explain that matter contained mostly empty space and just a few positively charged centres?

5 What information can you give about the two species: $^{35}_{17}X$ and $^{37}_{17}X$?

6 Find out what important discoveries were made by the following people: Moseley; J. J. Thomson; Mendeleev; Chadwick.

7

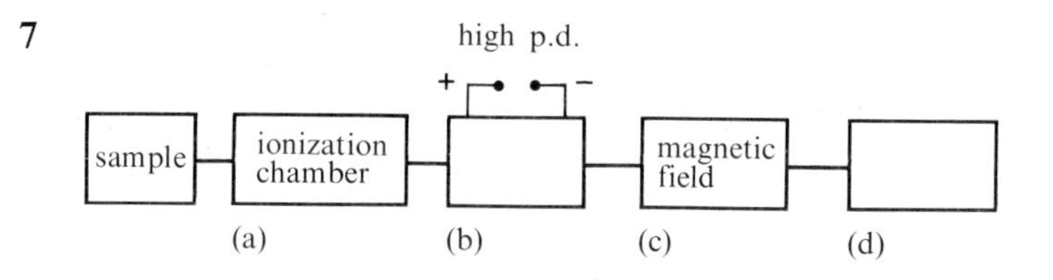

1 Above is a diagrammatic representation of a mass spectrometer. Explain what happens at (a), (b), (c), and (d).
2 What do you understand by the term 'isotopes'?
3 The following data refer to the element Y:

Isotopic mass	54	56	57
Percentage abundance	6.0	92.2	2.0

Calculate the relative atomic mass of Y. *P & W*

8 Atom A has a mass number of 239 and atomic number 93.
Atom B has a mass number of 239 and atomic number 94.
1 How many protons has atom A?
2 How many neutrons has atom B?
3 Are atoms A and B isotopes of the same element? Explain. *SCEEB*

9 1 Outline the operating principles of the mass spectrometer,
2 The trace shown was obtained for an element A from a mass spectrometer.

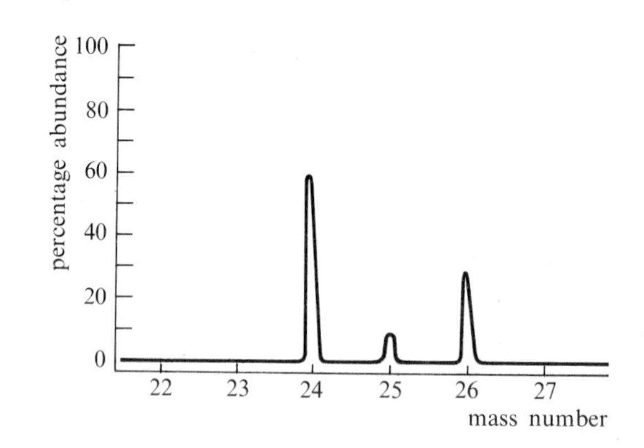

Calculate the relative atomic mass of A and identify it. *P & W*

10 1 In the atomic theory of matter proposed by John Dalton in 1808, it was suggested that matter was composed of small, indestructible particles called atoms, and that atoms of the same element were identical.
In the light of modern atomic theory, comment on Dalton's ideas.
2 In an experiment set up by Geiger and Marsden, fast moving, positively charged α-particles were directed on to a thin piece of metal foil and the scattering pattern observed.

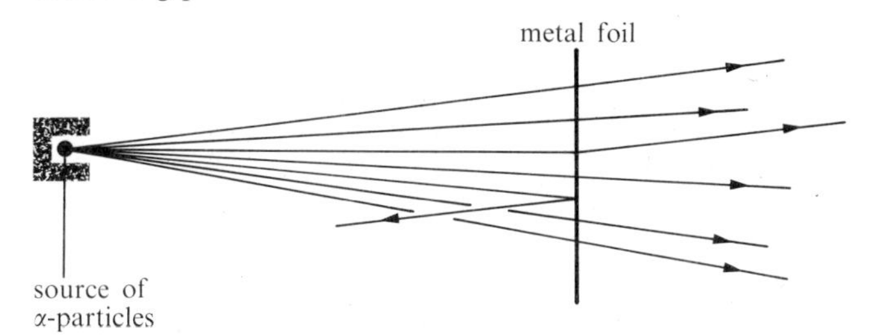

As shown in the diagram most of the α-particles pass through the foil with little or no deflection. However, a few completely rebound.
2.1 How can the scattering pattern of 'invisible' particles be observed?
2.2 Which metal foil was used in this experiment?
2.3 By means of a diagram, explain how some of the α-particles are able to pass through the foil undeflected, and how others completely rebound.
2.4 What is the significance of the fact that only a few particles completely rebound?
2.5 What was the name of the scientist who saw the significance of this fact, and interpreted it correctly? *P & W*

11 In each of the following groups of substances one item does not belong to the group. Select this item and explain why it does not belong.
1 Hydrogen, oxygen, steam, chlorine.
2 Calcium, magnesium, sodium, beryllium.
3 $^{27}_{13}X$, $^{24}_{12}X$, $^{23}_{11}X$, $^{20}_{10}X$.

3 Chemical bonding

Consider the electron arrangement for the noble gases.

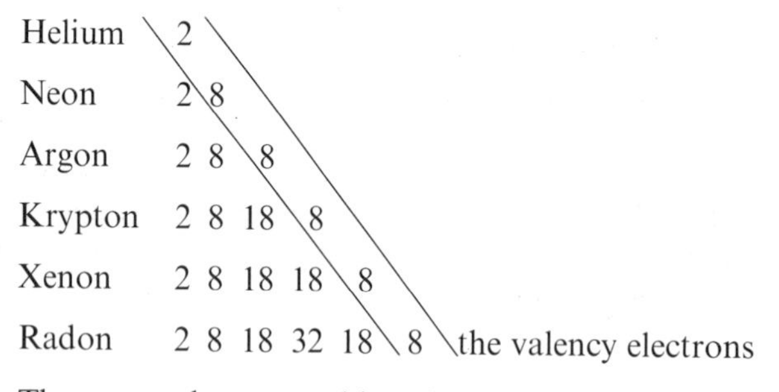

Helium	2					
Neon	2	8				
Argon	2	8	8			
Krypton	2	8	18	8		
Xenon	2	8	18	18	8	
Radon	2	8	18	32	18	8

These gases have two things in common.

1 They all (except helium) have eight electrons in the highest energy level.
2 They are all extremely unreactive, and indeed they were often called the 'inert gases'.

It seems reasonable to suppose that these two statements are related. If the gases do not react because they have an electron arrangement which is a stable one, the other elements must react because their electron arrangement is less stable than that of the noble gases, and the reaction takes place in order to obtain this arrangement.

3.1 A simple model

If one ring magnet is dropped down a brass rod on to another ring magnet with like poles facing, the force of repulsion gets bigger as the magnets approach each other, until the force of repulsion is equal to the force of gravity of the top magnet.

Figure 3.1

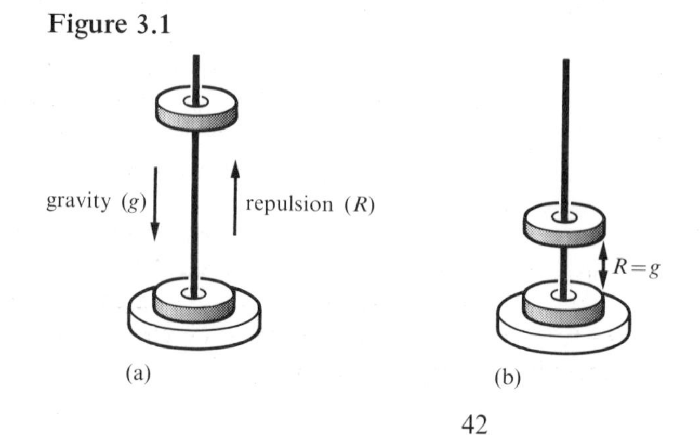

The top magnet in position (b) is now in a stable position because, if it is displaced upwards or downwards, it will return to its position when released. A bond has been formed between the magnets.

3.2 The real thing

The ways in which atoms achieve the electron arrangement of a noble gas can be explained in terms of the attraction of an atom's nucleus for the electrons of its neighbour, the forces of repulsion between the nuclei, and the forces of repulsion between the electrons.

Evidence from the mass spectrometer indicates that hydrogen gas is made of **diatomic molecules.** A molecule is the smallest part of a substance which can exist separately at normal temperatures and pressures. A diatomic molecule contains two atoms. Imagine two hydrogen atoms travelling towards each other. Each atom consist of a nucleus, which has a positive charge, surrounded by an **electron cloud** with a negative charge. The electron cloud represents the region of space where the electron is most likely to be found.

Figure 3.2

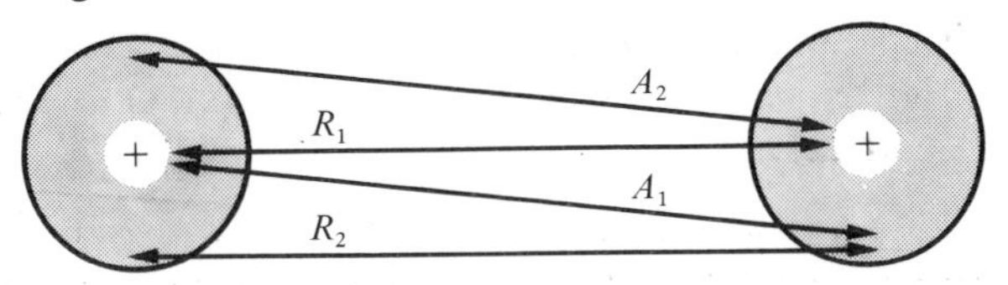

In Figure 3.2

1. R_1 represents the force of repulsion between the two nuclei.
2. R_2 represents the force of repulsion between the two electron clouds.
3. A_1 and A_2 represent the forces of attraction between one nucleus and the electrons of the other atom.

The atoms will arrive at a certain distance from each other where the forces of attraction are exactly balanced by the forces of repulsion:

$$R_1 + R_2 = A_1 + A_2$$

When this occurs, a **bond** has been formed between the atoms.

Since the atoms approaching each other are both hydrogen atoms with the same numbers of protons and electrons, the electrons will be evenly distributed between the nuclei. This is called a **covalent bond.**

If one atom has a much larger charge on its nucleus than the other, the electrons will not be evenly distributed between the nuclei. This is called a **polar covalent bond.**

In the ultimate case, one nucleus may pull electrons off the other atom. This is called an **ionic** or **electrovalent bond.**

Although the chemical properties of elements and compounds depend on the type of bonding involved, the different types of bonding are all represented by the ring magnet model.

3.3 The covalent bond

The covalent bond can be described as an even sharing of electrons between atoms such that each of the atoms in the molecule has the electron arrangement of a noble gas. The covalent bond is an overlap of electron clouds. Two clouds, containing one electron each, overlap to form a single cloud between the atoms. Full electron clouds associated with an atom are unavailable for bonding. They contain pairs of electrons, which are known as **lone pairs.**

Examples of covalent molecules

We will now consider the bonding in some common covalent molecules.

Hydrogen

Hydrogen gas, H_2, is diatomic. There is a **single** covalent bond between the atoms.

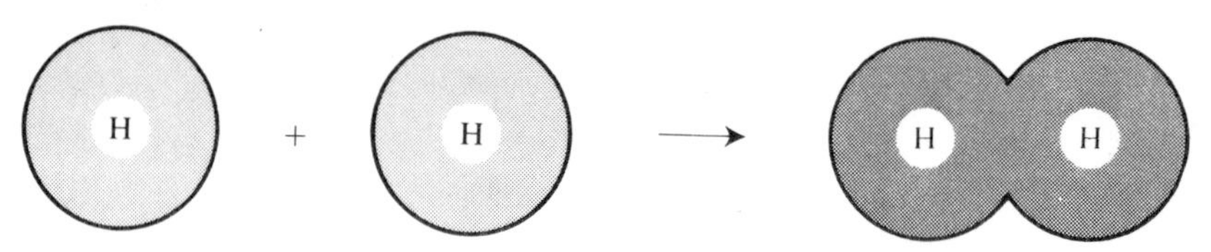

This method of representing the molecule gives some idea of its shape, but it is sometimes a bit cumbersome. The covalent bond is often represented by a short line joining the symbols for the atoms: H—H.

Chlorine

Chlorine gas, Cl_2, is diatomic.

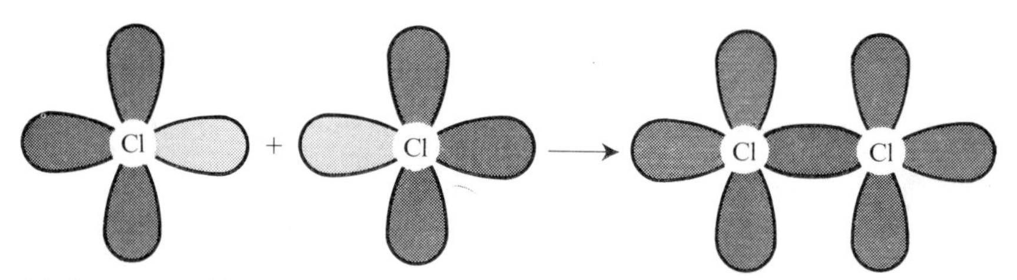

chlorine atoms with 7 valency electrons

chlorine molecule Cl —— Cl

each chlorine has a share of eight electrons–a stable arrangement

Oxygen

Oxygen gas, O_2, is diatomic. There is a **double** bond between the atoms.

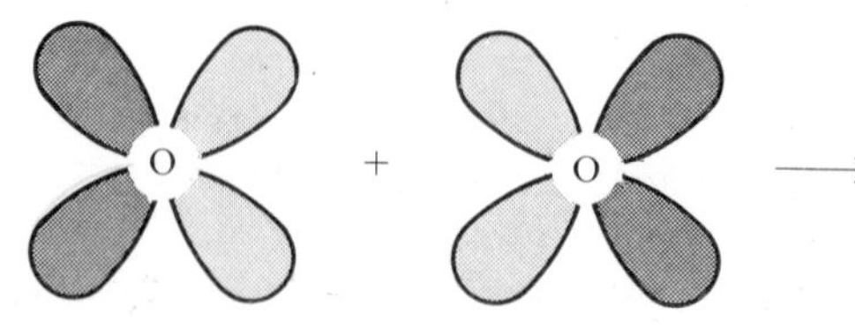

oxygen atoms with 6 valency electrons

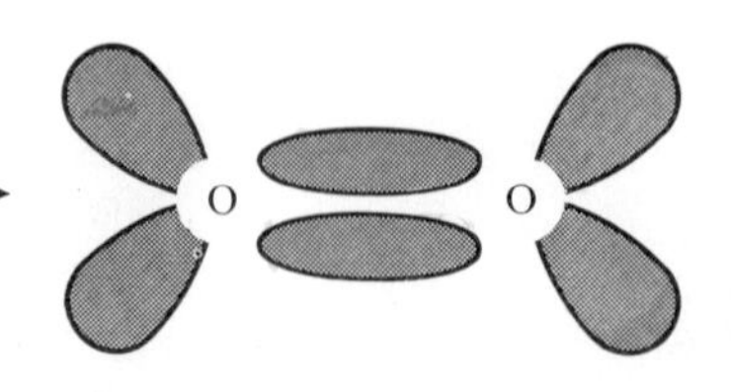

oxygen molecule O══O

each oxygen has a share of eight electrons–a stable arrangement

Nitrogen

Nitrogen gas, N_2, is diatomic. There is a **triple** bond between the atoms.

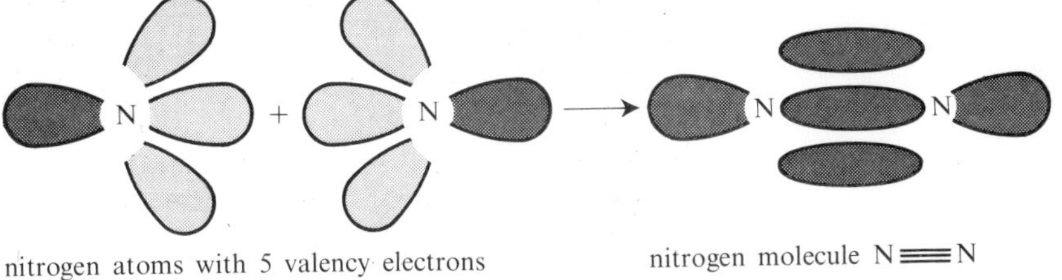

nitrogen atoms with 5 valency electrons

nitrogen molecule $N \equiv N$

each nitrogen has a share of eight electrons–a stable arrangement

3.4 The polar covalent bond

The polar covalent bond is formed in exactly the same way as the covalent bond, but one of the nuclei attracts the shared electrons more than the other, resulting in an uneven electron distribution.

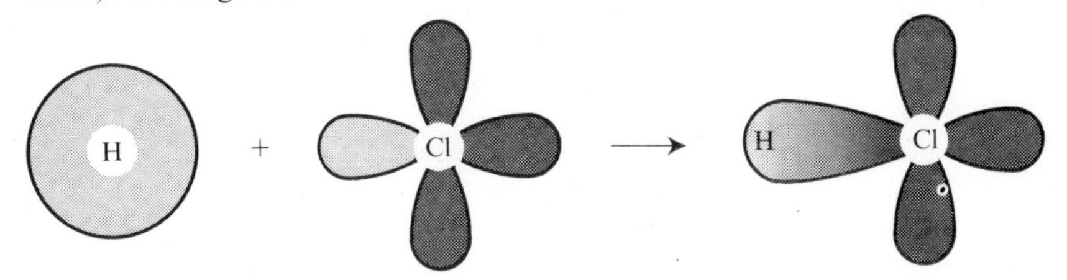

The pair of electrons shared by the two nuclei lie much closer to the nucleus of the chlorine since it has seventeen protons compared to the single proton in the hydrogen nucleus.
Consider the molecule of methane gas, CH_4.

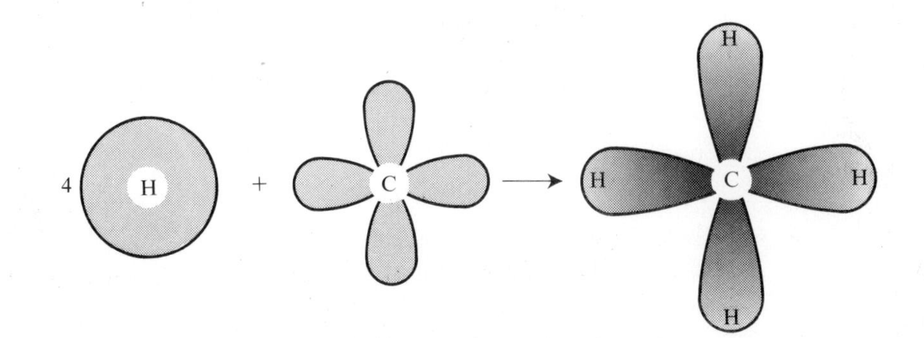

The pairs of electrons shared between the carbon and hydrogen nuclei lie close to the carbon nucleus since it has six protons compared to the single proton in the hydrogen nucleus.

The polarity of the covalent bonds in a molecule can have an effect on the overall polarity of that molecule. It is important to note that the bond polarity is not the only factor. The lone pairs and the shape of the molecule also play a part. Consider the molecule of hydrogen chloride again.

1 The shared electrons are displaced towards the chlorine.
2 There are three lone pairs of electrons at the chlorine end of the molecule.
3 The molecule is linear in shape. Hence the chlorine end of the molecule is relatively negative compared to the hydrogen end. This uneven distribution of charge is usually represented by the symbols $\delta+$ and $\delta-$.

$^{\delta+}H-Cl^{\delta-}$

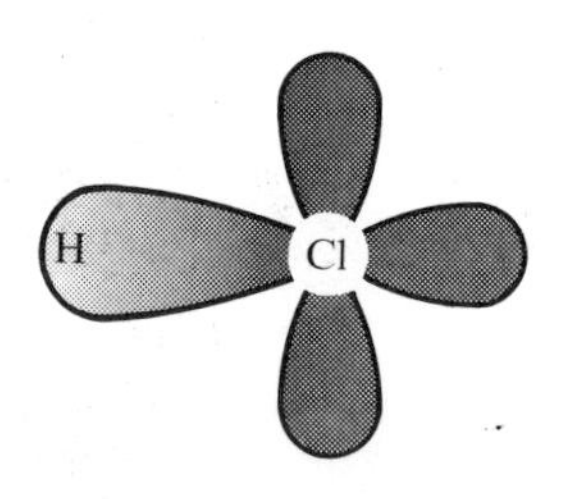

Consider the molecule of methane again.

1 The shared electrons are displaced towards the carbon.
2 There are no lone pairs.
3 The molecule is tetrahedral in shape.

Although the bonds are polar the molecule is non-polar because of its symmetrical shape.

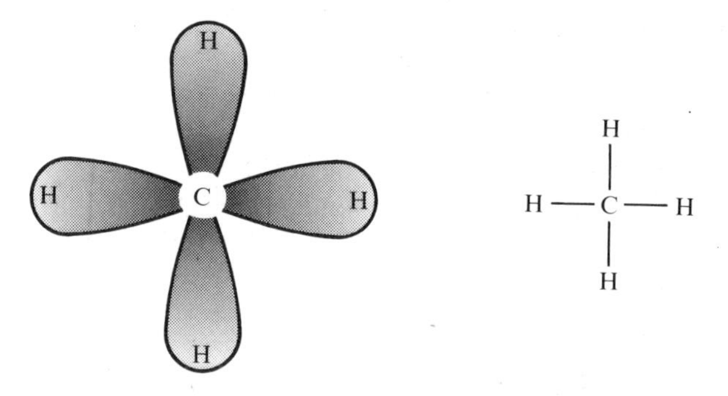

Examples of non-polar molecules

We will now discuss two more common non-polar molecules.

Tetrachloromethane

Tetrachloromethane has the formula CCl_4.

1 Each of the C—Cl bonds has the electrons displaced towards the chlorine.
2 Each chlorine has three lone pairs.
3 The molecule is tetrahedral in shape, so in spite of the bonds themselves being polar, the molecule is non-polar.

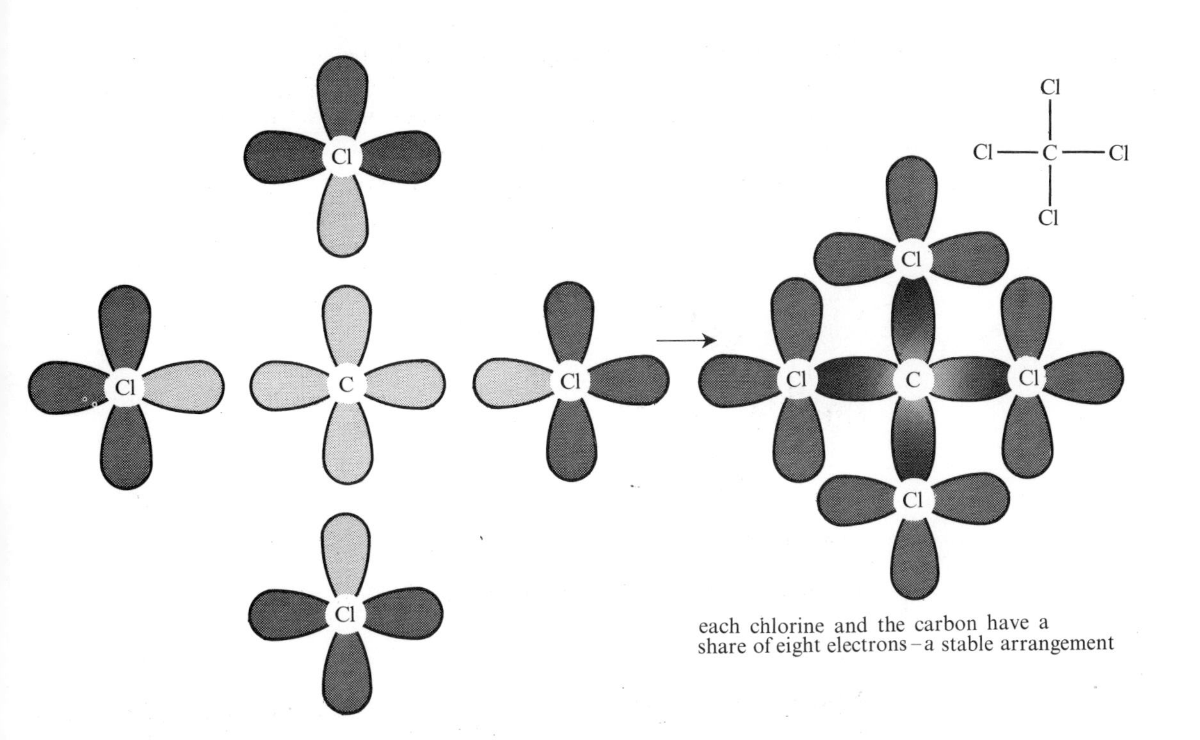

each chlorine and the carbon have a share of eight electrons – a stable arrangement

Carbon dioxide

Carbon dioxide has the formula CO_2.

1. Each of the C=O double bonds has the electrons displaced towards the oxygen.
2. Each oxygen atom has two lone pairs.
3. The molecule is linear and the charge differences cancel each other out. Thus the molecule is non-polar in spite of the bonds themselves being polar.

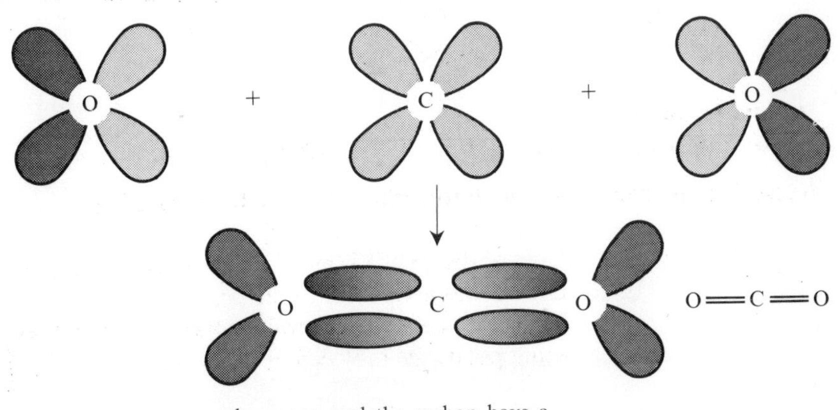

each oxygen and the carbon have a share of eight electrons – a stable arrangement

Examples of polar molecules

We will now discuss three common polar molecules.

Water Water has the formula H_2O.

1 Oxygen has eight protons in the nucleus compared with one in the hydrogen nucleus.
2 Oxygen has two lone pairs of electrons.
3 The molecule is asymmetric.

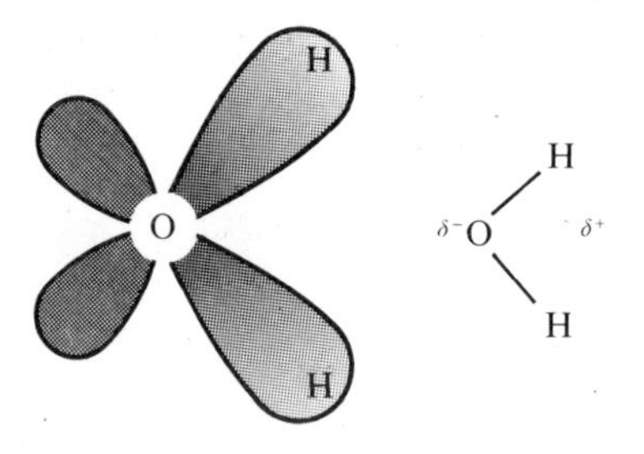

Ammonia Ammonia has the formula NH_3.

1 Nitrogen has seven protons in the nucleus compared with one in the hydrogen nucleus.
2 Nitrogen has one lone pair of electrons.
3 The molecule is asymmetric.

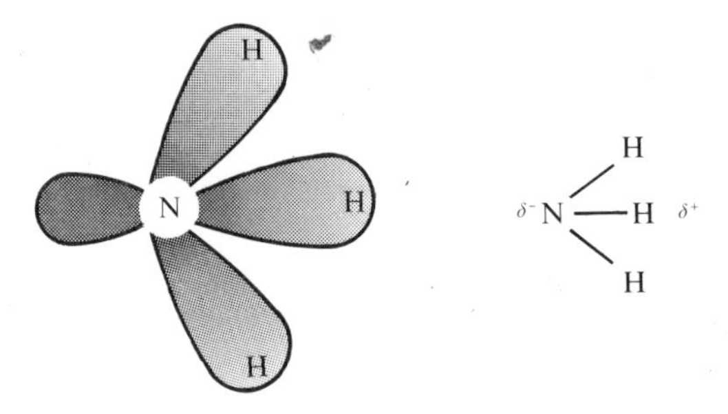

Chloromethane Chloromethane has the formula CH_3Cl.

1 Each of the C—H bonds has the electrons displaced towards the carbon.
2 The C—Cl bond has the electrons displaced towards the chlorine.
3 The chlorine atom has three lone pairs.
4 The molecule is asymmetric.

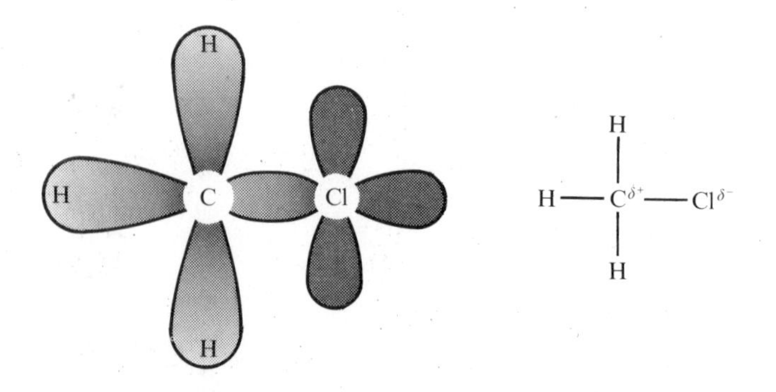

3.5 Identification of polar liquids

If a liquid is run from a burette and a charged poly(ethene) rod is brought close to a stream of the liquid, one of two things can happen.

1 The polar molecules will flip over in such a way that the positive ends of the molecules will point towards the negatively charged rod, and the molecules will then be attracted to the rod, causing the stream to bend.
2 The non-polar molecules will be unaffected by the presence of the charged rod and the stream will not bend.

Both these possibilities are illustrated in Figure 3.3.

Figure 3.3

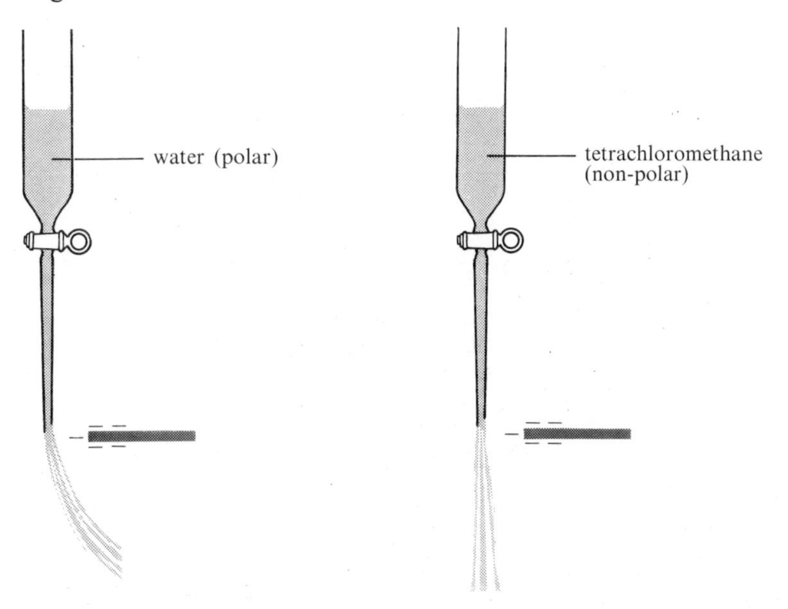

3.6 The ionic bond

Where there is a large difference in the nuclear charges it is possible for electrons to be transferred from one atom to another. Consider a sodium atom travelling towards a chlorine atom.

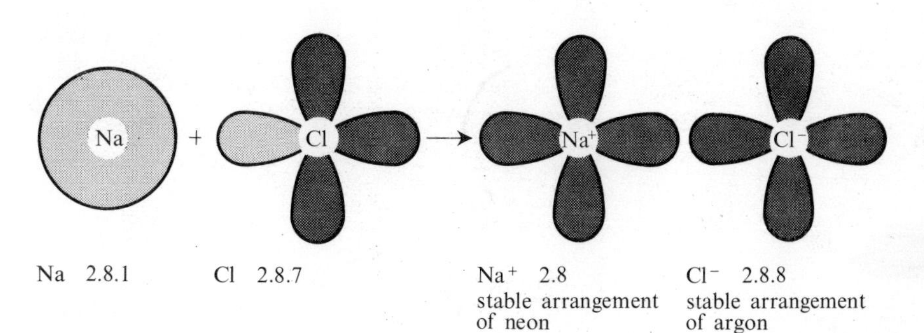

The sodium atom has lost an electron. Although it now carries a positive charge, it is stable as it has the electron arrangement of neon. Similarly, the chlorine atom has gained an electron. It now carries a negative charge, but is also stable as it has the electron arrangement of argon. These charged particles are called **ions.** In the compound sodium chloride there are no sodium atoms and chloride atoms, but instead the entire crystal structure is made up of sodium ions and chloride ions which attract each other because of their opposite charges. The force of attraction between the ions is called the **ionic bond** (electrovalent bond). Figure 3.4 represents a model of sodium chloride, and shows how the sodium ions and the chloride ions are arranged in the compound.

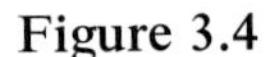

Figure 3.4

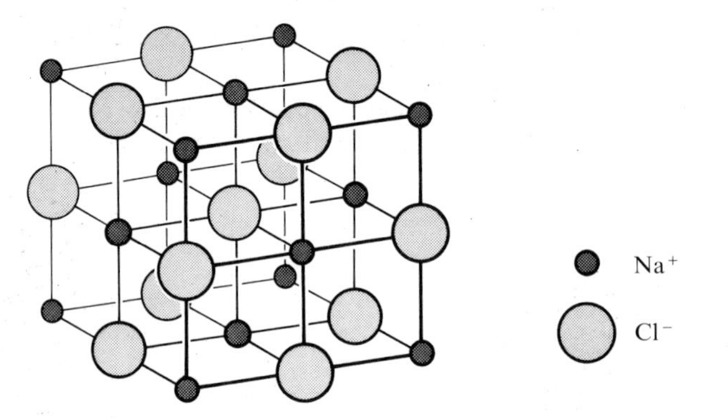

The number of sodium ions is equal to the number of chloride ions. We can represent the compound by the formula Na^+Cl^-, although there is no molecule corresponding to this formula. This is generally true for all ionic compounds.

Examples of ionic compounds

The following examples discuss the bonding in some common ionic compounds.

Potassium bromide

Potassium has the electron arrangement 2.8.8.1. Bromine has the electron arrangement 2.8.18.7. We can represent the atoms as:

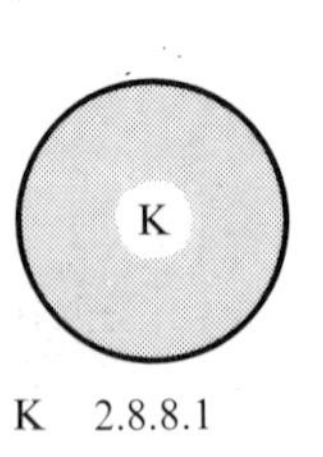

K 2.8.8.1

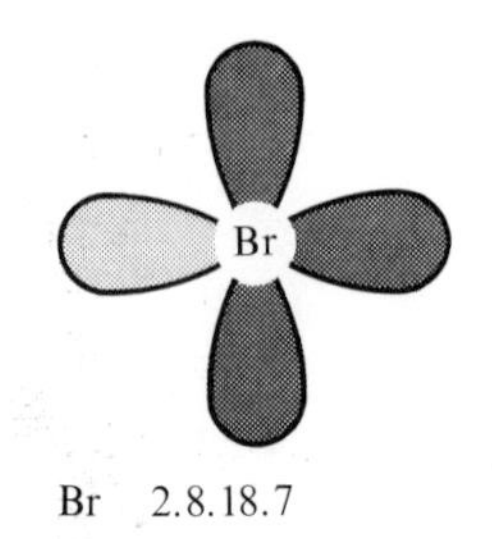

Br 2.8.18.7

By considering the electron arrangements we can see that potassium would reach the stable arrangement of argon by losing one electron, and bromine would reach the stable arrangement of krypton by gaining one electron. This would result in the formation of two charged particles with stable electron arrangements. They would attract each other and form an ionic bond.

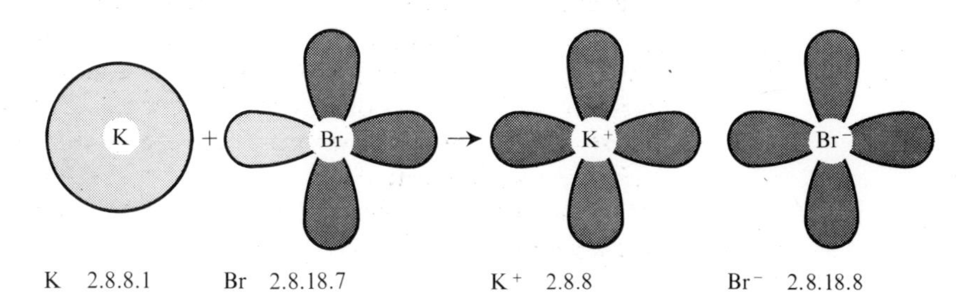

The formula of potassium bromide will be K^+Br^-. The ions will be arranged in a similar way to sodium and chloride ions in sodium chloride.

Calcium fluoride Calcium has the electron arrangement 2.8.8.2. Fluorine has the electron arrangement 2.7. We can represent the atoms as:

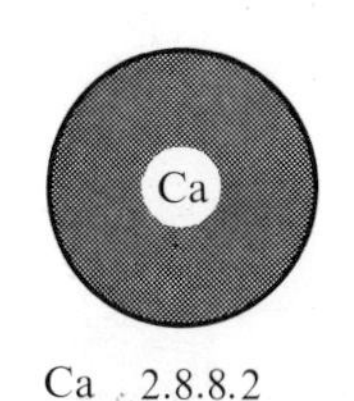

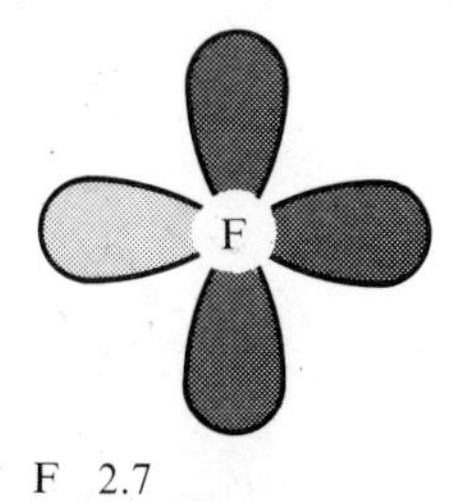

By considering the electron arrangements we can see that calcium would reach the stable electron arrangement of argon by losing two electrons, and fluorine would reach the stable electron arrangement of neon by gaining one electron. This would result in the formation of a calcium ion with a 2+ charge and a fluoride ion with a 1− charge.

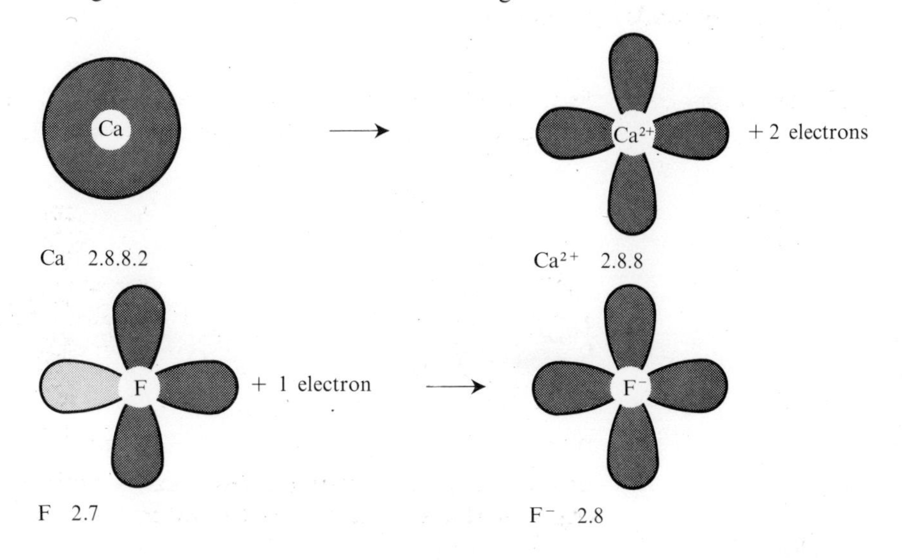

There will be an attraction between the positive ions and the negative ions. As the the compound is electrically neutral, the formula must be $Ca^{2+}(F^{-})_2$. In the compound calcium fluoride the number of fluoride ions is twice the number of calcium ions.

Magnesium oxide Magnesium has the electron arrangement 2.8.2. Oxygen has the electron arrangement 2.6. We can represent the atoms as:

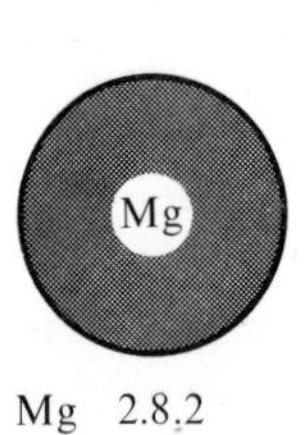

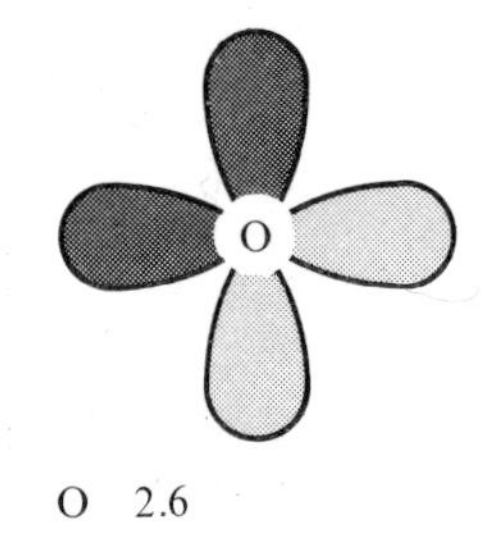

By considering the electron arrangements, we can see that magnesium would reach the stable electron arrangement of neon by losing two electrons, and oxygen would reach the stable electron arrangement of neon by gaining two electrons. This would result in the formation of a magnesium ion with a 2+ charge and an oxide ion with a 2− charge.

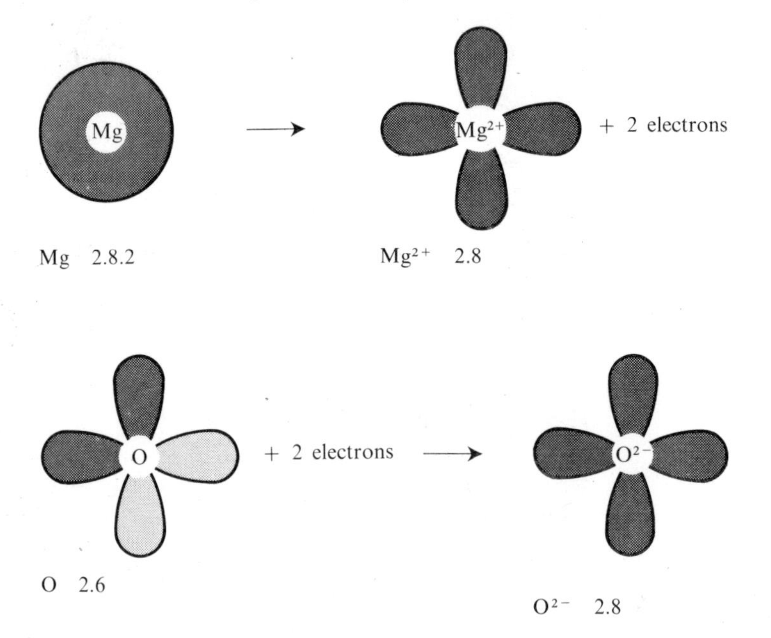

There will be an attraction between the ions, and an ionic bond will be formed. The formula will be $Mg^{2+}O^{2-}$.

Aluminium oxide

Aluminium has the electron arrangement 2.8.3. Oxygen has the electron arrangement 2.6. We can represent the atoms as:

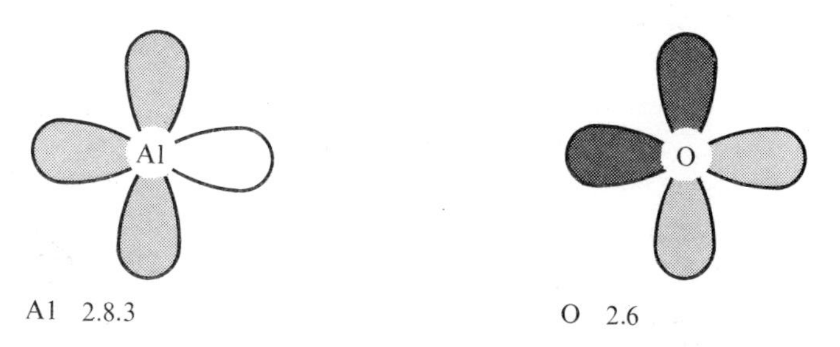

By considering the electron arrangements we can see that aluminium would reach the stable electron arrangement of neon by losing three electrons and oxygen would reach the stable electron arrangement of neon by gaining two electrons. This would result in the formation of an aluminium ion with a 3+ charge and an oxide ion with a 2− charge.

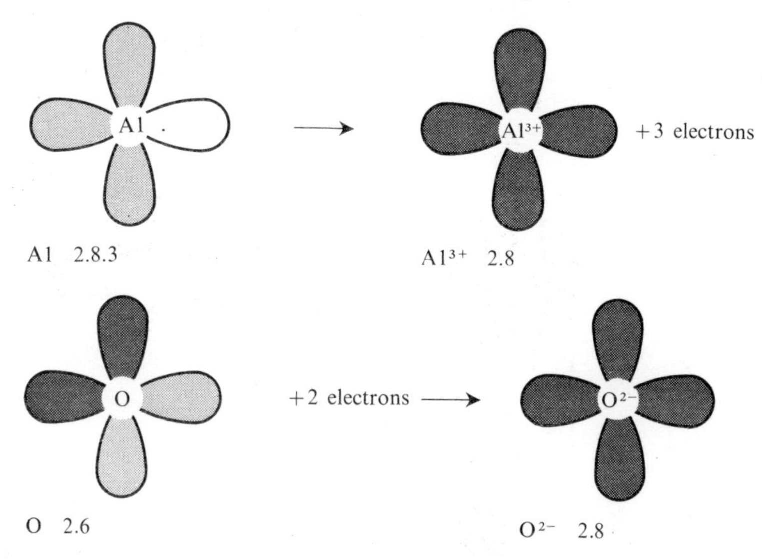

There will be an attraction between the positive ions and the negative ions to form an ionic bond. The compound is electrically neutral, so the formula must be $(Al^{3+})_2(O^{2-})_3$. In the compound aluminium oxide there are three oxide ions for every two aluminium ions.

Summary

From this chapter you should know:

1 Noble gases owe their lack of reactivity to their electron arrangement.

2 Other elements form bonds to achieve this stable arrangement.

3 The bonds formed are the result of attractions and repulsions in neighbouring atoms.

4 There are three types of bond:
Covalent—equal sharing of electrons.
Polar covalent—unequal sharing of electrons.
Ionic (electrovalent)—transfer of electrons producing ions.

An experiment for this chapter is on page 255.

Questions

1 1 Draw the structures of the compounds formed between:
1.1 Carbon and chlorine.
1.2 Lithium and chlorine.
2 Why does the chlorine bond differently in the above compounds? *P & W*

2 Using sodium chloride and hydrogen as examples, explain what happens to electrons in the formation of ionic (electrovalent) compounds and covalent compounds. *SCEEB*

3 1 An atom X has mass number 40 and contains 21 neutrons. To what column of the Periodic Table does it belong?
2 X forms a compound X_2Y. Suggest an element that Y might be and give reasons for your choice. *P & W*

4 The following facts are known about the three elements X, Y, and Z.
The atoms of X have 11 protons.
The atoms of Y have 16 electrons.
The relative atomic mass of Z is 24.3.
1 Name X, Y, and Z.
2 What is the formula of the compound between X and Y?
3 What is the formula of the compound between Y and Z? *SCEEB*

4 Properties associated with types of bonds

4.1 Electrical conductivity

Substances which allow an electric current to flow through them are called **conductors** of electricity, while those which do not are called **non-conductors.** The apparatus shown in Figure 4.1 can be used to determine whether substances conduct or not.

Figure 4.1

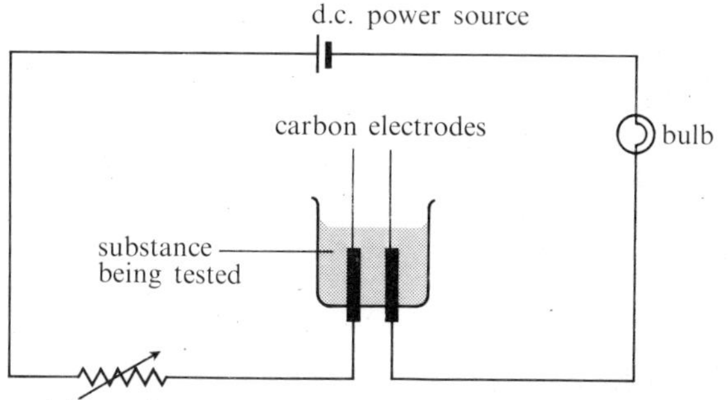

This apparatus is designed for investigating the conductivity of liquids, but it can be adapted for solids by putting crocodile clips on the electrodes and holding the test-piece of the solid between the crocodile clips. If the bulb lights up the substance is a conductor.

Table 4.1 A typical set of results

Conductors when solid	*Non-conductors when solid, conductors when molten or in aqueous solution*	*Non-conductors when solid, molten or in aqueous solution*
Magnesium	Sodium chloride	Glucose
Copper	Copper(II) sulphate	Sulphur
Zinc	Zinc(II) sulphate	Tetrachloromethane
Tin	Sodium carbonate	Ethanol
Aluminium	Silver(I) nitrate	Pure water
Iron	Sodium hydroxide	Methylbenzene
Carbon rod	Nickel(II) sulphate	
	Potassium bromide	

4.2 A closer look at solid conductors

Electricity is a phenomenon associated with electrons. An electric current is a flow of electrons. With the exception of carbon, which we will consider in chapter 14, all the substances which conduct when solid are metals. It seems that a metal has a structure which allows electrons to flow through it. Consider the arrangement of atoms in a copper wire shown in Figure 4.2.

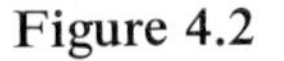

Figure 4.2

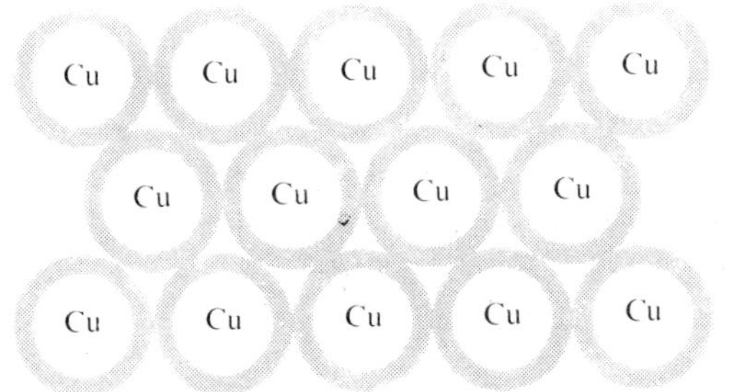

The electron arrangement for each atom of copper is 2.8.18.1, which means that each atom has one electron at rather a long distance from the nucleus. In a close-packed structure, the attraction of the nucleus of the parent atom for the electron is about the same as the attraction of the neighbouring nuclei for the same electron. The electrons in this situation are no longer associated with the original nuclei, but are free to move through the material. However, at any given time, the number of electrons in the bulk of the metal will be the correct number to make the atoms of the metal electrically neutral. When the current is switched on, electrons are pushed into one end of the wire and the same number of electrons are removed from the other end (Figure 4.3).

Figure 4.3

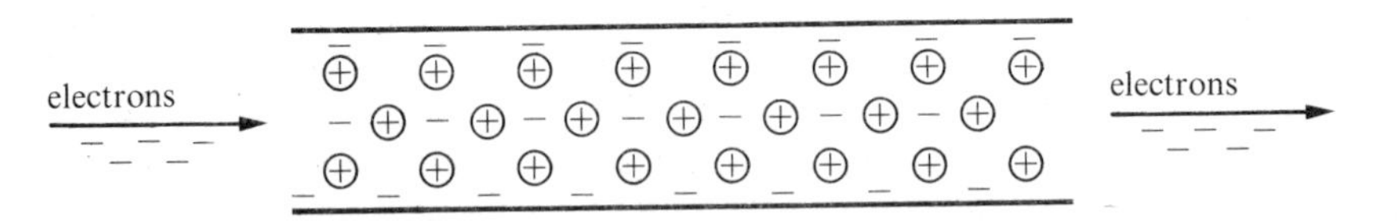

The number of protons and electrons in the wire is unchanged. This means that no chemical change is taking place when electrons are flowing through the wire.

4.3 A closer look at liquid conductors

For the bulb to light in Figure 4.1, electrons must be flowing through the circuit. To allow this, there must be some mechanism for transferring electrons from one carbon electrode to the other. Figure 4.4 shows what happens when molten sodium chloride is tested in the circuit. At the cathode

Figure 4.4

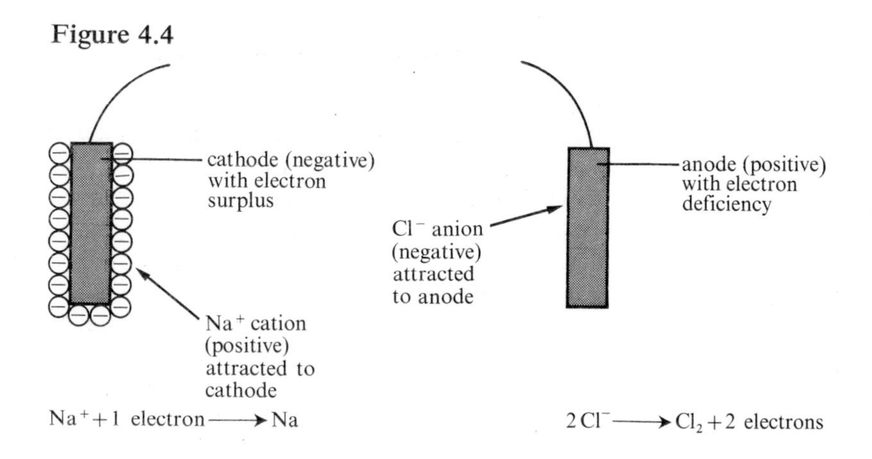

the sodium ion is forced to accept an electron and become a neutral sodium atom. At the anode the chloride ion has the extra electron taken off by the electrode leaving a neutral chlorine atom. The chlorine atoms then combine to form chlorine molecules. The net effect is that the cathode is losing electrons at the same rate as the anode is gaining electrons. This mechanism explains why the bulb lights up, since the electrons are apparently flowing round the circuit.

4.4 Evidence for ions

So far we have considered the formation of ions from a bonding point of view, and then used the theory of ions to explain conduction of certain solutions. This is bound to raise the question: 'Do we have any evidence to support the existence of ions?'

Table 4.2 The colour of some compounds in dilute aqueous solution

	Dichromate(VI)[1]	*Chloride*	*Sulphate*	*Nitrate*	*Manganate(VII)*
Na	orange	colourless	colourless	colourless	purple
K	orange	colourless	colourless	colourless	purple
NH_4	orange	colourless	colourless	colourless	purple
Ca	yellow	colourless	colourless[2]	colourless	purple
Cu(II)	lime green	blue	blue	blue	purple
Pb	yellow	colourless[2]	colourless[2]	colourless	purple
Co	orange	pink	pink	pink	purple
Ag	orange	colourless	colourless	colourless	purple
Fe(III)	yellow	yellow	colourless	colourless	purple
Al	orange	colourless	colourless	colourless	purple
Zn	orange	colourless	colourless	colourless	purple

[1]Solution made acid enough to ensure that the dichromate(VI) ion is present rather than the chromate(VI) ion

[2]Sparingly soluble or insoluble

If we consider the colours of the compounds in Table 4.2, we can assume that the colours are either associated with the compound or with the individual ions which make the compound. For example, the compound sodium manganate(VII) is purple whereas sodium chloride, sodium sulphate, and sodium nitrate are all colourless. This suggests that the sodium ion is colourless and the manganate(VII) ion is purple. Similar reasoning leads us to suspect that copper ions are blue or green, that dichromate ions are orange or yellow, and so on. These are plausible suggestions but it could be that the colour is associated with the compound itself and we will have to investigate further. If the colours are associated with the ions, it should be possible to take a compound which we suspect is made of two coloured ions and separate the ions. A suitable compound is copper(II) manganate(VII), which ought to be made of blue and purple ions. A suitable arrangement is shown in Figure 4.5.

Figure 4.5

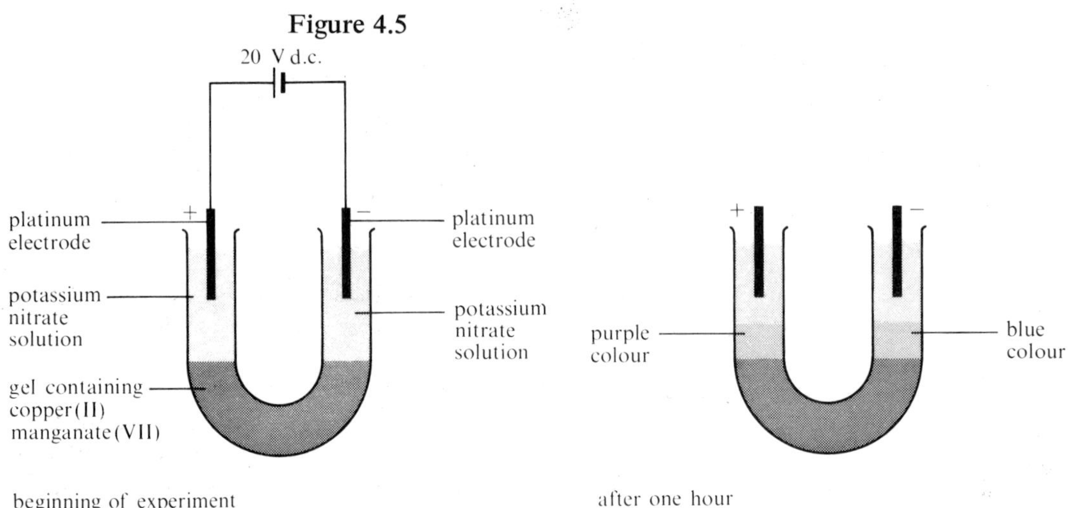

After one hour the purple colour has moved towards the anode and the blue colour has moved towards the cathode. This supports our original reasoning, showing that the copper ion is blue and positively charged, while the manganate(VII) ion is purple and negatively charged. Another way of presenting this argument is to mix two solutions, and if the solutes are ionized, it should be possible to obtain a compound by 'changing partners'.

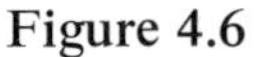

Figure 4.6

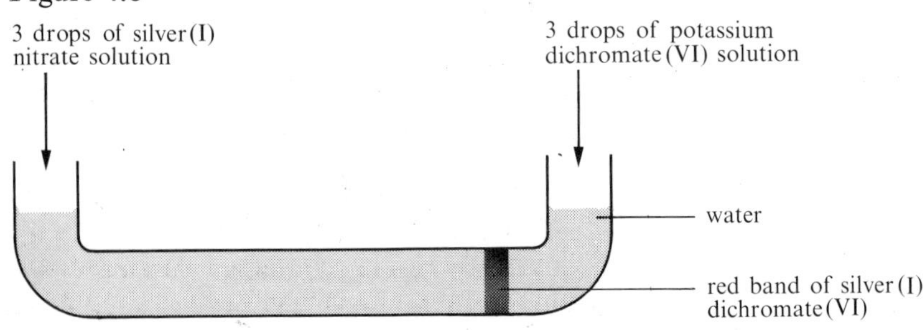

If you would like to try some of these experiments for yourself you will find them on pages 258–60.

4.5 Ions and conductivity

If we replace the bulb in Figure 4.1. by a milliammeter we can compare the conductivities of solutions. Consider the results in Table 4.3.

Table 4.3

Solution	*Conductivity* (mA)
(a) M hydrochloric acid[1]	100
$\frac{M}{10}$ hydrochloric acid	60
$\frac{M}{100}$ hydrochloric acid	45
$\frac{M}{1000}$ hydrochloric acid	5
(b) M sodium hydroxide	82
M sodium chloride	65

[1] M stands for molar, which will be explained on page 70. For the purposes of this experiment it measures the concentration of ions in solution.

From the results in (a), we can deduce that the conductivity depends on the number of ions present. From the results in (b), we can deduce that the hydroxide ion must travel through the solution faster than the chloride ion, since the conductivity due to the sodium ions is the same for both, and in each case the number of ions present is the same. Similar reasoning should lead you to deduce that the hydrogen ion is more mobile than the sodium ion. From this we can see that conductivity depends on two factors:

1. The concentration of ions present.
2. The mobility of the ions present.

4.6 Non-conductors

Compounds like glucose, tetrachloromethane, and methylbenzene are not conductors because there are no ions present nor are there any free electrons. They are covalent compounds. Conductivity gives us a laboratory tool for testing whether a compound is covalent or ionic.

4.7 Melting points and boiling points

From Table 4.4, we see that ionic compounds have high melting points and high boiling points, and that they are usually solids at room temperature.

On the other hand, covalent compounds have low melting points, low boiling points, and are usually liquids or gases at room temperature.

Table 4.4 Melting points and boiling points of some compounds

	Melting point		*Boiling point*			
Compound	K	C	K	°C	*Type of bond*	*State at room temperature*
Benzene	279	6	353	80	Covalent	l
Methane	90	−183	111	−162	Covalent	g
Sodium chloride	1073	800	1686	1413	Ionic	s
Tetrachloromethane	250	−23	350	77	Covalent	l
Trichloromethane (chloroform)	209	−64	334	61	Covalent	l
Calcium chloride	1045	772	>1870	>1600	Ionic	s
Ethanol	159	−114	351	78	Covalent	l
Lead bromide	646	373	1189	916	Ionic	s
Naphthalene	354	81	491	218	Covalent	s
Cadmium iodide	660	387	1069	796	Ionic	s

It would seem that melting points and boiling points should give an indication of the type of bonding in a compound. However, there are some well known exceptions to the general rule, so be prepared to consider further evidence before drawing conclusions about the type of bonding in a compound.

When an ionic crystal is heated to melting, the energy supplied is being used to break the forces of attraction between the ions, so that the ions become free to move about in the liquid state. In this condition the ions are able to conduct an electric current. Even in the liquid state the ions still attract each other strongly, and much heat energy is required to boil the liquid.

Figure 4.7

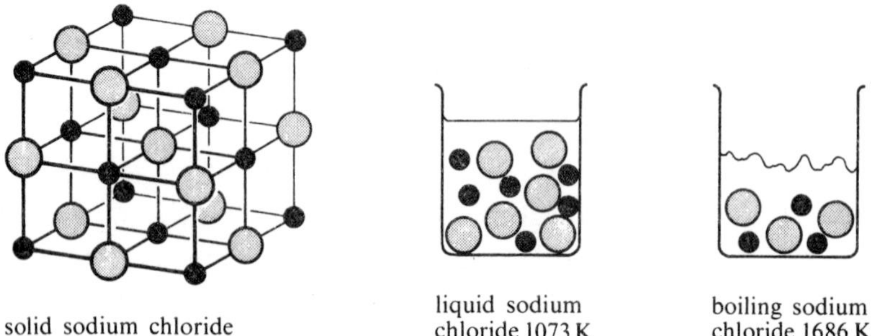

solid sodium chloride 293 K (20 °C)

liquid sodium chloride 1073 K (800 °C)

boiling sodium chloride 1686 K (1413 °C)

Since a great amount of energy was required to boil sodium chloride, we can draw the conclusion that the ionic bond is a strong bond. If we consider the melting points and boiling points of the covalent compounds, we might draw the conclusion that the covalent bond is weak. This, however, is a trap for the unwary. When trichloromethane is heated to boiling, the gas above the liquid is still composed of complete trichloromethane molecules, with all four covalent bonds intact. The small amount of heat energy supplied has been used to overcome the small forces of attraction between the molecules in the liquid. These small, intermolecular forces are called **Van der Waals' forces.** The energy required to break trichloromethane down to carbon and chlorine atoms is very great indeed. In fact the covalent bond is usually stronger than the ionic bond.

4.8 Solubility of compounds in water

Water is a rather remarkable compound in that it dissolves so many different substances. This can be attributed to the polar nature of the water molecule.

The fountain experiment

As soon as the first drop of water enters the flask, it dissolves enough hydrogen chloride to reduce the pressure in the flask. This causes the water to come in to the flask faster, dissolving more gas which, in turn, causes more water to come up to the flask. This gives the effect of a fountain.

Figure 4.8

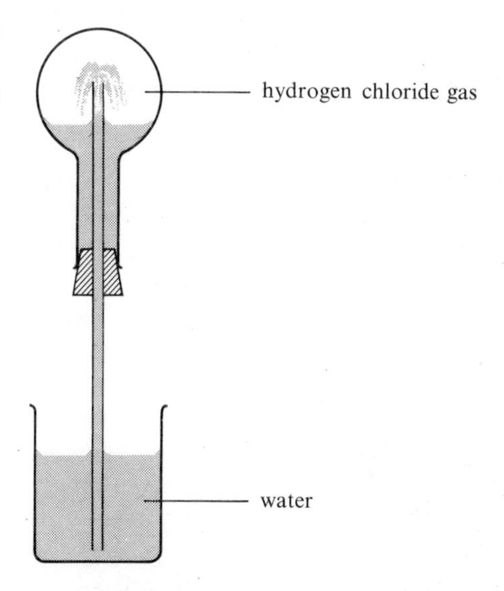

Hydrogen chloride gas is extremely soluble in water, as this experiment shows. This can be explained quite readily when it is appreciated that both hydrogen chloride and water are polar molecules.

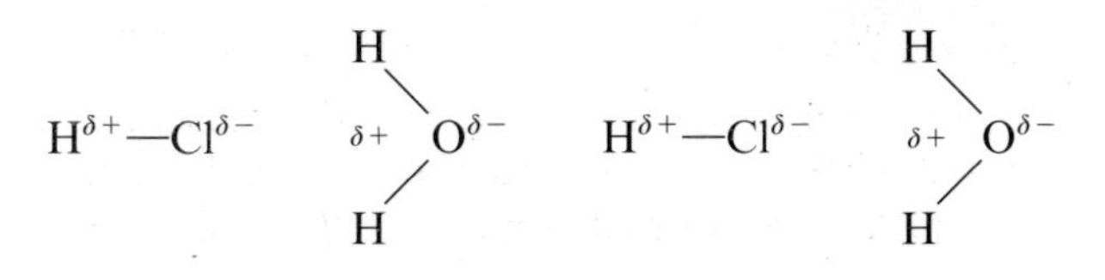

The hydrogen chloride and water molecules line up so that there is an attraction between the molecules. The molecules flip into the correct orientations and attract each other strongly. We shall look at this reaction again in more detail in chapter 7. The fountain experiment also works very well with ammonia gas because this compound is also polar and extremely soluble in water.

When an ionic compound is put into water, the extent to which it dissolves depends on:

1 The relative sizes of the forces holding the ions together in the crystal.
2 The forces of attraction of the water molecules on the ions.

Since sodium chloride dissolves easily in water (Figure 4.9.), the forces of attraction between the ions are smaller than those of the water molecules on the ions.

Figure 4.9

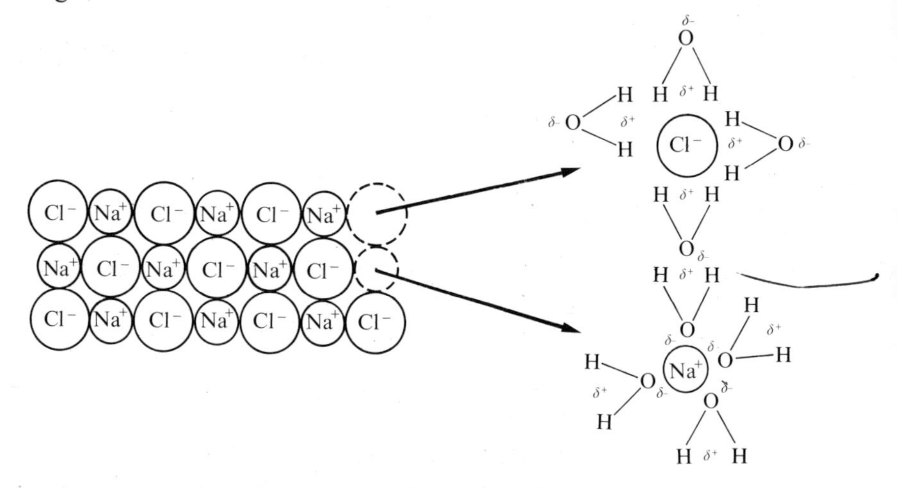

As calcium carbonate is sparingly soluble in water, the forces between the ions in the crystal are greater than the forces pulling the ions into solution.

Solubility in water can be used as a laboratory tool for discriminating between ionic or polar-covalent compounds and non-polar compounds, but again there are traps. Non-polar compounds tend to be insoluble in water, but they do dissolve in non-polar solvents. For instance, naphthalene is insoluble in water, but dissolves in tetrachloromethane.

Summary

From this chapter you should know:

1 An electric current is a flow of electrons.

2 Ions, when free to move, provide a mechanism for conducting electricity.

3 There is some experimental evidence for the existence of ions.

4 The conductivity of a solution or melt depends on the concentration and mobilities of the ions present.

5 Ionic compounds have high melting points and high boiling points. They conduct electricity if the ions are free to move and they may be soluble in water.

6 Covalent compounds have low melting points and low boiling points. They do not conduct electricity and they tend to be insoluble in water.

The experiments for this chapter are on pages 255–62.

Questions

1 Explain why solid sodium chloride does not conduct electricity but molten sodium chloride does.
Suggest another method which will show that sodium chloride is ionic.

2 **1** Explain how bonds are formed in:
1.1 Magnesium oxide
1.2 Hydrogen chloride.
2 The bonding between the atoms in hydrogen chloride molecules is strong. Why is hydrogen chloride a gas and magnesium oxide a solid? *P & W*

3 Why is sulphur a non-conductor of electricity whereas silver is a good conductor?

4 **1** What is thought to happen when atoms are bonded by:
1.1 an electrovalent (ionic) bond?
1.2 a covalent bond?
2 From the following list, name one compound which is electrovalent and one which is covalent:
Ethanol, potassium chloride, calcium nitrate, starch, copper(II) sulphate.
Describe one experiment which could be applied to each of the chosen compounds and would confirm this choice.
3 What is meant by the term 'molecule'?
Explain why the term has no meaning for an electrovalent compound.
SCEEB

5 The following table gives some information about the elements A,B,C,D, and E.

Element	*Atomic number*
A	3
B	9
C	12
D	17
E	18

1 Give the formulae of the compounds you would expect to be formed between:
1.1 C and D.
1.2 C and oxygen.
2 What will be the formula of a compound containing only A and B? Give two physical properties you would expect this compound to have.
3 Would you expect a compound to be formed between E and hydrogen? Explain your answer.

6 Give formulae for the compounds formed between:
1 Potassium and bromine.
2 Carbon and bromine.
Which type of bonding predominates in each?
Which is likely to have a higher boiling point?
Apart from using the boiling point or melting point, explain how you might distinguish between the two compounds.
3 Sketch a molecule of the compound formed when carbon combines with bromine. Why do we not normally speak of a molecule of the potassium–bromine compound? *SCEEB*

7 What type of bonding would you expect between the following pairs of elements:
1 Calcium and oxygen.
2 Carbon and chlorine.
3 Copper and zinc.
4 Hydrogen and chlorine.

8 Show by means of diagrams the three-dimensional structure or shape of the following substances:
1 A tetrachloromethane molecule.
2 A water molecule.
3 Part of a sodium chloride crystal. *SCEEB*

9 The apparatus in the diagram was set up to demonstrate the movement of ions.

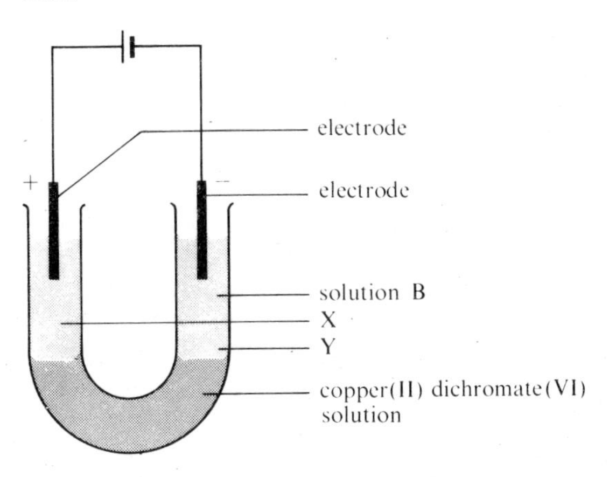

1 Would you use an a.c. or d.c. power supply? Explain your answer.
2 Suggest a suitable material for the electrodes.
3 Suggest a suitable solution for solution B.

10

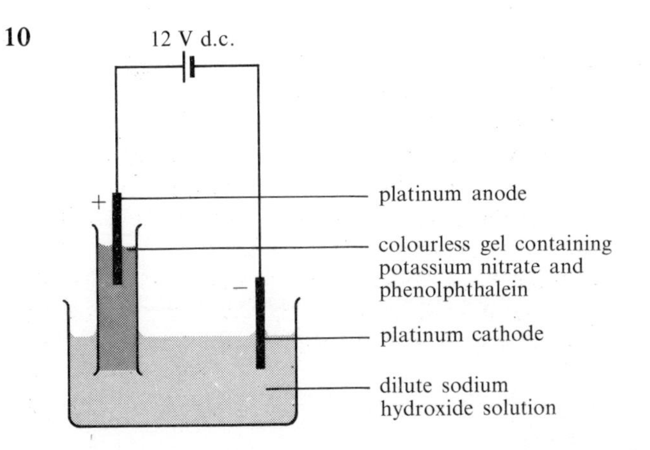

When a current flows in the circuit above, a pink colour travels slowly up the gel in the glass tube.

1 What is the function of the potassium nitrate?
2 Explain why the pink colour rises up the gel in the tube. *P & W*

5 Chemical formulae

5.1 Valency

When elements combine to form compounds they do so in fixed numbers depending on the capacities of the atoms involved to form bonds. This capacity or strength of the atom to form bonds is called its **combining power** or **valency.** The electrons in the highest energy level are involved in bonding, and they are called the valency electrons.

The valency of the element will depend on the number of valency electrons. It will be either the number of valency electrons, or the number of electrons required to make up the stable octet of a noble gas. The valency is equal to the charge on the ion when the element is involved in ionic bonding.

Table 5.1

Group	*1*	*2*	*3*	*4*	*5*	*6*	*7*	*8*
Valency	1	2	3	4	5 or 3	6 or 2	7 or 1	0
Charge on ion	1+	2+	3+		3−	2−	1−	0

The elements in Group 5, 6, and 7 have two possible valencies, depending on whether we consider the number of electrons in the highest energy level or the number of extra electrons required to give the element the structure of a noble gas. Chlorine has a valency of one (the number of electrons required to give the noble gas structure) in a large number of compounds, especially ionic compounds, but it does have a valency of seven (the number of electrons in the highest energy level) in the oxide, Cl_2O_7. Similarly we can reconcile the formulae PCl_5 and PCl_3 by giving chlorine a valency of one and phosphorus valencies of five and three respectively.

If we can give values for valency to the elements we can then deduce the formulae for compounds by balancing the valencies. Some examples are shown below.

1. Calcium bromide: Ca has a valency of two. Br has a valency of one. Formula is $CaBr_2$.
2. Potassium oxide: K has a valency of one. O has a valency of two. Formula is K_2O.
3. Magnesium nitride: Mg has a valency of two. N has a valency of three. Formula is Mg_3N_2.
4. Hydrogen oxide (water): O has a valency of two. H has a valency of one. Formula is H_2O.

The names of all the compounds so far have ended in -ide. This indicates that the compound contains only the elements mentioned in the name.

At first sight it looks as if we are well on the way to writing formulae easily, but there are difficulties which we have so far ignored:

1 Elements in the transition series show variable valencies.
2 Some ions contain several atoms combined together, and although it is possible to draw electron cloud diagrams for them from first principles, it is cumbersome and tedious.

Tables 5.2 and 5.3 should help you learn the valencies for some common ions.

Table 5.2 Valencies of cations

Valency of one		*Valency of two*		*Valency of three*	
Li^+	lithium	Be^{2+}	beryllium	Cr^{3+}	chromium(III)
Na^+	sodium	Mg^{2+}	magnesium	Al^{3+}	aluminium
K^+	potassium	Ca^{2+}	calcium	Fe^{3+}	iron(III)
NH_4^+	ammonium	Ba^{2+}	barium		
Cu^+	copper(I)	Cu^{2+}	copper(II)		
Hg^+	mercury(I)	Fe^{2+}	iron(II)		
Ag^+	silver	Hg^{2+}	mercury(II)		
		Zn^{2+}	zinc(II)		
		Pb^{2+}	lead(II)		
		Sn^{2+}	tin(II)		

Table 5.3 Valencies of anions

Valency of one		*Valency of two*		*Valency of three*	
F^-	fluoride	O^{2-}	oxide	N^{3-}	nitride
Cl^-	chloride	S^{2-}	sulphide	P^{3-}	phosphide
Br^-	bromide	SO_4^{2-}	sulphate	PO_4^{3-}	phosphate
I^-	iodide	SO_3^{2-}	sulphite		
NO_3^-	nitrate	CO_3^{2-}	carbonate		
NO_2^-	nitrite	CrO_4^{2-}	chromate(VI)		
OH^-	hydroxide	$Cr_2O_7^{2-}$	dichromate(VI)		
MnO_4^-	manganate(VII)				
HCO_3^-	hydrogencarbonate				

Examples

Sodium sulphate Na_2SO_4
Iron(II) hydroxide $Fe(OH)_2$
Potassium manganate(VII) $KMnO_4$
Silver(I) chromate(VI) Ag_2CrO_4
Lithium hydrogencarbonate $LiHCO_3$
Barium carbonate $BaCO_3$
Copper(II) nitrate $Cu(NO_3)_2$
Aluminium sulphate $Al_2(SO_4)_3$
Chromium(III) oxide Cr_2O_3
Tin(II) phosphate $Sn_3(PO_4)_2$

5.2 Formula weight and the mole

The **formula weight** of a compound is obtained by writing down the formula for the compound and adding up the relative atomic masses of all the atoms in the compound. Values of relative atomic masses are given in the Periodic Table inside the front cover of the book.

Example Find the formula weight of sodium sulphate.
Formula is Na_2SO_4.

$$
\begin{aligned}
\text{Relative atomic mass of Na} &= 23 \\
\text{S} &= 32 \\
\text{O} &= 16 \\
\text{Formula weight} &= 23\times2+32+16\times4 \\
&= 46+32+64 \\
&= 142.
\end{aligned}
$$

A **mole** is the amount of substance corresponding to the formula weight expressed in gram units. Thus, 142 g of sodium sulphate represents one mole of the compound.

Examples NaOH: formula weight $= 23+16+1$
$= 40.$
One mole of sodium hydroxide $\equiv$ 40 g of the compound.
Na_2CO_3: formula weight $= 46+12+48$
$= 106.$
One mole of sodium carbonate $\equiv$ 106 g of the compound.

Although the mole bridges the gap between atomic mass units and the laboratory units of gram, there is a more fundamental connection. A mole is the mass of a fixed number of formula weight units. This is a very large number, 6×10^{23}, which is called the Avogadro Constant. The number was obtained from very complicated experiments. The importance of the Avogadro Constant lies in the fact that statements about moles can be related back to the atoms themselves, and this in turn means that formulae for compounds can be determined from simple analysis. To change from gram units to moles you divide the mass in grams by the formula weight:

$$
\begin{aligned}
\text{6 g of carbon C} &\equiv \frac{6}{12} \text{ moles or 0.5 of a mole.} \\
\text{4 g of sodium hydroxide NaOH} &\equiv \frac{4}{40} \text{ moles or 0.1 of a mole.} \\
\text{53 g of sodium carbonate } Na_2CO_3 &\equiv \frac{53}{106} \text{ moles or 0.5 of a mole.} \\
\text{0.17 g of ammonia } NH_3 &\equiv \frac{0.17}{17} \text{ moles or 0.01 of a mole.}
\end{aligned}
$$

Example To find the formula of a compound from simple analysis, the following method can be used.
From analysis 5.0 g of chalk contain 2.0 g of calcium, 0.6 g carbon and 2.42 g of oxygen. Find the formula for chalk.

Table 5.4

Element	*Mass*(g)	*Relative atomic mass*	*Number of moles*	*Ratio*
Ca	2.0	40	$\frac{2.0}{40} = 0.05$	1
C	0.6	12	$\frac{0.6}{12} = 0.05$	1
O	2.4	16	$\frac{2.4}{16} = 0.15$	3

From the ratios between the elements, the formula of chalk must be $CaCO_3$.

This is the **empirical formula** for chalk and we see that it is calcium carbonate. An empirical formula is one found from experiment and very often, since it gives only the ratio of atoms in the compound, it requires to be multiplied by a factor to obtain the correct formula.

Example A compound contains 26.7 per cent carbon, 2.2 per cent hydrogen and 71.1 per cent oxygen by weight. From the mass spectrometer the formula weight of the compound is found to be 90. Find the molecular formula for the compound.

Table 5.5

Element	*Mass*(g)	*Relative atomic mass*	*Number of moles*	*Ratio*
C	26.7	12	$\frac{26.7}{12} = 2.2$	1
H	2.2	1	$\frac{2.2}{1} = 2.2$	1
O	71.1	16	$\frac{71.1}{16} = 4.4$	2

The empirical formula is CHO_2.
The formula weight of CHO_2 is 45.
The mass spectrometer tells us that the compound has a formula weight of 90.

Therefore
$$(CHO_2)_n = 90$$
$$45n = 90$$
$$n = 2$$

Thus the molecular formula is $(CHO_2)_2$ or $C_2H_2O_4$.

It is possible to calculate the percentage composition of elements in a compound.

Example Calculate the percentage composition of hydrogen and oxygen in water.

Formula weight of H_2O $= 2+16$
$= 18$

$$\text{The proportion of hydrogen} = \frac{\text{Formula weight of hydrogen in compound}}{\text{Formula weight of compound}}$$

$$\text{The percentage of hydrogen} = \frac{\text{Formula weight of hydrogen in compound} \times 100}{\text{Formula weight of compound}}$$

$$= \frac{2 \times 100}{18}$$

$= 11$ per cent

$$\text{The proportion of oxygen} = \frac{\text{Formula weight of oxygen in compound}}{\text{Formula weight of compound}}$$

$$\text{The percentage of oxygen} = \frac{\text{Formula weight of oxygen in compound} \times 100}{\text{Formula weight of compound}}$$

$$= \frac{16 \times 100}{18}$$

$= 89$ per cent

5.3 Concentration and molarity

A solution of known concentration is called a **standard solution**. The units can be any units of mass per unit of volume, but the most common in a chemistry laboratory are grams per litre of solution ($g\,l^{-1}$). However, since chemical elements and compounds react in simple molar ratios, it is more convenient to express the concentration in moles per litre of solution ($mole\,l^{-1}$).

A **molar solution** contains one mole of **solute** per litre of **solution**.

Example 1 What mass of sodium hydroxide is required to make 500 cm^3 of 1M sodium hydroxide solution?

Formula of sodium hydroxide is NaOH
Formula weight $= 40$
40 g of sodium hydroxide make 1000 cm^3 of 1M solution.
Therefore 20 g of sodium hydroxide make 500 cm^3 of 1M solution.

Example 2 What is the molarity of a solution containing 0.53 g of sodium carbonate in 250 cm^3 of solution?

Formula of sodium carbonate is Na_2CO_3
Formula weight $= 106$

$$\text{Concentration} = 0.53 \text{ g in } 250 \text{ cm}^3$$
$$= 4 \times 0.53 \text{ g l}^{-1}$$
$$= \frac{4 \times 0.53}{106} \text{ mol l}^{-1}$$
$$= 0.02\text{M}$$

Example 3 What mass of sodium chloride is contained in 2 litres of a 0.1M solution?

2 litres of 0.1M solution contains the same mass of NaCl as 200 cm^3 of 1M solution.
But 1000 cm^3 of 1M solution contains 58.5 g.
Therefore 200 cm^3 of 1M solution contains $\frac{58.5}{5}$ g = 11.7 g

The importance of molar solutions will be realized when volumetric calculations are discussed in chapter 8.6.

5.4 What the formula does not tell

The formula for a compound does not tell us anything about the type of bonding in the compound. It simply shows the relative number of atoms in it. We have to have some other information about the compound before we can speculate on the bonding. Experimental evidence about melting point, boiling point, and conductivity is required.

However, if we have no evidence, then we may speculate on the type of bonding by referring to the positions of the elements in the Periodic Table. Elements far apart horizontally tend to form ionic compounds, and elements near the middle tend to form covalent compounds. From the positions of sodium and chlorine in the Periodic Table we might expect sodium chloride to be ionic. Sodium is in Group 1 and chlorine is in Group 7. They are far apart horizontally and do form the ionic compound sodium chloride NaCl. Since carbon and oxygen are close together and in the middle of the Table we might expect carbon dioxide to be covalent. Carbon is in Group 4 and oxygen is in Group 6, and they do form the covalent compound carbon dioxide CO_2. This is a generalization, and although it does give an indication of the bonding, it is not always true.

Summary

From this chapter you should know:

1. Valency is a number associated with group number.
2. Formulae are obtained by balancing valencies.
3. How to calculate formula weights.
4. The mole is the amount of substance corresponding to the formula weight in gram units.
5. The mole is the bridge between gram units and atomic mass units.
6. How to determine the experimental formula.
7. How to calculate the molarity of a solution.

The experiments for this chapter are on pages 263–4.

Questions

1 Write formulae for the following compounds and comment on the type of bonding likely in each case.

1	Potassium iodide	6	Lead bromide
2	Zinc(II) oxide	7	Tin(II) carbonate
3	Ammonium sulphate	8	Tetrachloromethane
4	Silicon oxide	9	Silver(I) nitrate
5	Copper(II) dichromate(VI)	10	Iron(III) hydroxide

2 Find the mass of one mole of each of the compounds in question 1.

3 How many moles of sodium hydroxide are there in 10 g of the compound?

4 How many moles of each ion are present in 5.3 g of sodium carbonate?

5 Find the empirical formula for each of the following compounds from the composition by mass.
1 Na, 29.1%; S, 40.5%; O, 30.4%
2 Na, 37.1%; C, 9.7%; O, 38.7%; H_2O, 14.5%
3 K, 42.4%; Fe, 15.2%; C, 19.5%; N, 22.8%

6 A well known anaesthetic contains 64.9 per cent carbon, 13.5 per cent hydrogen, and 21.6 per cent oxygen by mass. If one mole of the compound has a mass of 74 g, find the formula for the compound.

7 1 Calculate the formula weights of:
1.1 Calcium nitrate
1.2 Chromium(III) sulphide.
2 How many moles of anhydrous sodium carbonate are present in 5.3 g of the salt? *P & W*

8 1 Calculate the percentage composition of sodium hydroxide.
2 Calculate the empirical (simplest) formula of a substance which contains 49.5 per cent manganese and 50.5 per cent oxygen. *P & W*

9 1 Calculate the weight of one mole of calcium phosphate.
2 Analysis of a hydrated salt showed that it contained 56.2 per cent of barium and 29.1 per cent of chlorine, by mass. Find the empirical (simplest) formula of the salt. *P & W*

10 A sample of lead was weighed and dissolved in nitric acid. The resultant solution was diluted with water and potassium iodide solution was added until precipitation was complete. The precipitate of lead iodide was filtered, dried and weighed. The results obtained were:
Weight of lead = 0.63 g
Weight of lead iodide = 1.41 g
1 How would you ensure that all the lead iodide has been precipitated?
2 Calculate the formula of lead iodide. *P & W*

11 1 In the following account there are certain errors and omissions. Make a list of these and give the corrections required.
'From the formula PbO it can be calculated that 1 g oxygen combines with 10.25 g lead. To check this experimentally the following procedure should be carried out: From the bottle labelled lead oxide (technical) carefully weigh a sample in a container. Place the container in a glass tube and pass coal gas over it. As soon as some lead is seen in the container, reweigh.'
2 From a properly conducted experiment on an oxide of lead, the following results were obtained.

Weight of porcelain boat = 5.20 g
Weight of porcelain boat + the oxide of lead = 7.60 g
Weight of porcelain boat + lead = 7.28 g

What weight of lead combines with 1 g of oxygen?
3 Given that one atom of lead is thirteen times as heavy as one atom of oxygen, what is the simplest formula for this oxide?
4 White lead, $Pb_3(OH)_2(CO_3)_2$, and chrome yellow, $PbCrO_4$ are used as pigments in paint. Calculate which has the higher percentage of lead. Show your working clearly. *SCEEB*

12 Calculate the molarity of the following solutions:
1 4.0 g of sodium hydroxide in 100 cm^3 of solution.
2 10.6 g of sodium carbonate in 500 cm^3 of solution.
3 5.85 g of sodium chloride in 1 litre of solution.

13 Calculate the mass of solute in each of the following solutions:
1 200 cm^3 of 0.1M potassium hydroxide.
2 500 cm^3 of 1M potassium carbonate.
3 2 litres of 0.5M potassium chloride.

6 Equations

6.1 Introduction

When a mixture of hydrogen and oxygen explodes, water is formed. Unless the masses of the gases in the mixture are exactly those required to make water, there will be an excess of one of the gases.

Reactions can be summarized by using **equations,** but it is important to realize that these equations are precise quantitative statements and not simply a form of shorthand. The above reaction can be illustrated by the following equation:

$$2H_2(g) + O_2(g) \rightarrow 2H_2O(l)$$

It should be read as follows: two moles of hydrogen gas combine with one mole of oxygen gas to produce two moles of water. Bearing in mind the significance of the Avogadro Constant, it is possible to read the equation as two molecules of hydrogen combine with one molecule of oxygen to form two molecules of water. Unless otherwise stated we shall interpret an equation in the mole form.

It is worth noticing at this point that 4 g of hydrogen combine with 32 g of oxygen to form 36 g of water. This is only to be expected because matter is neither created nor destroyed in a chemical reaction. This is known as the Law of Conservation of Mass.

6.2 Rules for writing equations

1. Be sure that the chemical reaction really does take place.
2. Write the correct formula for each of the reactants and products.
3. Balance the equation by using multiples of these formulae.
4. After each reactant and product put in the physical state.
5. Do not change the formula of a compound or element to balance the equation.

Example 1 Finely divided copper burns in chlorine gas to form a dense smoke of copper(II) chloride. Following the rules above:

1. Unless you have seen this reaction you will need to accept that it does in fact take place.
2. Write the formulae.

   $$Cu + Cl_2 \rightarrow CuCl_2$$

3. Balance the equation.
   In this case the equation is already balanced.

4 Put in physical states.

$Cu(s) + Cl_2(g) \rightarrow CuCl_2(s)$

One mole of copper (63.5 g) combines with one mole of chlorine gas (71 g) to form one mole of copper(II) chloride (134.5 g).

Example 2 Sodium metal reacts with water to give off hydrogen gas and leave a solution of sodium hydroxide.

$$Na + H_2O \rightarrow NaOH + H_2$$
$$2Na + 2H_2O \rightarrow 2NaOH + H_2$$
$$2Na(s) + 2H_2O(l) \rightarrow 2NaOH(aq) + H_2(g)$$

Two moles of sodium react with two moles of water to produce two moles of sodium hydroxide and one mole of hydrogen gas. The symbol (aq) is used in the equation above. This is an abbreviation for aqueous, and indicates that the substance is dissolved in water.

Example 3 When dilute hydrochloric acid is added to marble chips (calcium carbonate), carbon dioxide gas is given off and a solution of calcium chloride is produced.

$CaCO_3 + HCl \rightarrow CaCl_2 + CO_2$

This equation is not going to balance, because water is also a product.

$CaCO_3 + HCl \rightarrow CaCl_2 + CO_2 + H_2O$

Inspection of the products should lead you to write

$CaCO_3(s) + 2HCl(aq) \rightarrow CaCl_2(aq) + CO_2(g) + H_2O(l)$

One mole of calcium carbonate reacts with two moles of hydrochloric acid to produce one mole of calcium chloride, one mole of carbon dioxide gas and one mole of water.

Reactions which take place between ionic compounds in aqueous solution can be written in the ionic form and it becomes apparent that some of the ions react while others do not.

Example 1 Sodium hydroxide solution reacts with hydrochloric acid to form sodium chloride solution and water.

$NaOH(aq) + HCl(aq) \rightarrow NaCl(aq) + H_2O(l)$
or
$Na^+(aq) + OH^-(aq) + H^+(aq) + Cl^-(aq) \rightarrow Na^+(aq) + Cl^-(aq) + H_2O(l)$

Example 2 Sodium hydroxide solution reacts with nitric acid to form sodium nitrate solution and water.

$NaOH(aq) + HNO_3(aq) \rightarrow NaNO_3(aq) + H_2O(l)$
or
$Na^+(aq) + OH^-(aq) + H^+(aq) + NO_3^-(aq) \rightarrow Na^+(aq) + NO_3^-(aq) + H_2O(l)$

Example 3 Potassium hydroxide solution reacts with hydrochloric acid to form potassium chloride solution and water.

$$KOH(aq) + HCl(aq) \rightarrow KCl(aq) + H_2O(l)$$

or

$$K^+(aq) + OH^-(aq) + H^+(aq) + Cl^-(aq) \rightarrow K^+(aq) + Cl^-(aq) + H_2O(l)$$

Example 4 Calcium hydroxide solution reacts with hydrochloric acid to form calcium chloride solution and water.

$$Ca(OH)_2(aq) + 2HCl(aq) \rightarrow CaCl_2(aq) + 2H_2O(l)$$

or

$$Ca^{2+}(aq) + 2OH^-(aq) + 2H^+(aq) + 2Cl^-(aq) \rightarrow Ca^{2+}(aq) + 2Cl^-(aq) + 2H_2O(l)$$

Example 5 Sodium hydroxide solution reacts with sulphuric acid to form sodium sulphate solution and water.

$$2NaOH(aq) + H_2SO_4(aq) \rightarrow Na_2SO_4(aq) + 2H_2O(l)$$

or

$$2Na^+(aq) + 2OH^-(aq) + 2H^+(aq) + SO_4^{2-}(aq) \rightarrow 2Na^+(aq) + SO_4^{2-}(aq) + 2H_2O(l)$$

In each of these reactions the hydroxide ion OH^- and the hydrogen ion H^+ are reacting to form water. The other ions are merely spectators and can be left out of the equation. Thus,

$$OH^-(aq) + H^+(aq) \rightarrow H_2O(l)$$

represents all of the above equations. One mole of hydroxide ions reacts with one mole of hydrogen ions to form one mole of water in each equation.

6.3 Calculations from equations

Since equations are quantitative statements, it is possible to calculate the exact quantities of reactants required to produce the products. We can solve chemical problems of this type by following the simple rules.

1. Write the equation for the reaction.
2. Write the mole ratio for the chemicals in question.
3. Express the mole in the appropriate units.
4. Find the quantity required by simple proportion.

Example 1 What mass of carbon dioxide will be given off by heating 10 g of calcium carbonate?

$CaCO_3(s) \rightarrow CaO(s) + CO_2(g)$	
1 mole	1 mole
100 g	44 g
10 g	4.4 g

10 g of calcium carbonate will yield 4.4 g of carbon dioxide.

Example 2 What mass of oxygen would be required to convert 7.5 g of sulphur to sulphur dioxide?

$S(s)$ +	$O_2(g) \rightarrow SO_2(g)$
1 mole	1 mole
32 g	32 g
7.5 g	7.5 g

7.5 g of sulphur require 7.5 g of oxygen.

Example 3 How many moles of hydrochloric acid would be required to neutralize exactly 80 g of sodium hydroxide?

$NaOH(aq)+$	$HCl(aq) \rightarrow NaCl(aq)+H_2O(l)$
1 mole	1 mole
40 g	1 mole
80 g	2 moles

80 g of sodium hydroxide would require two moles of hydrochloric acid to neutralize it.

Example 4 What mass of phosphorus(V) oxide would be formed by burning 4g of phosphorus in 8g of oxygen, and how much oxygen would be left?

$4P(s)$ +	$5O_2(g)$ $\rightarrow$	$2P_2O_5(s)$
4 moles	5 moles	2 moles
(4×31) g	(5×32) g	(2×142) g
4 g	5.16 g	9.16

4 g of phosphorus would burn to form 9.16g of phosphorus(V) oxide and 2.84g of oxygen would be left.

This chapter is designed to help you write equations with speed and accuracy since both are essential if quantitative chemistry is to be more than a lesson in arithmetic

Summary

From this chapter you should know:

1 An equation is a precise quantitative statement.

2 There are simple rules for writing equations:
Know the reaction.
Write the formulae for the reactants and products.
Balance the equation.
Put in the physical states.

3 Calculations from equations require the use of simple proportion.

Questions

1 Write equations for the following reactions.
1 Calcium metal reacts with water, giving off hydrogen gas and leaving a solution of calcium hydroxide.
2 Mercury(II) oxide decomposes on heating to produce its elements.
3 Carbon dioxide dissolved in aqueous sodium hydroxide produces a solution of sodium hydrogencarbonate.
4 Iron(III) oxide reacts with carbon monoxide to give iron and carbon dioxide.
5 Ammonia gas reacts with hydrogen chloride gas forming solid ammonium chloride.

2 Calculate the mass of oxygen required to burn 6g of magnesium.

3 How many moles of sodium hydroxide would be required if 4.9 g of sulphuric acid reacted completely to give sodium sulphate and water?

4 Ammonium dichromate(VI) $(NH_4)_2Cr_2O_7$ decomposes on heating, forming chromium(III) oxide Cr_2O_3, water, and nitrogen. Calculate the mass of nitrogen gas formed by heating one mole of ammonium dichromate(VI).

5 How many moles of sodium are there in 9.2g sodium?
What weight of hydrogen is produced when 9.2g sodium reacts with water.
P & W

6 In an experiment to determine the composition of an oxide of copper, 1.43g of the oxide were found to yield 1.27g of copper metal.
1 Draw a labelled diagram showing the apparatus and chemicals which could be used in the experiment.
2 From the results given above calculate the simplest formula of the oxide.
3 Write a balanced chemical equation for the reaction taking place in the experiment.

7 1 What is the weight in grams of a mole of (a) calcium and (b) sodium?
2 What do a mole of calcium and a mole of sodium have in common?
3 What weight of hydrogen would be obtained by reaction of 0.1 mole of calcium with water?
4 Explain if there would be any difference in the weight of hydrogen obtained if 0.1 mole of sodium were used. *P & W*

8 In an experiment 36g of an oxide of copper was reduced to metal by passing hydrogen gas over the heated oxide. 32g of copper remained.
1 Calculate a possible formula for the copper oxide.
2 What weight of water was formed? *SCEEB*

9 In an experiment, 20 litres of hydrogen and 10 litres of oxygen are obtained from water.

1 The density of hydrogen is 0.1 grams per litre. What weight of hydrogen is obtained in the experiment?

2 The density of oxygen is 1.6 grams per litre. What weight of oxygen is obtained in the experiment?

3 How many moles of hydrogen are obtained in the experiment?

4 How many moles of oxygen are obtained in the experiment?

5 Use your answers to justify that the formula for water is H_2O. *SCEEB*

7 Acids, bases, and salts

7.1 Water equilibrium

In chapter 4 we observed that pure water is apparently a non-conductor (see Table 4.1). If we change the milliammeter (see page 59) for a micro-ammeter, a small amount of current is observed. The implication of this is that there are some ions present in the pure water, although a very low concentration:

$$H_2O(l) \rightleftharpoons H^+(aq) + OH^-(aq)$$

Water exists in equilibrium with hydrogen ions and hydroxide ions. The double arrow indicates a reversible reaction in which the water molecules are being ionized at the same rate as the ions are combining to form water molecules. The large arrow indicates that when the system is at equilibrium the concentration of water molecules is very large compared to the concentration of the ions. In one litre of water there are only 10^{-7} moles of each ion, whereas there are about fifty moles of water molecules.

Since water is such a common solvent, we use it as the reference when describing solutions as being **neutral.** A neutral solution is one in which the concentration of $H^+(aq)$ is equal to the concentration of $OH^-(aq)$. If $H^+(aq)$ is in excess the solution is described as being **acidic,** and if $OH^-(aq)$ is in excess the solution is described as being **alkaline.**

$H^+(aq) = OH^-(aq)$ Neutral
$H^+(aq) > OH^-(aq)$ Acidic
$H^+(aq) < OH^-(aq)$ Alkaline

7.2 pH scale

In pure water the concentration of hydrogen ions is 10^{-7} moles per litre. We call this a pH of seven. We are taking the **p**ower of the **H**ydrogen ion but ignoring the minus sign. The pH of a solution is measured using pH paper, which changes colour at different values of pH. The $H^+(aq)$ ion is very mobile. Small changes in its concentration will lead to significant changes in the conductivity of the solution. A millivoltmeter can be calibrated to detect these changes, and we call it a pH meter. pH paper, however, will indicate pH accurately enough for our purposes.

pH indicator papers are supplied with a colour chart for reference, and there is no need to learn the colours. The smaller the number on the pH scale the larger is the concentration of hydrogen ions. This is confusing until you realize that we are ignoring a minus sign in the index. As soon as you see that 10^{-2} is bigger than 10^{-3}, you will understand that a solution with a pH of two has more hydrogen ions than one with a pH of three.

Figure 7.1 (a) the pH scale; (b) colours of pH paper

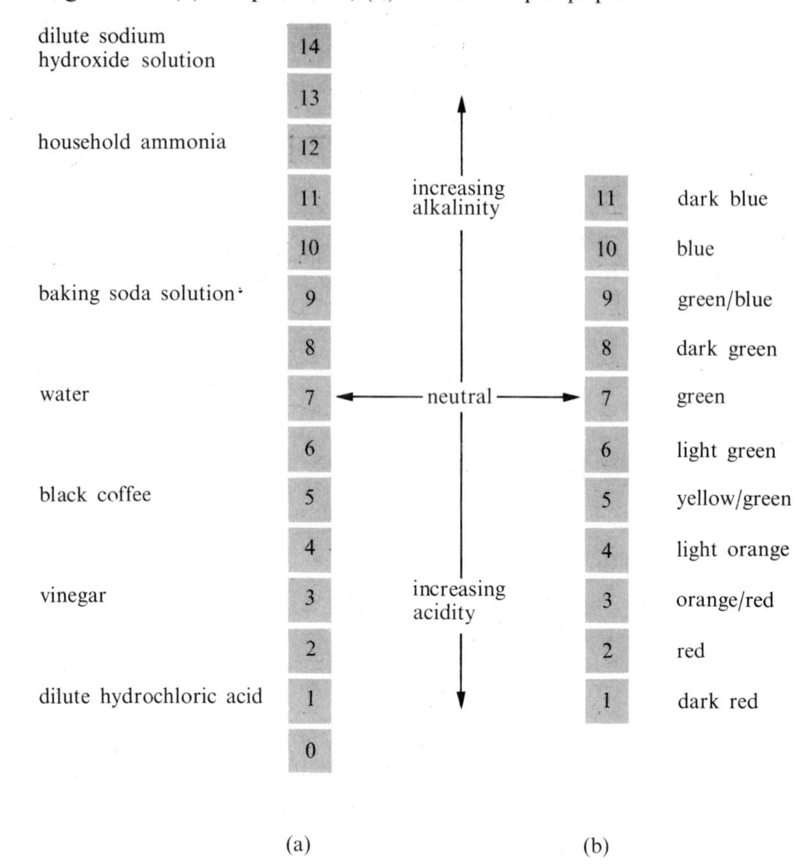

7.3 Acidic and basic oxides

When elements are burned in oxygen, the products dissolved in water, and the pH of the resulting solutions measured, results of the kind shown in Table 7.1 are obtained.

Table 7.1

	Substance burned	*pH of the resulting solution*	
Metals	Sodium	11	Alkaline
	Calcium	10	
	Magnesium	8	
Non-metals	Carbon	4	Acidic
	Phosphorus	2	
	Sulphur	2	

From Table 7.1 it is apparent that metal oxides form alkaline solutions and non-metal oxides form acidic solutions when they are dissolved in water. Metal oxides are **basic oxides** which give alkaline solutions if they are soluble in water. Non-metal oxides are **acidic oxides** which give acid solutions if they are soluble in water.

7.4 Acids

By definition, an **acid** is a substance which produces hydrogen ions in aqueous solution, that is a **proton donor.**

Table 7.2

Acid	*Formula*	
Hydrochloric	HCl	Monoprotic
Nitric	HNO_3	
Nitrous	HNO_2	
Sulphuric	H_2SO_4	Diprotic
Sulphurous	H_2SO_3	
Carbonic	H_2CO_3	
Phosphoric	H_3PO_4	Triprotic

An acid always contains hydrogen. The names monoprotic, diprotic, and triprotic refer to the number of hydrogen atoms in the formula that are capable of being easily removed from the molecule as protons. Since protons are extremely small, and consequently carry a high charge, they attach themselves readily to polar molecules. With water they form oxonium ions H_3O^+.

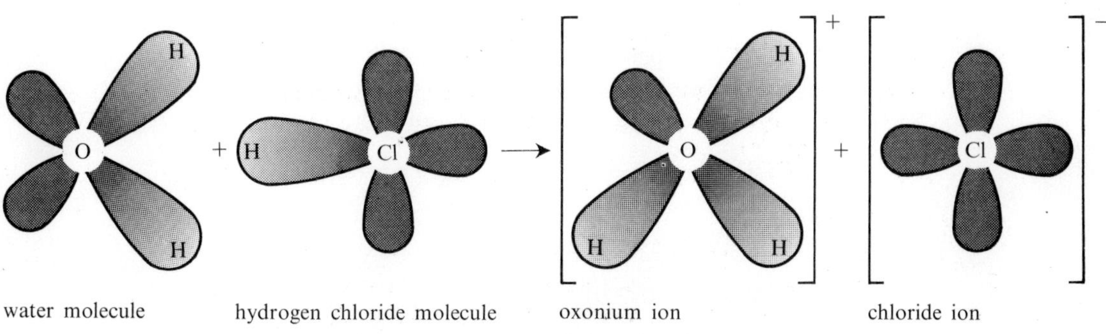

water molecule hydrogen chloride molecule oxonium ion chloride ion

The oxonium ion can cause an unnecessary complication in writing equations. It is often more convenient to write $H^+(aq)$ to represent the proton from the acid in solution, provided that you understand that the proton cannot exist as a single entity in solution.

$$HCl(g) \rightarrow H^+(aq) + Cl^-(aq)$$
$$HNO_3(l) \rightarrow H^+(aq) + NO_3^-(aq)$$

$$H_2SO_4(l) \rightarrow 2H^+(aq) + SO_4^{2-}(aq)$$
$$H_3PO_4(l) \rightarrow 3H^+(aq) + PO_4^{3-}(aq)$$

The terms monoprotic, diprotic, and triprotic become obvious when we consider these equations. However, not all the hydrogen atoms in an acid are easily removed as protons. Ethanoic acid CH_3COOH and phosphonic acid are examples of monoprotic and diprotic acids respectively.

$$CH_3COOH(l) \rightarrow H^+(aq) + CH_3COO^-(aq)$$
$$H_3PO_3(l) \rightarrow 2H^+(aq) + HPO_3^{2-}(aq)$$

7.5 Strong and weak acids

Some acids are completely ionized in aqueous solution and these are called **strong acids,** even when dilute. It is important to note that the word 'strong' relates to the degree of ionization and not to the concentration. Some examples of strong acids are:

$$HCl(g) \rightarrow H^+(aq) + Cl^-(aq)$$
$$H_2SO_4(l) \rightarrow 2H^+(aq) + SO_4^{2-}(aq)$$
$$HNO_3(l) \rightarrow H^+(aq) + NO_3^-(aq)$$

Such acids have a low pH and a high conductivity because of the high concentration of hydrogen ions.

Some acids in water ionize partially, producing a smaller number of hydrogen ions than might be expected from the formula. These are called **weak acids.** Some examples of weak acids are:

$$HNO_2(aq) \rightleftharpoons H^+(aq) + NO_2^-(aq)$$
$$H_2SO_3(aq) \rightleftharpoons 2H^+(aq) + SO_3^{2-}(aq)$$
$$H_2CO_3(aq) \rightleftharpoons 2H^+(aq) + CO_3^{2-}(aq)$$

Vinegar is a solution of ethanoic acid (CH_3COOH) whose concentration is about one mole per litre. However, it has a pH of three, and the conductivity of vinegar is lower than that of a molar solution of hydrochloric acid. From this we should deduce that ethanoic acid is a weak acid.

$$CH_3COOH(aq) \rightleftharpoons H^+(aq) + CH_3COO^-(aq)$$

7.6 Characteristics of acids

1. Acids have a sour taste. This can be demonstrated by tasting things like lemons, grapefruit, rhubarb, and vinegar and testing them with pH paper. Do not taste acid in the bottles in the laboratory as this is very dangerous.

2. Acids liberate carbon dioxide from carbonates:

$$Na_2CO_3(s) + 2HCl(aq) \rightarrow 2NaCl(aq) + H_2O(l) + CO_2(g)$$
$$CuCO_3(s) + 2HCl(aq) \rightarrow CuCl_2(aq) + H_2O(l) + CO_2(g)$$
$$CaCO_3(s) + 2HCl(aq) \rightarrow CaCl_2(aq) + H_2O(l) + CO_2(g)$$

3 Acids react with certain metals to liberate hydrogen gas:

$$Zn(s)+2HCl(aq) \rightarrow ZnCl_2(aq)+H_2(g)$$
$$Mg(s)+H_2SO_4(aq) \rightarrow MgSO_4(aq)+H_2(g)$$
$$Sn(s)+2HCl(aq) \rightarrow SnCl_2(aq)+H_2(g)$$

4 Acids react with metal oxides and hydroxides to produce salts:

$$CuO(s)+2HCl(aq) \rightarrow CuCl_2(aq)+H_2O(l)$$
$$NaOH(aq)+HCl(aq) \rightarrow NaCl(aq)+H_2O(l)$$
$$Ca(OH)_2(aq)+2HNO_3(aq) \rightarrow Ca(NO_3)_2(aq)+2H_2O(l)$$

7.7 Bases

By definition, a **base** is a substance that accepts hydrogen ions, that is a **proton acceptor.** If ammonia gas and hydrogen chloride gas come into contact with each other, ammonium chloride forms as a white smoke:

$$NH_3(g)+HCl(g) \rightarrow (NH_4^+ + Cl^-)(s)$$

The ammonia molecule is accepting a proton to become the ammonium ion, so the ammonia molecule is acting as a base.

When hydrogen chloride gas is passed over heated iron(II) oxide, iron(II) chloride is formed:

$$(Fe^{2+} + O^{2-})(s)+2HCl(g) \rightarrow (Fe^{2+} + 2Cl^-)(s)+H_2O(l)$$

The oxide ion is accepting protons to become water, so the oxide ion is acting as a base.

Table 7.3 Names and formulae of some bases

Base	*Formula*	*Solubility in water*
Sodium hydroxide	$NaOH$	Soluble
Potassium oxide	K_2O	
Ammonia	NH_3	
Calcium oxide	CaO	Less soluble
Magnesium oxide	MgO	
Barium hydroxide	$Ba(OH)_2$	
Copper(II) oxide	CuO	Insoluble
Iron(III) hydroxide	$Fe(OH)_3$	

Bases which are soluble in water are called **alkalis.** This means they produce hydroxide ions to form an alkaline solution. Sodium hydroxide dissolves in water producing the calculated concentration of ions. It is a **strong base** and the sodium hydroxide solution is a **strong alkali.**

$$NaOH(s) \rightarrow Na^+(aq)+OH^-(aq)$$

1 mole 1 mole 1 mole

Potassium oxide is a strong base. It reacts with water to produce potassium hydroxide, which is fully ionized:

$$K_2O(s)+H_2O(l) \rightarrow 2K^+(aq)+2OH^-(aq)$$

Calcium oxide reacts with water to form calcium hydroxide, which is not very soluble in water. Consequently the ions in the saturated solution are in equilibrium with the solid. Calcium oxide is a **weak base** and the calcium hydroxide solution a **weak alkali:**

$$CaO(s)+H_2O(l) \rightarrow Ca(OH)_2(s) \rightleftharpoons Ca^{2+}(aq)+2OH^-(aq)$$

Magnesium oxide and barium hydroxide are also weak bases:

$$MgO(s)+H_2O(l) \rightarrow Mg(OH)_2(s) \rightleftharpoons Mg^{2+}(aq)+2OH^-(aq)$$
$$Ba(OH)_2(s) \rightleftharpoons Ba^{2+}(aq)+2OH^-(aq)$$

It might appear from this that soluble bases produce strong alkalis and less soluble bases produce weak alkalis, but beware. Ammonia gas is extremely soluble, but measurement of the pH of its solution shows that it is, in fact, a weak alkali. This is because aqueous ammonia is only partially ionized:

$$NH_3(g)+H_2O(l) \rightarrow NH_3(aq)+H_2O(l) \rightleftharpoons NH_4^+(aq)+OH^-(aq)$$

7.8 Salts

When acids and bases react, **salts** are formed and we can consider all salts as having been theoretically produced from an acid and a base. Sodium sulphate can be considered to be formed from sulphuric acid and sodium hydroxide, although it may have been prepared by some other method. It would seem a reasonable assumption that the solution of a salt should be neutral, and indeed for a great many this is so. However, there are also salts which do not dissolve to give neutral solutions, and we shall therefore have to look at the parent acid and parent base from which it is derived.

Table 7.4

Solution	*pH*
Sodium chloride	7
Potassium sulphate	7
Sodium carbonate	9
Ammonium chloride	6
Sodium ethanoate	8

Sodium chloride is formed from sodium hydroxide and hydrochloric acid, both of which are strong. Likewise potassium sulphate is formed from a strong acid, sulphuric acid, and a strong base, potassium hydroxide. It seems that salts formed from strong acids and strong bases give neutral solutions.

Sodium carbonate is derived from a strong base, sodium hydroxide, and a weak acid, carbonic acid. The weak acid upsets the water equilibrium leaving the solution with more hydroxide ions in it than hydrogen ions.

$$Na_2CO_3(s) \longrightarrow 2Na^+(aq) + CO_3^{2-}(aq)$$
$$2H_2O(l) \rightleftharpoons 2OH^-(aq) + 2H^+(aq)$$
$$\Downarrow\Uparrow$$
$$H_2CO_3(aq)$$

The formation of carbonic acid molecules removes hydrogen ions from solution, causing the water equilibrium to move to the right. When the system comes to equilibrium again, there is an excess of hydroxide ions, and the pH of the solution is greater than seven. Salts of strong bases and weak acids yield solutions which are alkaline.

Ammonium chloride is derived from a weak base, aqueous ammonia and a strong acid, hydrochloric acid. The weak base upsets the water equilibrium leaving the solution with more hydrogen ions than hydroxide ions.

$$NH_4Cl(s) \longrightarrow NH_4^+(aq) + Cl^-(aq)$$
$$H_2O(l) \rightleftharpoons OH^-(aq) + H^+(aq)$$
$$\Downarrow\Uparrow$$
$$NH_3(aq) + H_2O(l)$$

The formation of aqueous ammonia removes hydroxide ions from solution, causing the water equilibrium to move to the right. When the system comes to equilibrium again there is an excess of hydrogen ions and the pH of the solution is less than seven. Salts of strong acids and weak bases yield solutions which are acidic.

When a salt reacts with the water in which it dissolves, we say that the salt has been **hydrolysed,** or that it has undergone **hydrolysis.**

7.9 Acid salts and normal salts

Theoretically salts are formed by replacing a proton in the acid by a metal ion or an ammonium ion. A monoprotic acid is capable of forming only one series of salts, but a diprotic acid can form two series and a triprotic acid, three series.

Table 7.5

Acid	*Normal salt*	*Acid salt*
Hydrochloric HCl	Chloride Cl^-	
Nitric HNO_3	Nitrate NO_3^-	
Nitrous HNO_2	Nitrite NO_2^-	
Ethanoic CH_3COOH	Ethanoate CH_3COO^-	
Sulphuric H_2SO_4	Sulphate SO_4^{2-}	Hydrogensulphate HSO_4^-
Sulphurous H_2SO_3	Sulphite SO_3^{2-}	Hydrogensulphite HSO_3^-
Carbonic H_2CO_3	Carbonate CO_3^{2-}	Hydrogencarbonate HCO_3^-
Phosphoric H_3PO_4	Phosphate PO_4^{3-}	Hydrogenphosphate HPO_4^{2-}
		Dihydrogenphosphate $H_2PO_4^-$

7.10 Preparation of salts

The method of preparing a salt usually depends on the solubility of the salt in water and some general rules are given in Table 7.6.

Table 7.6

Soluble salts	*Insoluble salts*
Nitrates	Carbonates (except Na, K, NH_4)
Chlorides (except AgCl, $PbCl_2$)	
Sulphates (except $BaSO_4$, $CaSO_4$, $PbSO_4$)	Sulphides (except Na, K, NH_4)
All sodium, potassium, and ammonium salts	

Insoluble salts By mixing the appropriate solutions the required salt can be precipitated from the solution, filtered off, washed, and dried.

$$CuSO_4(aq) + Na_2CO_3(aq) \rightarrow CuCO_3(s) + Na_2SO_4(aq)$$
$$AgNO_3(aq) + HCl(aq) \rightarrow AgCl(s) + HNO_3(aq)$$
$$Pb(NO_3)_2(aq) + Na_2S(aq) \rightarrow PbS(s) + 2NaNO_3(aq)$$

Soluble salts We will now consider some of the preparations of soluble salts.

1 Action of acid on a metal:

$$Zn(s) + H_2SO_4(aq) \rightarrow ZnSO_4(aq) + H_2(g)$$

An excess of the metal is added to the acid to make sure that all the acid is used up. The excess solid is removed by filtration. The filtrate is then evaporated to small bulk and left to crystallize. This method is not suitable for very reactive metals such as sodium and potassium.

2 Action of acid on an insoluble base or an insoluble carbonate:

$$CuO(s) + H_2SO_4(aq) \rightarrow CuSO_4(aq) + H_2O(l)$$
$$CaCO_3(s) + 2HCl(aq) \rightarrow CaCl_2(aq) + H_2O(l) + CO_2(g)$$

An excess of the solid is added to the acid to make sure that all the acid is used up. The excess solid is removed by filtration. The filtrate is then evaporated to small bulk and left to crystallize.

3 Action of acid on alkali:

$$NaOH(aq) + HCl(aq) \rightarrow NaCl(aq) + H_2O(l)$$

The acid is run from a burette into the alkali until the solution is neutral. When the solution is neutral, it is evaporated to small bulk and left to crystallize. This method is particularly suitable for strong acids and strong bases.

For the normal salt sodium sulphate, two moles of sodium hydroxide are required for every mole of sulphuric acid:

$$2NaOH(aq) + H_2SO_4(aq) \rightarrow Na_2SO_4(aq) + 2H_2O(l)$$
2 moles 1 mole

For the acid salt sodium hydrogencarbonate, one mole of sodium hydroxide is required for every mole of sulphuric acid:

$$NaOH(aq) + H_2SO_4(aq) \rightarrow NaHSO_4(aq) + H_2O(l)$$
1 mole 1 mole

It is easier experimentally to prepare the normal salt first and then to add the same amount of acid again, rather than to half the amount of sodium hydroxide used:

$$Na_2SO_4(aq) + H_2SO_4(aq) \rightarrow 2\,NaHSO_4(aq)$$

On crystallization, salts are often associated with a certain amount of water. This is known as the **water of crystallization.** One mole of copper(II) sulphate crystals is associated with five moles of water of crystallization, and the formula for this substance is $CuSO_4.5H_2O$. The water of crystallization can be removed by heating:

$$CuSO_4.5H_2O(s) \xrightarrow{heat} CuSO_4(s) + 5H_2O(l)$$

The substance produced is called **anhydrous** copper(II) sulphate. There are, therefore, two forms of copper(II) sulphate:

1 Copper(II) sulphate-5-water $CuSO_4.5H_2O$.
2 Anhydrous copper(II) sulphate $CuSO_4$.

Summary

From this chapter you should know:

1 Water is in equilibrium with its ions.

2 The pH scale measures the concentration of $H^+(aq)$.

3 Metals form basic oxides while non-metals form acidic oxides.

4 Acids are proton donors.

5 Bases are proton acceptors.

6 'Strong' and 'weak' refer to the degree of ionization in acids and bases.

7 Methods of preparing salts depend on the solubility of the salt.

The experiments for this chapter are on pages 265–6.

Questions

1 1 What is meant by the 'pH' of a solution?
2 How can pH be measured?
3 Suggest an approximate pH for solutions of each of the following and explain your reason for assigning each value:
Limewater (calcium hydroxide solution), vinegar, salt, baking soda. *P & W*

2 1 What is the difference between a strong and a weak acid?
2 How could you show that ethanoic acid, CH_3COOH, is a weak acid?
3 Briefly describe how you would make crystals of lead nitrate? *P & W*

3 Ethanoic acid is a weak electrolyte and sodium hydroxide is a strong electrolyte. If equal volumes of solutions of equal concentration of the substances are mixed together, the solution of sodium acetate formed is alkaline. How could you explain this? How would solutions of ammonium sulphate and sodium chloride affect litmus? *P & W*

4 Dry hydrogen chloride gas has no effect on Universal Indicator paper. Its solution in water, however, turns the paper red. Which of the following conclusions are correct and which are incorrect? Explain your answer.
1 Hydrogen chloride gas is neutral.
2 Hydrogen chloride gas has a pH of seven.
3 Water is acidic.
4 Hydrogen chloride gas is a covalent substance.
5 Hydrogen chloride gas reacts with water forming an acidic solution.
P & W

5 Which of the following elements would form oxides which would indicate pH values less than seven, using moist pH paper:
Magnesium, carbon, sulphur, hydrogen, copper?
Explain briefly the difference between 'strong' and 'weak' acids, and give an example of each. *SCEEB*

6 When asked how they would prepare some silver chloride, the members of a class made the following suggestions:
1 Pass chlorine gas over silver foil.
2 Add dilute hydrochloric acid to silver foil.
3 Add silver nitrate solution to sodium chloride solution.
Comment briefly on each of these methods, indicating whether you think each is suitable or unsuitable, and why. *SCEEB*

7 Calculate which of the following will give more hydrogen gas with excess of an acid, showing your calculation clearly.
1 0.243g magnesium.
2 0.327g zinc. *SCEEB*

8 Neutralization reactions

8.1 Neutralization

Neutralization can be defined as any change in the hydrogen ion concentration which makes a solution neutral, that is any change in the hydrogen ion concentration which brings the pH to seven. When preparing salts by neutralization of acids with alkalis or soluble carbonates, we use a method called **titration.** This involves careful addition of the acid to the alkali or carbonate solution until the **end-point,** when the solution is completely neutralized, is reached. The end-point can be judged by means of indicators, pH meters, or conductivity measurements.

8.2 Use of indicators and pH meters

An indicator is a dye which changes colour within a specific pH range. Table 8.1 gives examples of the colours which some indicators exhibit under different conditions.

Table 8.1 Some typical indicators

Indicator	*Colour in acidic solution*	*Colour in alkaline solution*	*pH range over which colour changes*
Phenolphthalein	Colourless	Pink	8–10
Litmus	Red	Blue	7–8
Methyl orange	Orange	Yellow	3–5

Universal Indicator is a mixture of several indicators and changes colour gradually, from red through green to violet, over a wide pH range.

By using a pH meter to follow the course of neutralization reactions, we can eliminate the use of indicators. The pH meter is an instrument which gives direct readings of pH on the scale 0–14. Figure 8.1 shows how pH varies as 1 M hydrochloric acid is titrated against 10 cm^3 of 1 M sodium hydroxide.

The graph shows that the pH drops rapidly between B and C. This is the neutral point. The volume of acid used to neutralize the alkali can be read from the graph. This technique is used in many industrial laboratories.

Figure 8.1

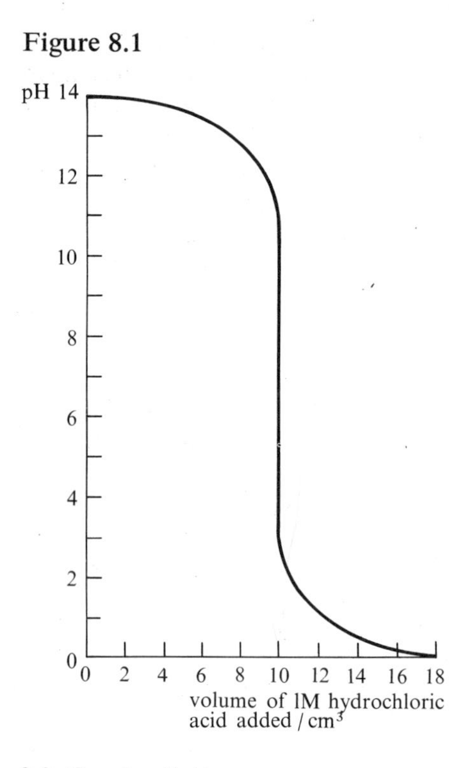

8.3 Conductivity measurement

As we discovered in chapter 4, changing the concentration of hydrogen or hydroxide ions in a solution causes a change in the conductivity of that solution. As neutralization reactions involve change of ionic concentrations, then the reactions can be followed by means of conductivity measurements. A suitable type of apparatus for following neutralization reactions is shown in Figure 8.2.

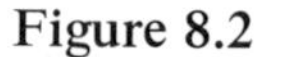

Figure 8.2

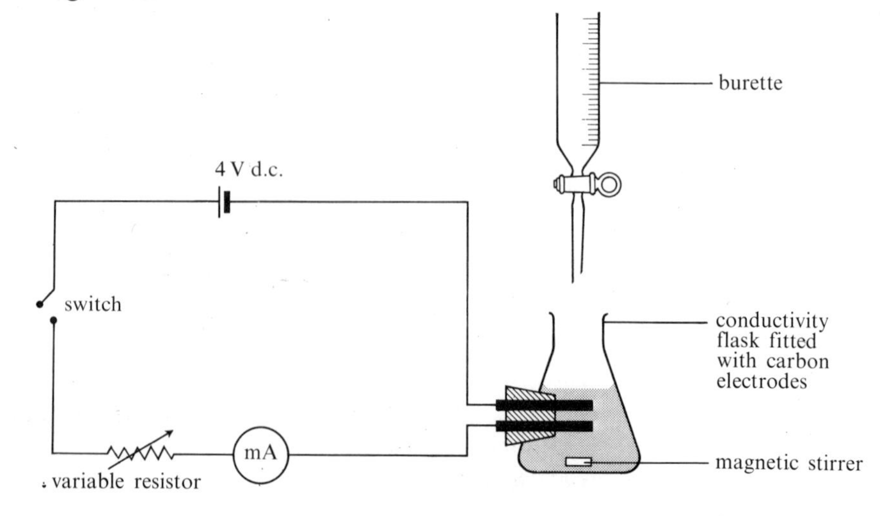

The alkali solution is placed in the flask, and the variable resistor adjusted to give almost a full scale deflection on the milliammeter. The acid is added from the burette, $1.0\,cm^3$ at a time, and the reading on the milliammeter is recorded after each addition.

To understand the conductivity changes involved in neutralization reactions it is best to consider specific examples.

Example 1 Neutralization of 0.1M sodium hydroxide with 0.1M hydrochloric acid (strong base/strong acid).

Figure 8.3

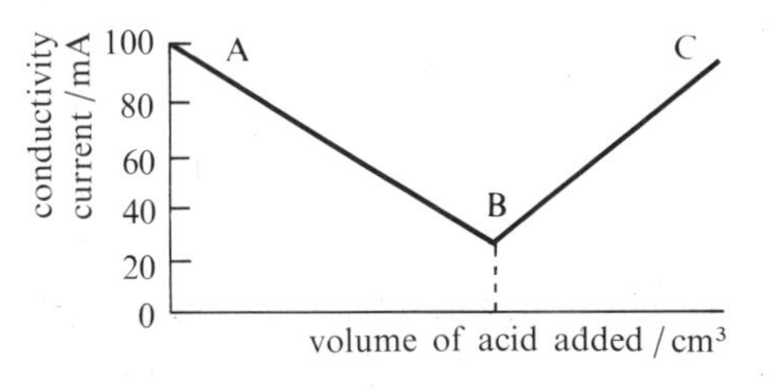

At A — The conductivity is high due to the presence of large numbers of mobile hydroxide ions in the sodium hydroxide.

A to B — The conductivity falls as the mobile hydroxide ions are replaced by the less mobile chloride ions.

At B — The end-point. The conductivity is at a minimum when the neutralization is complete.

$$Na^+(aq)+OH^-(aq)+H^+(aq)+Cl^-(aq) \rightarrow Na^+(aq)+Cl^-(aq)+H_2O(l)$$

The conductivity at the end-point is not zero as the solution contains sodium and chloride ions.

B to C — The conductivity increases due to the addition of excess mobile hydrogen ions from the strong acid. The graph rises more steeply as hydrogen ions are more mobile than hydroxide ions.

Example 2 Neutralization of 0.1M sodium hydroxide with 0.1M ethanoic acid (strong base/weak acid).

Figure 8.4

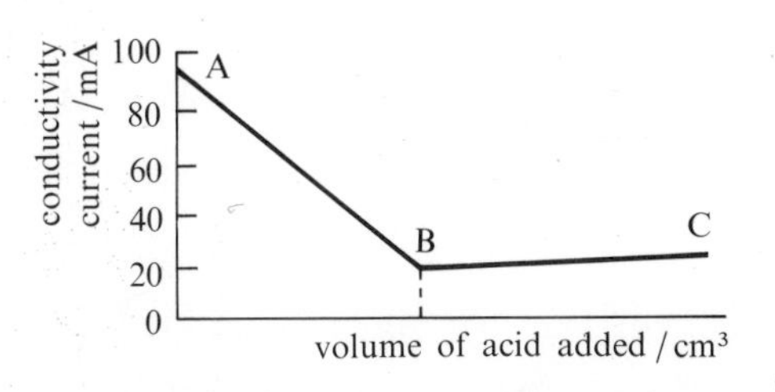

The explanation for this curve is much the same as that in Example 1.

A to B — The conductivity falls due to the replacement of mobile hydroxide ions by less mobile ethanoate ions.

At B — The end-point.

B to C The conductivity rises, but only gradually as the acid is weak and therefore only partially ionized.

Example 3 Neutralization of 0.1M aqueous ammonia with 0.1M hydrochloric acid (weak base/strong acid).

Figure 8.5

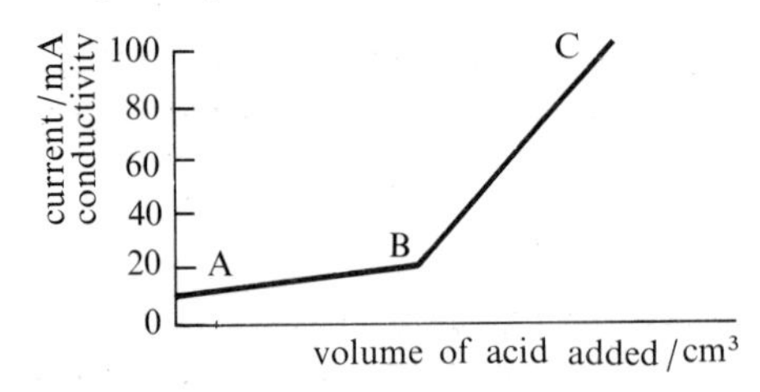

At A The conductivity is low as the aqueous ammonia is a weak base and is therefore only partially ionized.

A to B The conductivity increases as the partially ionized aqueous ammonia becomes fully ionized ammonium chloride.

At B The end-point. In this case the end-point is not a minimum as the conductivity is increasing throughout the titration.

B to C The conductivity increases as excess hydrogen ions are added.

8.4 Further applications of conductivity

Conductivity measurements can also be used to follow the course of other reactions.

Example The precipitation of barium sulphate by the addition of barium hydroxide solution to dilute sulphuric acid.

Figure 8.6

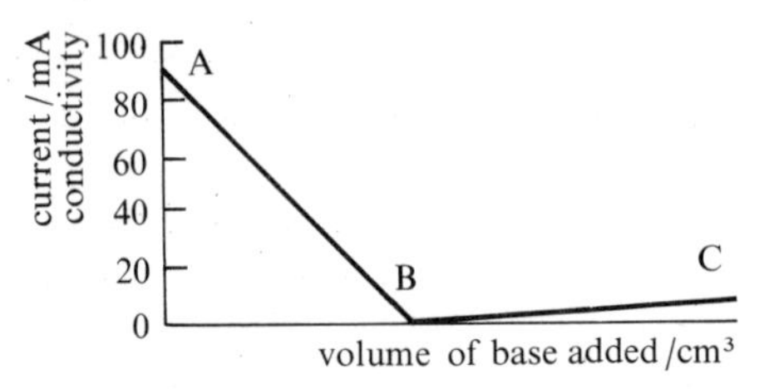

A to B The conductivity decreases because the barium ions are precipitated as insoluble barium sulphate and the hydrogen and hydroxide ions unite to form water.

At B The conductivity is zero as there are no ions in solution:

$$Ba^{2+}(aq)+2OH^-(aq)+2H^+(aq)+SO_4^{2-}(aq) \rightarrow (Ba^{2+}+SO_4^{2-})(s)+2H_2O(l)$$

B to C The conductivity rises slightly as excess barium hydroxide is added. The barium hydroxide is sparingly soluble and there are therefore some barium and some hydroxide ions present.

8.5 Heat of neutralization

Most chemical reactions are accompanied by a heat change. This results from the energy difference between making and breaking chemical bonds. Neutralization reactions are always accompanied by a heat loss. We call such a reaction an **exothermic** reaction. The heat energy given out when a strong acid is neutralized by a strong alkali to produce one mole of water is called the **heat of neutralization.** It is of the order of 57 kilojoules per mole. The heat of neutralization is the same irrespective of which strong acid and strong alkali are used, as the same reaction is taking place each time.

$$H^+(aq) + OH^-(aq) \rightarrow H_2O(l) \qquad \Delta H = -57 \text{ kJ mol}^{-1}$$

ΔH represents the energy change in the system. In this case the system has lost 57 kilojoules to the surroundings for the formation of one mole of water, which is the reason for the negative sign.

8.6 Volumetric calculations

When working with acids and alkalis of accurately known concentrations, i.e. standard solutions, it is possible to make a neutral solution without the use of indicators, pH meters or conductivity measurements. Consider the following examples.

Example 1

$HCl(aq) + NaOH(aq) \rightarrow NaCl(aq) + H_2O(l)$
1 mole 1 mole 1 mole 1 mole
For neutralization:
1 mole of HCl requires 1 mole of NaOH,
i.e. 1 litre of 1M HCl requires 1 litre of 1M NaOH.
Therefore 20 cm^3 of 1M HCl requires 20 cm^3 of 1M NaOH
or 2×20 cm^3 of 0.5M NaOH
or $\frac{1}{2} \times 20$ cm^3 of 2M NaOH
or $1/x \times 20$ cm^3 of xM NaOH.

This pattern is followed by other monoprotic acids.

Example 2

$H_2SO_4(aq) + 2NaOH(aq) \rightarrow Na_2SO_4(aq) + 2H_2O(l)$
1 mole 2 moles 1 mole 2 moles
For neutralization:
1 mole of H_2SO_4 requires 2 moles of NaOH,
i.e. 1 litre of 1M H_2SO_4 requires 2 litres of 1M NaOH.
Therefore 20 cm^3 of 1M H_2SO_4 requires 2×20 cm^3 of 1M NaOH
or $1/x \times 2 \times 20$ cm^3 of xM NaOH.
This pattern is followed by other diprotic acids.

Example 3

$H_3PO_4(aq) + 3NaOH(aq) \rightarrow Na_3PO_4(aq) + 3H_2O(l)$
1 mole 3 moles 1 mole 3 moles
For neutralization:
1 mole of H_3PO_4 requires 3 moles of NaOH,

i.e. 1 litre of 1M H_3PO_4 requires 3 litres of 1M NaOH.
Therefore 20 cm^3 of 1M H_3PO_4 requires 3×20 cm^3 of 1M NaOH
or $1/x \times 3 \times 20$ cm^3 of xM NaOH.

This pattern is followed by other triprotic acids.

8.7 Determination of molarity and concentration

Volumetric techniques can be used to determine the molarity and concentration of acids and alkalis. The best way to show this is to consider some examples.

Example 1 Calculate the molarity and concentration of a sodium hydroxide solution of which 30 cm^3 were required to neutralize 25 cm^3 of 0.1M hydrochloric acid.

$HCl(aq) + NaOH(aq) \rightarrow NaCl(aq) + H_2O(l)$
1 mole 1 mole

From the equation we see that for neutralization:
1 mole of HCl requires 1 mole of NaOH,
i.e. 25 cm^3 of 0.1M HCl requires 25 cm^3 of 0.1M NaOH.

25 cm^3 of 0.1M HCl $\equiv$ 2.5 cm^3 of 1M HCl
$\equiv$ (2.5 cm^3 of 1M NaOH)

From the experiment:
25 cm^3 of 0.1M HCl required 30 cm^3 of xM NaOH
25 cm^3 of 0.1M HCl $\equiv$ 30 cm^3 of xM NaOH
$\equiv$ (30x cm^3 of 1M NaOH)

Therefore $30x = 2.5$

$$x = \frac{2.5}{30} = 0.083$$

The sodium hydroxide is 0.083M.

The concentration is 0.083 mol l^{-1}.
To change this to g l^{-1}:
1 mole of sodium hydroxide $\equiv$ 40 g
Therefore concentration $= 40 \times 0.083$
$= 3.32$ g l^{-1}.

We can express the concentration as 0.083 mol l^{-1} or as 3.32 g l^{-1}.

Example 2 In making a sample of ammonium sulphate, 20 cm^3 of 1M aqueous ammonia were neutralized by 12 cm^3 of sulphuric acid. Calculate the molarity and concentration of the acid.

$H_2SO_4(aq) + 2NH_3(aq) \rightarrow (NH_4)_2SO_4(aq) + 2H_2O(l)$
1 mole 2 moles

From the equation we see that for neutralization:
2 moles of NH_3(aq) requires 1 mole of H_2SO_4,
i.e. 20 cm^3 of 1M NH_3(aq) requires 10 cm^3 of 1M H_2SO_4
20 cm^3 of 1M NH_3(aq) $\equiv$ (10 cm^3 of 1M H_2SO_4)

From the experiment:

$20\,cm^3$ of $0.1M\ NH_3(aq)$ required $12\,cm^3$ of $xM\ H_2SO_4$

$$20\,cm^3 \text{ of } 1M\ NH_3(aq) \equiv 12\,cm^3 \text{ of } xM\ H_2SO_4$$
$$\equiv (12x\,cm^3 \text{ of } 1M\ H_2SO_4)$$

Therefore $12x = 10$

$$x = \frac{10}{12} = 0.83$$

The sulphuric acid is 0.83M.

The concentration is $0.83\ mol\ l^{-1}$.

To change this to $g\,l^{-1}$:

1 mole of $H_2SO_4 = 98\,g$

Therefore $\text{concentration} = 98 \times 0.83 = 81.3\,g\,l^{-1}$.

We can express the concentration as $0.83\ mol\ l^{-1}$ or as $81.3\,g\,l^{-1}$

8.8 Standard solutions

It might be of interest here to explain just how standard solutions are made. The most general method involves weighing out accurately the required mass of solute, dissolving that mass in a small amount of solvent (usually de-ionized water), and then making up the solution to a definite volume in a standard flask. The complete procedure is illustrated in Figure 8.7.

Figure 8.7

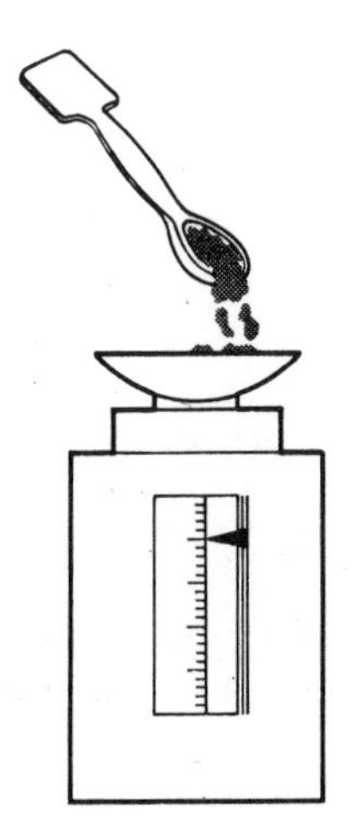

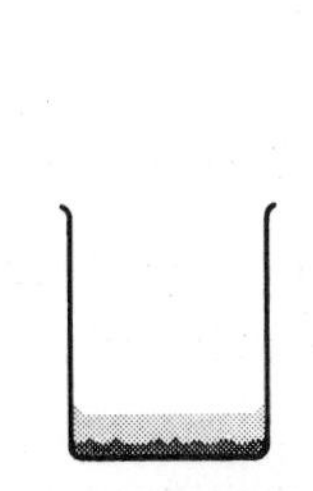

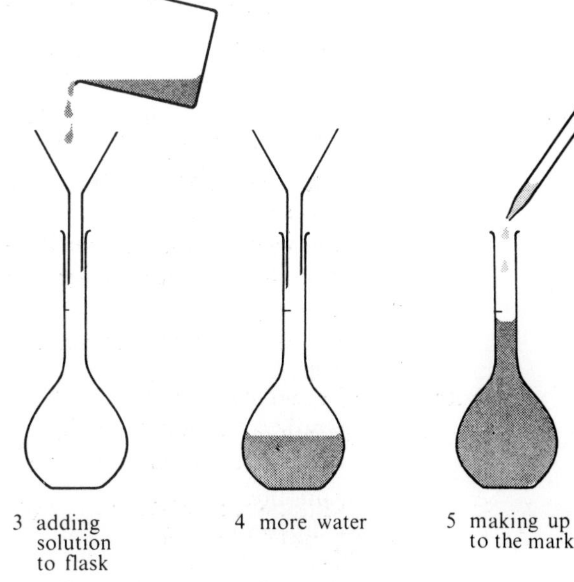

Summary

From this chapter you should know:

1. A neutralization reaction is one in which the hydrogen ion concentration is changed to give a solution with a pH of seven.
2. The course of a neutralization reaction can be followed using indicators, pH meters, or conductivity measurements.
3. The course of precipitation reactions can be followed using conductivity measurements.
4. Neutralization reactions are exothermic.
5. The heat energy evolved when a strong acid is neutralized by a strong alkali to produce a mole of water is called the heat of neutralization.
6. Volumetric techniques, i.e. titration, can be used to determine the molarity and concentration of acids and alkalis.

The experiments for this chapter are on pages 266–9.

Questions

1
1. What do you understand by the term 'neutralization'?
2. How can you test a solution to see if it is neutral?
3. How can you combat 'acid indigestion'?

2 Some indicators change colour over a wide pH range.
Table 1 shows the colours observed above and below certain pH values with different indicators.

Table 1

Indicator	*Below pH*	*Colour*	*Above pH*	*Colour*
Bromothymol blue	6.0	Yellow	7.6	Blue
Methyl orange	3.1	Red	4.4	Yellow
Phenolphthalein	8.0	Colourless	9.9	Red

Table 2 shows the results obtained when three substances A, B, and C were tested using the indicators named in Table 1.

Table 2

Substance	*Bromothymol blue*	*Methyl orange*	*Phenolphthalein*
A	Blue	Yellow	Red
B	Yellow	Yellow	Colourless
C	Yellow	Red	Colourless

Explain what each indicator tells you about the pH of each substance and give an approximate pH value for A, B, and C. *P & W*

3 Given bottles of sodium hydroxide solution and dilute sulphuric acid, Universal Indicator and all the necessary glassware, describe carefully how you would prepare a reasonably pure crystalline sample of sodium sulphate. Give an equation for the reaction.

4 The conductivity of 50 cm^3 of barium chloride solution was measured. Dilute suphuric acid was then added drop by drop. The change in conductivity is shown by the graph.

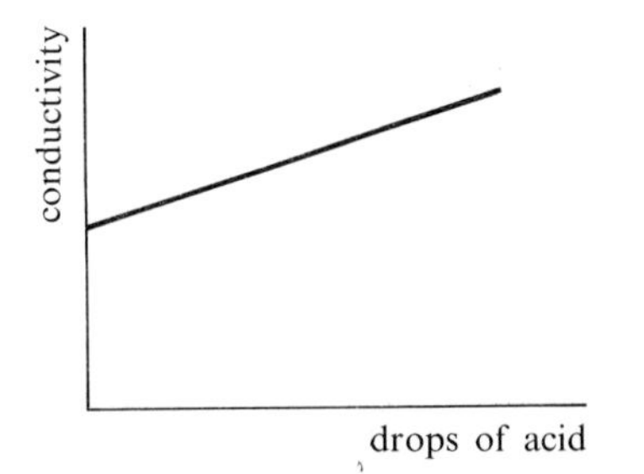

Here are the possible explanations for the shape of the graph.
Comment on each explanation.

1 More ions are being added so the conductivity rises.

2 The mobile hydrogen ions of the acid are taking the place of the less mobile barium ions.

3 The electrodes are being immersed more deeply in the solution and so the conductivity rises. *SCEEB*

5 The following graph was obtained when 0.1M sodium hydroxide was added to 0.1M sulphuric acid.

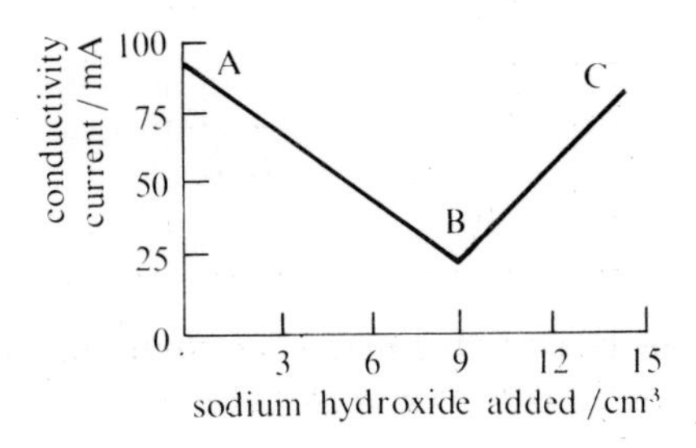

1 Draw a diagram of the circuit you would expect to use to carry out the experiment.
2 What is the conductivity at the end-point?
3 What was the volume of the sulphuric acid used?
4 Explain why the conductivity:
4.1 Falls from A to B.
4.2 Is not zero at B.
4.3 Rises from B to C. *P & W*

6 1 Draw the conductivity curve which you would expect to obtain when $10\,cm^3$ of 0.1M hydrochloric acid is titrated with excess 0.1M sodium hydroxide solution.
1.1 Write the equation for the reaction.
1.2 What ionic species are present at the beginning of the experiment?
1.3 What ionic species will be present at the end of the experiment?
2 Add to your graph (using a dotted line) the curve which you would expect to obtain when the hydrochloric acid is replaced by $10\,cm^3$ of 0.1M sulphuric acid.
Explain any differences in the shape of the curves. *P & W*

7 The conductivity of a dilute solution of hydrochloric acid was measured. Small quantities of powdered calcium carbonate were added until there was a definite excess of the carbonate. The conductivity of the solution was measured after each addition.
Draw a graph showing how the conductivity of the solution changed during the experiment.

8 1 Place the following molar solutions in order of increasing conductivity: Ethanoic acid, hydrochloric acid, sodium chloride, sodium hydroxide. Give reasons for the order chosen.
2 Draw a graph to show how the conductivity would change during the neutralization of dilute suphuric acid solution by barium hydroxide solution. Clearly label the following points on the graph:
A Initial conductivity of the dilute sulphuric acid.
B Conductivity of the products on completion of the reaction.
C Effect on the conductivity by adding excess barium hydroxide solution.
How else could the end-point of the reaction be shown? *P & W*

9 A pupil neutralized $20\,cm^3$ of saturated barium hydroxide solution with dilute hydrochloric acid while his neighbour neutralized $20\,cm^3$ of the same solution with dilute sulphuric acid.
Which of these two neutral solutions will have the higher conductivity and why? (You may assume total immersion of the electrodes.) *SCEEB*

10 A piece of magnesium ribbon is added to some dilute sulphuric acid in a conductivity apparatus.
Write an ionic equation for the reaction that takes place and *explain* which one of the following will happen to the meter reading as the magnesium reacts.

1 It will increase.
2 It will decrease.
3 It will increase, then decrease.
4 It will decrease, then increase.
5 It will not change. *SCEEB*

11 In experiments to determine heats of neutralization, sufficient 0.5M sulphuric acid was added, with efficient stirring, to each of three beakers containing (a) 50 cm^3 of 1M sodium hydroxide. (b) 50 cm^3 of 1M potassium hydroxide. (c) 50 cm^3 of 1M aqueous ammonia.
The temperature rise was noted in each case.
1 What volume of acid is required for exact neutralization of each of the alkalis?
2 If the temperature rise in experiment (a) was found to be 6.5 °C, explain whether you expect the temperature rises in (b) and (c) to be the same, more, or less. *P & W*

12 1 'When an acid reacts with a carbonate, a colourless gas is evolved.' What is this gas and how could it be identified?
2 Write a balanced equation for the reaction between dilute nitric acid and sodium carbonate.

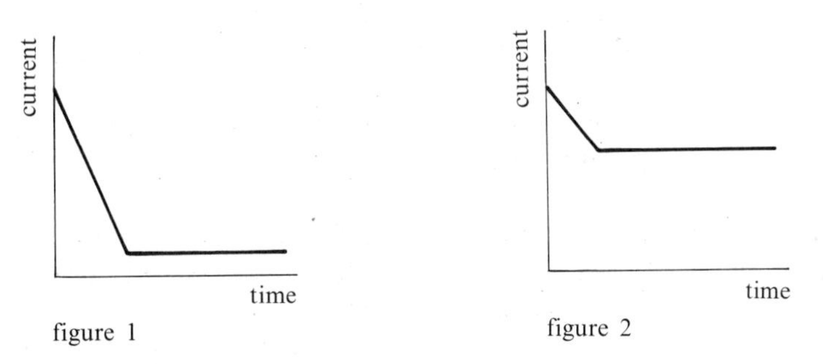

figure 1 figure 2

3.1 The graph obtained from the readings taken when an excess of marble chips is added to dilute sulphuric acid with stirring is shown in figure 1. Explain the graph.
3.2 When the experiment is repeated without stirring, figure 2 is obtained.
Suggest an explanation for the difference between the two graphs. *P & W*

9 Reactivity and the electrochemical series

9.1 Reactivity of metals

It is impossible to find deposits of sodium metal in the earth, although many sodium salts do exist. When sodium metal is extracted from its salts, the process requires the use of an oxygen-free and moisture-free atomosphere. The sodium metal must then be stored under oil to prevent reaction with oxygen and moisture. On the other hand, gold can be found in the gravel of river beds, and gold ornaments made thousands of years ago are still in

Table 9.1 Reactions of some metals with oxygen, hydrochloric acid, and water

	Reaction with		
Metal	*Oxygen*	*Hydrochloric Acid*	*Water*
Potassium	Burns when heated to form the metal oxide	Acid decomposes explosively	Reacts with cold water to form hydrogen gas
Sodium			
Calcium		Reacts to form metal chloride and hydrogen gas	
Magnesium			
Aluminium			No reaction with cold water. Reacts with steam to form hydrogen gas
Zinc			
Iron			
Tin	Metal oxide formed slowly on heating		No reaction
Lead			
Copper		No reaction	
Mercury			
Silver	No reaction		
Gold			

perfect condition today. Obviously gold is an unreactive metal and sodium, by comparison, is a very reactive one. By considering the reactions of metals, it should be possible to determine an order of reactivity for metals.

As you can see from Table 9.1, some metals react vigorously with oxygen, hydrochloric acid, and water, but others do not react with any of these substances. These are two extremes. The majority of the metals react to some extent. Let us consider the reactions of sodium, calcium, zinc, mercury and gold:

With oxygen

If a metal reacts with oxygen, the oxide of that metal is formed.

$$4Na(s)+O_2(g) \rightarrow 2Na_2O(s)$$
$$2Ca(s)+O_2(g) \rightarrow 2CaO(s)$$
$$2Zn(s)+O_2(g) \rightarrow 2ZnO(s)$$
$$2Hg(l)+O_2(g) \rightarrow 2HgO(s)$$

Gold does not react with oxygen.

With water

If a metal reacts with water, the metal hydroxide and hydrogen gas are formed.

$$2Na(s)+2H_2O(l) \rightarrow 2NaOH(aq)+H_2(g)$$
$$Ca(s)+2H_2O(l) \rightarrow Ca(OH)_2(aq)+H_2(g)$$

Zinc, mercury, and gold do not react with water.

With hydrochloric acid

If a metal reacts with hydrochloric acid, the metal chloride and hydrogen gas are formed. Sodium reacts explosively with hydrochloric acid.

$$2Na(s)+2HCl(aq) \rightarrow 2NaCl(aq)+H_2(g)$$
$$Ca(s)+2HCl(aq) \rightarrow CaCl_2(aq)+H_2(g)$$
$$Zn(s)+2HCl(aq) \rightarrow ZnCl_2(aq)+H_2(g)$$

Mercury and gold do not react with hydrochloric acid.

Of the five metals, sodium is the most reactive and gold is the least reactive. By considering the reactions of the other metals, a reactivity series (Figure 9.1) can be constructed.

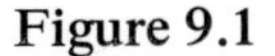

Figure 9.1

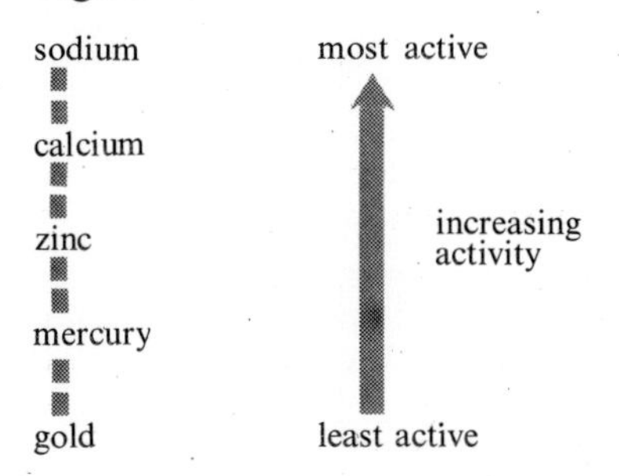

By considering all the metals in Table 9.1, a fuller reactivity series can be drawn up (Figure 9.2). This is called the **electrochemical series.**

Figure 9.2

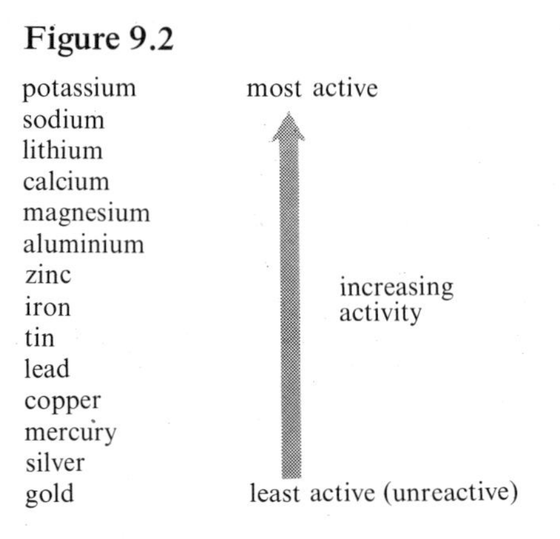

9.2 Reactions of oxides and carbonates

We have constructed a reactivity series for metals and it would seem reasonable to assume that the reactions of metal oxides and carbonates will in some way be related to the reactivity series. The following tables show reactions of metal oxides and metal carbonates.

Table 9.2 Reactions of some metal oxides with hydrogen, carbon, and when heated

	Reaction with		
Oxide	*Carbon*	*Hydrogen*	*Heat*
Sodium oxide	No reaction ↓	No reaction ↓	No reaction ↓
Calcium oxide			
Magnesium oxide			
Aluminium oxide			
Zinc(II) oxide	Zinc and carbon dioxide formed		
Iron(III) oxide	Iron and carbon dioxide formed		
Tin(II) oxide	Tin and carbon dioxide formed	Tin and water formed	
Lead(II) oxide	Lead and carbon dioxide formed	Lead and water formed	

	Reaction with		
Oxide	Carbon	Hydrogen	Heat
Copper(II) oxide	Copper and carbon dioxide formed	Copper and water formed	
Mercury(II) oxide	Mercury and carbon dioxide formed	Mercury and water formed	Mercury and oxygen formed
Silver(I) oxide	Silver and carbon dioxide formed	Silver and water formed	Silver and oxygen formed
Gold(I) oxide	Gold and carbon dioxide formed	Gold and water formed	Gold and oxygen formed

Table 9.3 Reaction of some metal carbonates on heating

Carbonate	*Action of heat*	
Potassium carbonate Sodium carbonate	No reaction	
Calcium carbonate	Calcium oxide and carbon dioxide formed	Ease of production of oxide increasing ↓
Magnesium carbonate	Magnesium oxide and carbon dioxide formed	
Aluminium carbonate	Aluminium oxide and carbon dioxide formed	
Zinc(II) carbonate	Zinc(II) oxide and carbon dioxide formed	
Iron(III) carbonate	Iron(III) oxide and carbon dioxide formed	
Lead(II) carbonate	Lead(II) oxide and carbon dioxide formed	
Copper(II) carbonate	Copper(II) oxide and carbon dioxide formed	
Mercury(II) carbonate	Mercury, carbon dioxide, and oxygen formed	
Silver(I) carbonate	Silver, carbon dioxide, and oxygen formed	
Gold(I) carbonate	Gold, carbon dioxide, and oxygen formed	

From Table 9.2, you can see that the oxides which react with hydrogen, carbon, and when heated are all oxides of metals at the lower end of the reactivity series. The results from Tables 9.2 and 9.3 show that the oxides and carbonates react in reverse order of the reactivity series (Figure 9.3).

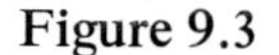

Figure 9.3

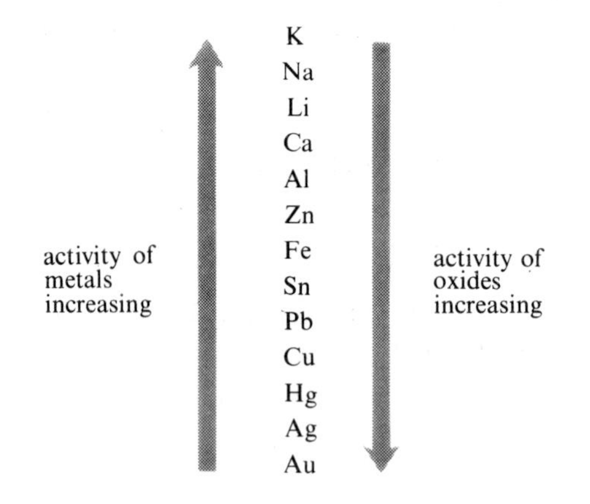

9.3 Displacement

If a piece of zinc metal is placed in a solution of copper(II) sulphate, the zinc gradually dissolves. The blue colour of the solution disappears and copper metal is formed. We can represent this reaction by means of **electron half-equations:**

$$Zn(s) \rightarrow Zn^{2+}(aq) + 2e^-$$
$$Cu^{2+}(aq) + 2e^- \rightarrow Cu(s)$$

The zinc is losing electrons (e^-) and forming zinc ions; the copper(II) ions are gaining electrons to form copper metal. We say that the zinc **displaces** the copper metal from the copper(II) sulphate solution. Similar reactions take place when:

1 A piece of iron is dropped into lead(II) nitrate solution:

$$Fe(s) \rightarrow Fe^{2+}(aq) + 2e^-$$
$$Pb^{2+}(aq) + 2e^- \rightarrow Pb(s)$$

2 A piece of copper is dropped into silver(I) nitrate solution:

$$Cu(s) \rightarrow Cu^{2+}(aq) + 2e^-$$
$$2Ag^+(aq) + 2e^- \rightarrow 2Ag(s)$$

If you drop a piece of copper into zinc(II) sulphate solution, no reaction occurs. This is also the case with silver in copper(II) sulphate solution and lead in iron(II) sulphate solution.

You should notice from the examples above that when a metal A is displaced from a solution by a metal B, that metal B is above metal A in the reactivity series.

Zinc/copper(II) sulphate: the copper is displaced—zinc is above copper in the reactivity series.
Iron/lead(II) nitrate: the lead is displaced—iron is above lead in the reactivity series.
Copper/silver(I) nitrate: the silver is displaced—copper is above silver in the reactivity series.
Copper/zinc(II) sulphate: no reaction—copper is below zinc in the reactivity series.

Consider the reaction between zinc and copper(II) sulphate solution. The electron half-equations are as follows:

$$Zn(s) \rightarrow Zn^{2+}(aq) + 2e^-$$
$$Cu^{2+}(aq) + 2e^- \rightarrow Cu(s)$$

By adding the two equations we can obtain the equation for the reaction in terms of the reacting species:

$$\begin{array}{r} Zn(s) \rightarrow Zn^{2+}(aq) + 2e^- \\ Cu^{2+}(aq) + 2e^- \rightarrow Cu(s) \\ \hline Zn(s) + Cu^{2+}(aq) + 2e^- \rightarrow Zn^{2+}(aq) + Cu(s) + 2e^- \end{array}$$

Since the number of electrons is the same on each side of the equation, they can be removed, giving

$Zn(s)$	$+Cu^{2+}(aq)$	$\rightarrow Zn^{2+}(aq)$	$+Cu(s)$
1 mole	1 mole	1 mole	1 mole
65.4 g	1 litre 1M	1 litre 1M	63.5 g

From the equation 1 mole (65.4 g) of zinc will react with 1 mole (1 litre 1M) of copper(II) ions to produce 1 mole (1 litre 1M) of zinc(II) ions and 1 mole (63.5 g) of copper metal.

9.4 Electrode potential

When a metal is placed in water, or in an ionic solution, the metal tends to dissolve. The surface layer of atoms changes to form ions which enter the solution, leaving electrons behind on the surface of the metal (Figure 9.4).

Figure 9.4

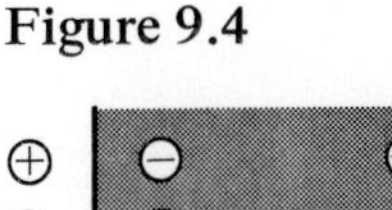

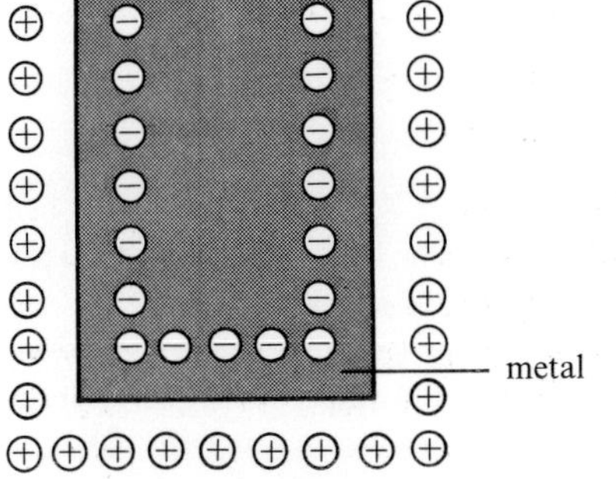

Two layers of opposite charges have been formed. These layers cause a potential difference between the negative charges on the metal and the positively charged ions in the solution. The greater the tendency for metals to ionize, the greater will be the potential difference. The potential difference between a metal and a solution of the metal ions is called the metal's **electrode potential.** We cannot measure the electrode potential for a single element, but we can measure the difference in potential between two electrodes. The hydrogen electrode (Figure 9.5) is used as a standard reference electrode, and all values of electrode potential are determined using hydrogen, which is given an arbitrary value of zero. Table 9.4 shows some standard values that have been determined in this way.

Figure 9.5 The hydrogen electrode

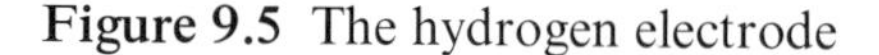

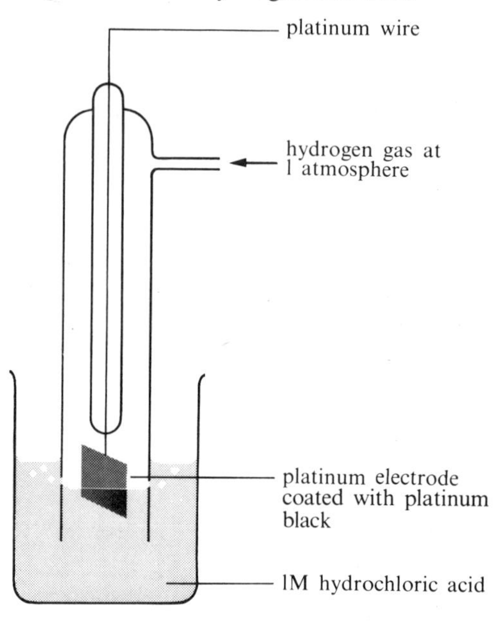

Table 9.4 Electrode potentials using standard H_2 reference

Metal	*Electrode potential* (V)	*Metal*	*Electrode potential* (V)
Potassium	−2.92	Tin	−0.14
Calcium	−2.87	Lead	−0.13
Sodium	−2.71	Hydrogen	0.00
Magnesium	−2.37	Copper	+0.34
Aluminium	−1.66	Silver	+0.80
Zinc	−0.76	Mercury	+0.85
Iron	−0.44	Gold	+1.68

You will see from Table 9.4 that hydrogen is given the value of 0.00 V. This standard value is assigned arbitrarily. The sign for the other values is given by the sign of the charge produced by the electrode relative to the hydrogen electrode. The most significant point which emerges from Table 9.4 is that it confirms the reactivity series. It gives us a measure of the readiness of a metal to form ions. If a metal has a high negative electrode potential, it will be very reactive. If it has a high positive electrode potential, it will be unreactive.

9.5 Electrochemical cells

We know that different metals have different electrode potentials. If we connect two metals with different electrode potentials and place each metal in contact with its own metal ion solution (Figure 9.6), then electrons will flow between the two metals.

Figure 9.6 An electrochemical cell

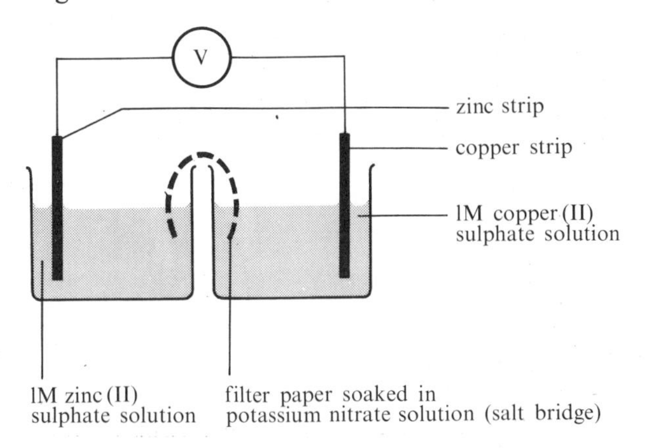

Since electricity is a flow of electrons, this arrangement will supply electricity and it is called an **electrochemical cell.** We can represent the cell as:

$Zn(s)|Zn^{2+}(aq)\vdots Cu(s)|Cu^{2+}(aq)$,

where the zinc electrode is in contact with zinc(II) ions, the copper electrode is in contact with copper(II) ions, and the two solutions are connected by a salt bridge. The reading on the voltmeter is due to a flow of electrons. Since zinc is higher in the reactivity series than copper, the electrons will flow from the zinc to the copper:

$$Zn(s) \rightarrow Zn^{2+}(aq) + 2e^-$$
$$Cu^{2+}(aq) + 2e^- \rightarrow Cu(s)$$

The zinc electrode will slowly dissolve as zinc ions are formed, and the copper electrode will increase in mass as the copper(II) ions accept electrons to form copper metal.

The salt bridge

The filter paper soaked in potassium nitrate is an example of a **salt bridge.** The salt bridge completes the circuit. Consider again the arrangement shown in Figure 9.6:

$Zn(s) \rightarrow Zn^{2+}(aq) + 2e^-$
Zinc atoms go into solution as zinc(II) ions and the electrons then flow in the external circuit to the copper. The salt bridge provides a mechanism for the positive ions in the solution to travel towards the copper strip.

$Cu^{2+}(aq) + 2e^- \rightarrow Cu(s)$
Copper(II) ions are discharged and deposited on the copper plate. The salt bridge allows the negative ions in solution to travel towards the zinc strip.

Remember that ions must be free to move to the electrodes to make the circuit complete, since they provide the mechanism for the transfer of charge. The cell will cease to function when:

1 The zinc electrode completely dissolves.
2 All copper(II) ions in the copper(II) sulphate solution form copper metal.

Summary

From this chapter you should know:

1. How metals react with oxygen, hydrochloric acid, and water.
2. How metal oxides react with hydrogen, with carbon, and on heating.
3. How metal carbonates react on heating.
4. A reactivity series exists. It can be constructed from the results obtained from 1, 2, and 3.
5. The meaning of the term displacement.
6. How to predict the behaviour of a metal when placed in a solution of a salt of another metal.
7. How to write electron half-equations when (a) metals lose electrons, and (b) ions gain electrons.
8. How to construct an equation for a reaction in terms of reacting species only.
9. Displacement reactions are quantitative: 1 mole of Zn(s) will displace 1 mole of Cu(s) from 1 mole of Cu^{2+}(aq).
10. The electrode potential is related to the ease with which a metal forms ions.
11. Electrode potentials can be related to the reactivity series.
12. How to construct an electrochemical cell.
13. The purpose of a salt bridge.

The experiments for this chapter are on pages 268–72.

Questions

1 Describe what you would see happening if a piece of zinc was dropped into a solution of:
1 Copper(II) chloride
2 Hydrogen chloride
3 Sodium chloride.
In your answer give chemical equation where appropriate. *P & W*

2 The oxides of metals X and Y are unaffected by heat, but the oxide of Z gives off oxygen when heated. The carbonate of Y is stable to heat but the carbonates of X and Z both give carbon dioxide on heating.
1 Place the three metals in order of reactivity and suggest a possible name for each.
2 Making use of your last answer, write balanced equations representing the action of heat on the oxide of Z and the carbonate of X.
3 By means of a fully labelled diagram, show how the elements X and Z may be used to make a cell. *P & W*

3

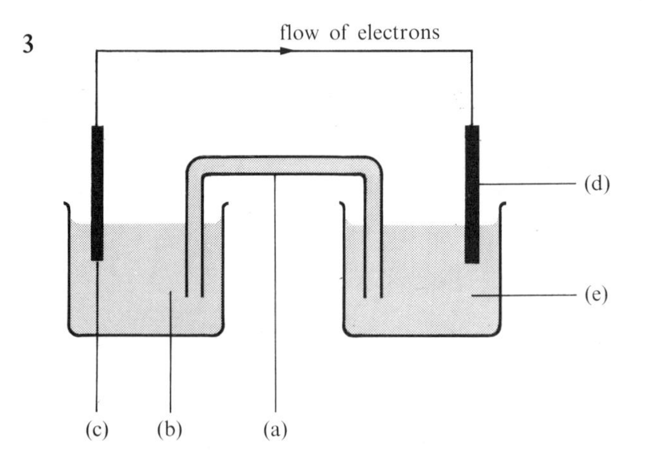

1 Using zinc, copper, zinc sulphate solution, and copper(II) sulphate solution, state what (b), (c), (d), and (e) must be to give the flow of electrons shown.
2.1 What is the device (a) known as?
2.2 Why is it necessary?
2.3 What substance could be used in it?
3 Explain how electrodes (c) and (d) change in weight while the cell is in operation.
4 What two substances would you mix together so that the overall reaction in the above cell could be carried out in a test-tube? *P & W*

4 Rods of zinc, copper, and silver are placed in solutions of lead nitrate as shown in the diagrams opposite.
In which of the experiments would the copper become coated with lead? Justify your answer briefly. *P & W*

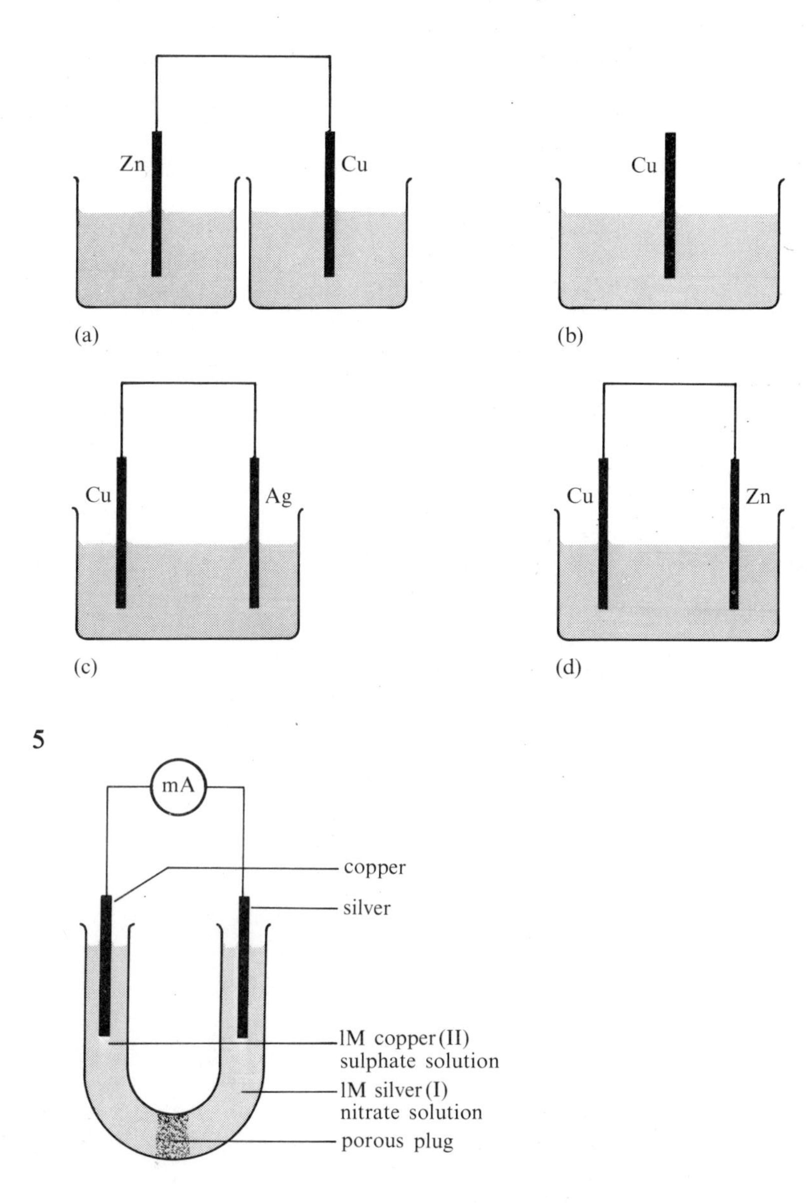

The arrangement above was set up to produce an electric current.

1 Write the ionic equation for the reaction at each electrode.
2 Which electrode increases in mass?
3 In which direction do the electrons flow through the current meter? Explain your choice. *SCEEB*

6 A, B, C, and D are four metals to be arranged in an order of reactivity. In each of the four cases **1** to **4,** state which of the two metals is the more reactive; also give the final order of reactivity (most reactive first).
1 The carbonate of C does not decompose on heating to redness, while that of A is too unstable to exist at room temperature.

2 B evolves hydrogen from dilute hydrochloric acid, but D does not.
3 When D is added to a solution containing ions of A, a precipitate of A is formed and D dissolves.
4 C reacts readily with cold water; B reacts slowly with steam. *SCEEB*

7 Several experiments are carried out to determine the order of reactivity of a number of metallic elements denoted by the symbols M, E, T, A, and L.
1 The results are as follows:
1.1 With water A reacts vigorously, M reacts slowly, while E, T, and L do not react. What information does this give about the relative reactivities of the metals?
1.2 T displaces E from an aqueous solution of the nitrate of E. What information does this give about the relative reactivities of the metals?
1.3 The oxides of E and T are reduced by heating with carbon; the oxides of the other metals are not. What information does this give about the relative reactivities of the metals?
1.4 M, A, and L react with dilute hydrochloric acid, T and E do not. What information does this give about the relative reactivities of the metals?
2 Place the metals in order of *increasing* reactivity.
3 What is the position of highest activity that hydrogen can occupy in this order?
4 Only *one* of these metals gives rise to a strong alkali. Which one?
5 When the nitrates of these metals are heated only *one* decomposes to leave the metal. Which is most likely to do so? *SCEEB*

10 Oxidation and reduction

10.1 Oxidation

At one time the name **oxidation** was given to any chemical reaction in which a substance combined with oxygen.

Example 1 When oxygen gas is passed over heated copper, the copper combines with the oxygen to form copper(II) oxide. In other words the copper is oxidized.

$2Cu(s) + O_2(g) \rightarrow 2CuO(s)$

What does the oxidation of copper mean in terms of electron transfer?

$2Cu(s) \rightarrow 2Cu^{2+}(s) + 4e^-$

The copper metal has lost electrons, and in doing so, it has formed copper(II) ions.

Example 2 When magnesium burns in oxygen, the magnesium combines with the oxygen to form magnesium oxide. In other words the magnesium is oxidized.

$2Mg(s) + O_2(g) \rightarrow 2MgO(s)$

What does the oxidation of magnesium mean in terms of electron transfer?

$2Mg(s) \rightarrow 2Mg^{2+}(s) + 4e^-$

The magnesium metal has lost electrons, and in doing so, it has formed magnesium ions.

The two examples would indicate that oxidation is a loss of electrons. All reactions concerning the gain of oxygen involve a loss of electrons. Oxidation, therefore, can be extended to include any reaction which involves a loss of electrons. **Oxidation** is now defined as a **loss of electrons.**

Example 3 Magnesium reacts with dilute hydrochloric acid to form magnesium chloride and hydrogen gas.

$Mg(s) + 2HCl(aq) \rightarrow MgCl_2(aq) + H_2(g)$

The magnesium is losing electrons to form magnesium ions.

$Mg(s) \rightarrow Mg^{2+}(aq) + 2e^-$

The magnesium is being oxidized.

10.2 Reduction

At one time the name **reduction** was given to any chemical reaction in which oxygen was removed from a substance.

Example 1 When hydrogen gas is passed over heated copper(II) oxide, the hydrogen removes the oxygen. In other words the copper(II) oxide is reduced.

$CuO(s) + H_2(g) \rightarrow Cu(s) + H_2O(l)$

What does the reduction of copper(II) oxide mean in terms of electron transfer?

$Cu^{2+} + 2e^- \rightarrow Cu(s)$

The copper(II) ion has gained electrons and in doing so has formed copper metal.

Example 2 When silver(I) oxide is heated, silver metal and oxygen gas are produced. The silver(I) oxide is reduced.

$2Ag_2O(s) \rightarrow 4Ag(s) + O_2(g)$

What does the reduction of silver(I) oxide mean in terms of electron transfer?

$4Ag^+(s) + 4e^- \rightarrow 4Ag(s)$

The silver(I) ion has gained electrons and in doing so has formed silver metal.

The two examples considered would indicate that reduction is a gain of electrons. All reactions concerning the loss of oxygen involve a gain of electrons. Reduction, therefore, can be extended to include any reaction which involves a gain of electrons. **Reduction** is now defined as a **gain of electrons.**

Example 3 Iron(III) oxide reacts with carbon monoxide gas to form iron metal and carbon dioxide gas.

$Fe_2O_3(s) + 3CO(g) \rightarrow 2Fe(s) + 3CO_2(g)$

The iron(III) ions are gaining electrons to form iron metal.

$2Fe^{3+} + 6e^- \rightarrow 2Fe(s)$

The iron(III) ion is being reduced.

10.3 Redox

Oxidation and reduction always occur at the same time in a chemical reaction. Every time a loss of electrons takes place in part of the reaction, there is an equivalent gain of electrons in another part of the reaction. Let us consider again the reaction between heated copper and oxygen. The oxidation process is:

$Cu(s) \rightarrow Cu^{2+}(s) + 2e^-$

The reduction process is:

$O_2(g) + 4e^- \rightarrow 2O^{2-}(s)$

If we adjust the equations so that the number of electrons lost is equal to the number of electrons gained, and add the two equations, we obtain the overall equation in terms of the reacting species.

$O_2(g) + 4e^- \rightarrow 2O^{2-}(s)$	reduction
$2Cu(s) \rightarrow 2Cu^{2+}(s) + 4e^-$	oxidation
$2Cu(s) + O_2(g) \rightarrow (2Cu^{2+} + 2O^{2-})(s)$	**redox**

This is called the **redox equation.**

A redox equation can be constructed in a similar way for the reaction of heat on silver(I) oxide. The oxidation process is:

$2O^{2-}(s) \rightarrow O_2(g) + 4e^-$

The reduction process is

$Ag^+(s) + 1e^- \rightarrow Ag(s))$

The equations are adjusted to ensure that the number of electrons lost is the same as the number of electrons gained and the redox equation is then obtained.

$4Ag^+(s) + 4e^- \rightarrow 4Ag(s)$	reduction
$2O^{2-}(s) \rightarrow O_2(g) + 4e^-$	oxidation
$(4Ag^+ + 2O^{2-})(s) \rightarrow 4Ag(s) + O_2(g)$	redox

In these two examples the redox equation is more or less the same as the overall equation, but this is not always the case.

Example When yellow iron(III) chloride solution is mixed with sodium sulphite solution, the solution changes to a pale green colour. Can we account for this in terms of redox? The colour change is due to the reduction of the yellow iron(III) ion to the green iron(II) ion.

$Fe^{3+}(aq) + 1e^- \rightarrow Fe^{2+}(aq)$

The corresponding oxidation step is the oxidation of the sulphite ion to the sulphate ion.

$SO_3^{2-}(aq) \rightarrow SO_4^{2-}(aq)$

This equation is not balanced but balancing it can be done in three steps.

1 Add sufficient water molecules to balance the number of oxygen atoms.

$SO_3^{2-}(aq) + H_2O(l) \rightarrow SO_4^{2-}(aq)$

2 Add sufficient hydrogen ions to balance the hydrogen in the water molecules.

$$SO_3^{2-}(aq) + H_2O(l) \rightarrow SO_4^{2-}(aq) + 2H^+(aq)$$

3 Add the correct number of electrons to make each side electrically equivalent.

$$SO_3^{2-}(aq) + H_2O(l) \rightarrow SO_4^{2-}(aq) + 2H^+(aq) + 2e^-$$

We now have the oxidation and reduction reactions.

$$Fe^{3+}(aq) + 1e^- \rightarrow Fe^{2+}(aq)$$
$$SO_3^{2-}(aq) + H_2O(l) \rightarrow SO_4^{2-}(aq) + 2H^+(aq) + 2e^-$$

The equations are now adjusted so that the number of electrons lost is equal to the number of electrons gained.

$$2Fe^{3+}(aq) + 2e^- \rightarrow 2Fe^{2+}(aq) \qquad \text{reduction}$$
$$SO_3^{2-}(aq) + H_2O(l) \rightarrow SO_4^{2-}(aq) + 2H^+(aq) + 2e^- \qquad \text{oxidation}$$

$$2Fe^{3+}(aq) + SO_3^{2-}(aq) + H_2O(l) \rightarrow 2Fe^{2+}(aq) + SO_4^{2-}(aq) + 2H^+(aq) \qquad \text{redox}$$

If we write the equation for the reaction between iron(III) chloride and sodium sulphite solution we obtain the following:

$$2FeCl_3(aq) + Na_2SO_3(aq) + H_2O(l) \rightarrow 2FeCl_2(aq) + Na_2SO_4(aq) + 2HCl(aq)$$
$$2Fe^{3+}(aq) + 6Cl^-(aq) + 2Na^+(aq) + SO_3^{2-}(aq) + H_2O(l) \rightarrow 2Fe^{2+}(aq) + 6Cl^-(aq) + 2Na^+(aq) + SO_4^{2-}(aq) + 2H^+(aq)$$

If we compare the redox equation and the complete equation we can see one significant difference. There are no sodium or chloride ions in the redox equation. These ions are unchanged during the reaction, and take no part in the reaction. These ions are called **spectator** ions. The redox equation shows how the reaction proceeds in terms of the reacting species only. We can show by using chemical tests that

$$Fe^{3+}(aq) \rightarrow Fe^{2+}(aq) \quad \text{and} \quad SO_3^{2-}(aq) \rightarrow SO_4^{2-}(aq)$$

Test for iron(II)/iron(III)

Iron(III) turns ammonium thiocyanate solution dark red.
Iron(II) does not turn ammonium thiocyanate solution red. Iron(II) gives a 'Prussian blue' precipitate with potassium hexacyanoferrate(III) solution.

Test for sulphite/sulphate

A sulphite, when added to barium chloride solution, forms a white precipitate of barium sulphite, which is soluble in dilute hydrochloric acid.
A sulphate, when added to barium chloride solution, forms a white precipitate of barium sulphate, which is insoluble in dilute hydrochloric acid.

10.4 Oxidizing and reducing agents

When zinc is dropped into copper(II) sulphate solution, the zinc displaces copper from the solution. The zinc is oxidized and the copper is reduced. **Oxidizing agents** are substances which accept electrons. In this case the copper ions are accepting electrons when the zinc is oxidized. **Reducing agents** are substances which donate electrons. In this case the zinc atoms are donating electrons when the copper(II) ion is reduced.

$$Cu^{2+}(aq)+2e^- \rightarrow Cu(s) \quad \text{reduction}$$
$$Zn(s) \rightarrow Zn^{2+}(aq)+2e^- \quad \text{oxidation}$$

$$Zn(s)+Cu^{2+}(aq) \rightarrow Zn^{2+}(aq)+Cu(s) \quad \text{redox}$$

The oxidizing agent is $Cu^{2+}(aq)$.
The reducing agent is $Zn(s)$.

10.5 Voltaic cells

A redox reaction involves a transfer of electrons. We can demonstrate this by using the apparatus shown in Figure 10.1.

Figure 10.1 A voltaic cell

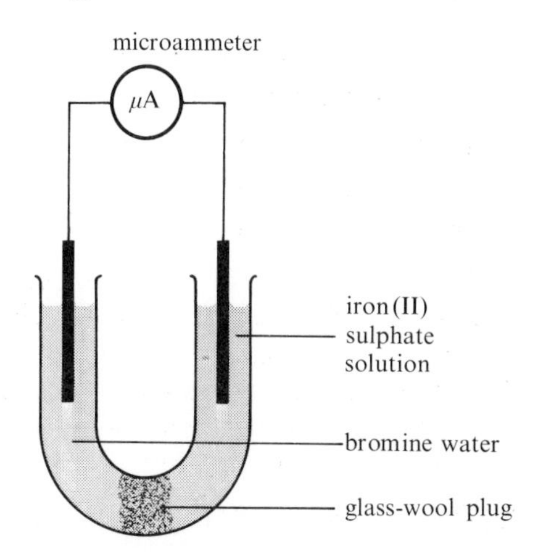

Almost immediately, the microammeter shows a current, indicating a flow of electrons. A transfer of electrons must be occurring. We can show this by means of visual observations and chemical tests.

The bromine water is a red-brown colour to begin with, due to the presence of molecular bromine Br_2. As the experiment progresses the colour gets lighter and lighter until the solution becomes colourless. It is known that the bromide ion is colourless. Therefore, the bromine has been reduced to form bromide ions.

$Br_2(aq)+2e^- \rightarrow 2Br^-(aq)$
red-brown colourless

We already know how to distinguish between iron(II) and iron(III) ions (section 10.3). If the iron(II) solution is tested with ammonium thiocyanate solution about fifteen minutes after setting up the experiment, a dark red colour is produced. Iron(III) ions have been formed. The iron(II) has been oxidized to iron(III).

$Fe^{2+}(aq) \rightarrow Fe^{3+}(aq) + 1e^-$

We can now construct the redox equation:

$Br_2(aq) + 2e^- \rightarrow 2Br^-(aq)$	reduction
$2Fe^{2+}(aq) \rightarrow 2Fe^{3+}(aq) + 2e^-$	oxidation
$2Fe^{2+}(aq) + Br_2(aq) \rightarrow 2Fe^{3+}(aq) + 2Br^-(aq)$	redox

From the meter reading we know there is a transfer of electrons and we have shown that oxidation and reduction (redox) have occurred.
We get similar reactions when chlorine water is used in place of bromine water. However, iron(II) ions cannot reduce iodine to iodide. In this case iron(III) ions oxidize iodide ions to iodine, since iodide ions are stronger reducing agents than iron(II) ions.

Test for chlorine/chloride

Chlorine water is yellow-green in colour.
Chloride ions in solution are colourless. Chloride ions give a white precipitate of silver(I) chloride with silver(I) nitrate solution.

Test for iodine/iodide

Iodine in water gives a brown colour.
Iodide ions in solution are colourless. Iodide ions give a yellow precipitate of silver(I) iodide with silver(I) nitrate solution.

Figure 10.1 is an example of a voltaic cell. Essentially, a voltaic cell consists of two electrodes combined in such a way that, when they are connected by a conductor, an electric current will be produced (Figure 10.2).

Figure 10.2

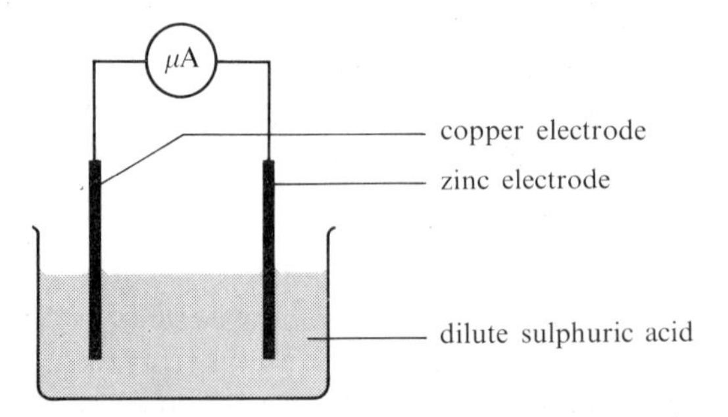

Zinc is higher in the reactivity series than copper and electrons will flow from the zinc to the copper. The zinc strip is being oxidized.

$Zn(s) \rightarrow Zn^{2+}(aq) + 2e^-$

We call the electrode at which oxidation occurs the **anode.** The electrons arriving at the copper electrode will not affect the copper, but they will combine with hydrogen ions from the sulphuric acid to form hydrogen gas:

$2H^+(aq) + 2e^- \rightarrow H_2(g)$

The hydrogen ion is being reduced and we call the electrode at which reduction occurs the **cathode.**

10.6 Electrolytic cells

In a voltaic (electrochemical) cell, a chemical reaction produces a flow of electrons. The reaction is spontaneous; it begins immediately the cell is set up and the energy comes from the cell.

An **electrolytic cell** is one in which no reaction occurs until an external energy source, in the form of an electric current, is applied. We have an electrolytic cell when an electric current is passed through a solution and the solution decomposes (Figure 10.3).

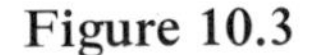

Figure 10.3

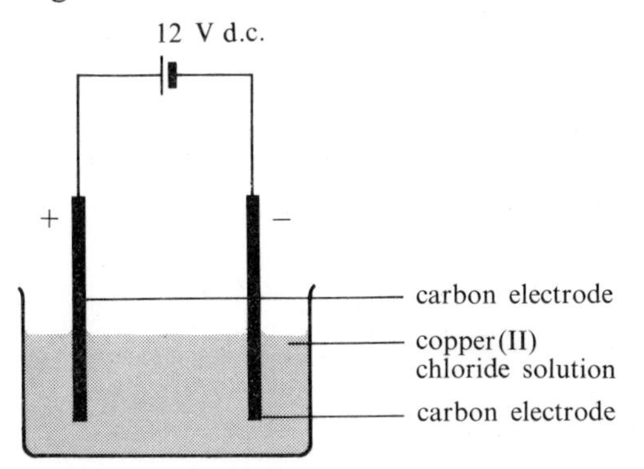

Since we are applying a voltage, one electrode will become positively charged and one will become negatively charged. In the copper(II) chloride solution, the copper(II) ions will be attracted to the negative electrode, where they will gain electrons to form copper metal. This electrode is, therefore, the cathode. The chloride ions will be attracted towards the positive electrode, where they will give up electrons to form chlorine gas. This electrode is, therefore, the anode.

At the cathode: $Cu^{2+}(aq) + 2e^- \rightarrow Cu(s)$
At the anode: $2Cl^-(aq) \rightarrow Cl_2(g) + 2e^-$

An ion which is attracted to the anode is called an **anion.** In this case the anion is the chloride ion $Cl^-(aq)$. An ion which is attracted to the cathode is called a **cation.** In this case the cation is the copper ion $Cu^{2+}(aq)$.

10.7 Electrolysis

When electricity is passed through a melt or an aqueous solution of a compound and decomposition of the compound occurs, the process is called **electrolysis.** We can use electrolysis to separate ionic compounds, but we must first consider the factors which affect the discharge of ions in these compounds.

Position in the electrochemical series

Figure 10.4

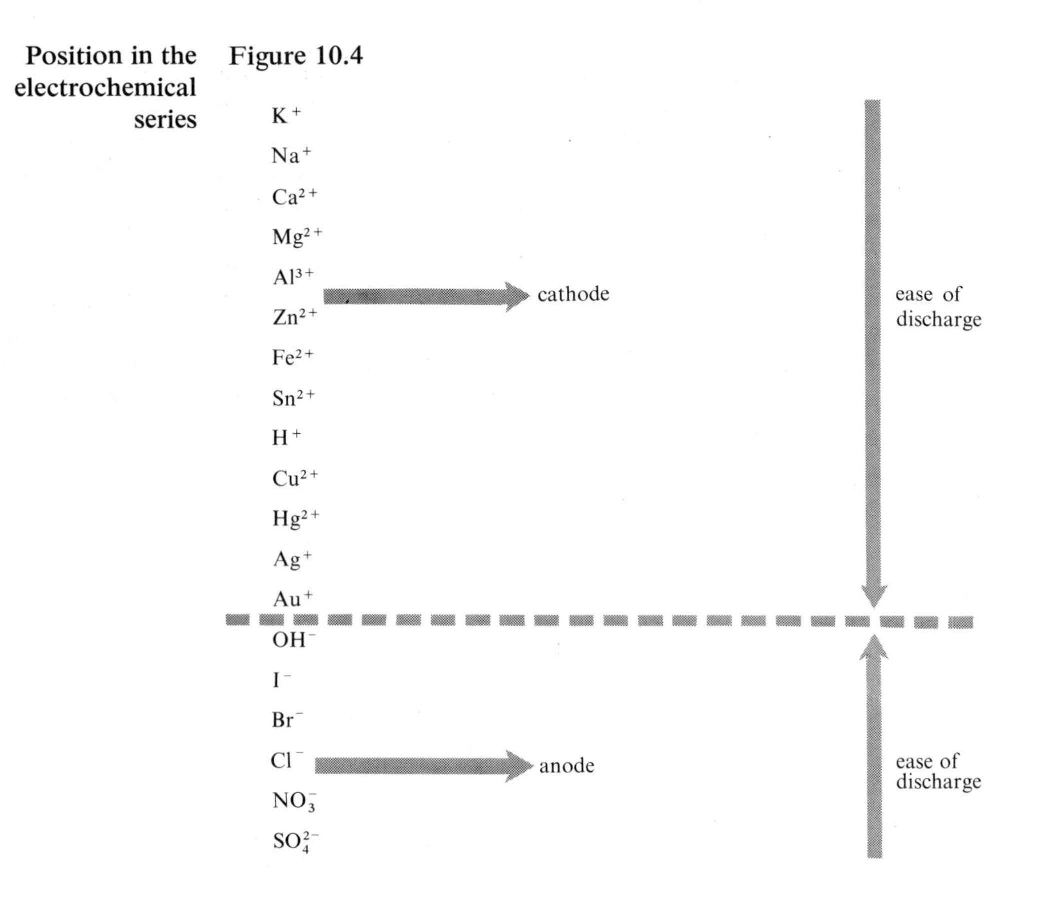

The ions discharge in reverse order of the electrochemical series. As you can see the hydroxide ion will discharge in preference to the chloride ion. The copper(II) ion will discharge in preference to the magnesium ion. This is known as **preferential discharge.**

Concentration

Let us consider the electrolysis of a sodium chloride solution. The ions present are:

Na^+ and Cl^- from sodium chloride
H^+ and OH^- from water

From the information given in Figure 10.4, we would expect the hydroxide ions to be discharged in preference to the chloride ions. However, the chloride ions are far more numerous than the hydroxide ions and they are discharged. This is called the **concentration effect.** In extremely dilute solutions, the hydroxide ions are discharged to a reasonable extent and a mixture of oxygen and chlorine is produced at the cathode.

Type of electrode

The choice of electrodes can control the discharge of ions. Let us consider again the electrolysis of sodium chloride. The ions present are Na^+, Cl^-, H^+, and OH^-.

At platinum cathode
Na^+ and H^+
H^+ will discharge in preference to Na^+
$2H^+(aq) + 2e^- \rightarrow H_2(g)$

At mercury cathode
Na^+ and H^+
The H^+ should discharge in preference to Na^+, but the Na^+ could discharge in concentrated solution.
$Na^+(aq) + 1e^- \rightarrow Na(s)$
The sodium metal would then form an amalgam with the mercury.

When considering the discharge of ions from melts or aqueous solutions these three factors must be considered. Let us consider some examples of electrolysis.

Electrolysis of dilute H_2SO_4

Figure 10.5 A Hoffmann voltameter is used for this experiment

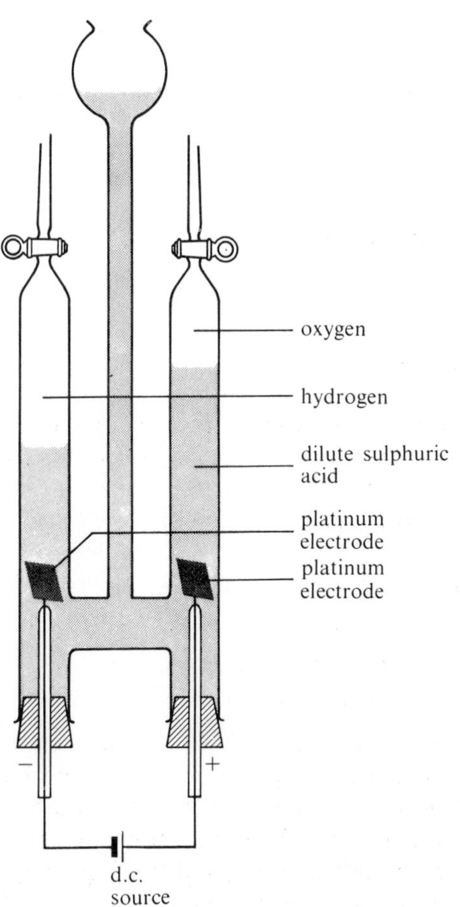

The ions present are H^+, SO_4^{2-}, and OH^-.

At cathode	*At anode*
H^+	SO_4^{2-} and OH^-
The hydrogen ions will accept electrons and hydrogen gas will be discharged.	The OH^- will discharge in preference to SO_4^{2-}.
$2H^+(aq)+2e^- \rightarrow H_2(g)$	
$4H^+(aq)+4e^- \rightarrow 2H_2(g)$	$4OH^-(aq) \rightarrow O_2(g)+2H_2O(l)+4e^-$

The volume of hydrogen liberated at the cathode is twice the volume of oxygen liberated at the anode.

Electrolysis of dilute NaOH

The apparatus used is that shown in Figure 10.5.
The ions present are Na^+, OH^-, and H^+

At cathode	*At anode*
Na^+ and H^+	OH^-
The H^+ will discharge in preference to Na^+.	The OH^- will discharge.
$2H^+(aq)+2e^- \rightarrow H_2(g)$	
$4H^+(aq)+4e^- \rightarrow 2H_2(g)$	$4OH^-(aq) \rightarrow O_2(g)+2H_2O(l)+4e^-$

The volume of hydrogen liberated at the cathode is twice the volume of oxygen liberated at the anode.

Electrolysis of NaCl

We will consider the electrolysis of solutions of different concentrations.

1 Sea water (very dilute sodium chloride)
The ions present are Na^+, Cl^-, H^+, and OH^-.

At cathode	*At anode*
Na^+ and H^+	Cl^- and OH^-
The H^+ will discharge in preference to Na^+.	Although there are many more Cl^- than OH^-, discharge of both ions will occur.
	$2Cl^-(aq) \rightarrow Cl_2(g)+4e^-$
$2H^+(aq)+2e^- \rightarrow H_2(g)$	$4OH^-(aq) \rightarrow O_2(g)+2H_2O(l)+4e^-$

The volumes of gases in this case have no simple relationships, since the chlorine gas dissolves to a large extent in water forming hypochlorous and hydrochloric acids.

$Cl_2(g)+H_2O(l) \rightarrow HClO(aq)+HCl(aq)$

2 1M sodium chloride
The ions present are Na^+, Cl^-, H^+, and OH^-.

At cathode	*At anode*
Na^+ and H^+	Cl^- and OH^-
The H^+ will discharge in preference to Na^+.	Since a high concentration of Cl^- is present, the Cl^- will discharge.
$2H^+(aq)+2e^- \rightarrow H_2(g)$	$2Cl^-(aq) \rightarrow Cl_2(g)+2e^-$

Equal volumes of hydrogen and chlorine are not obtained until the electrolysis has been running long enough for the solution to become saturated with chlorine.

Electrolysis of $CuSO_4$

Figure 10.6 Apparatus for the electrolysis of $CuSO_4$

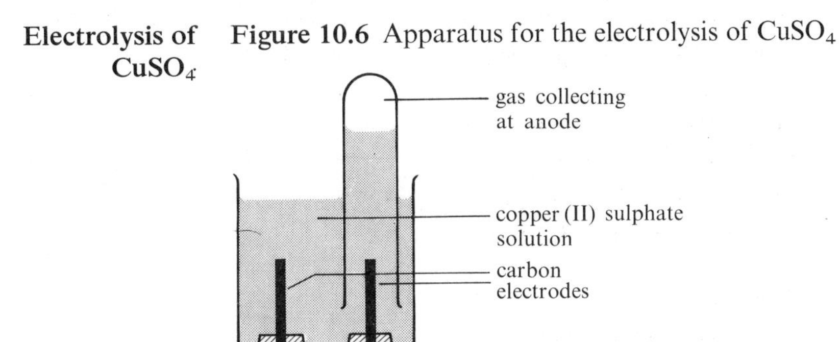

The ions present are Cu^{2+}, SO_4^{2-}, H^+, and OH^-.

At cathode
Cu^{2+} and H^+
Cu^{2+} will discharge in preference to H^+.

$$Cu^{2+}(aq)+2e^- \rightarrow Cu(s)$$
$$2Cu^{2+}(aq)+4e^- \rightarrow 2Cu(s)$$

At anode
SO_4^{2-} and OH^-
OH^- will discharge in preference to SO_4^{2-}.

$$4OH^-(aq) \rightarrow O_2(g)+2H_2O(l)+4e^-$$

Two moles of copper will be deposited at the cathode for every mole of oxygen liberated at the anode.

Electrolysis of molten NaCl

The ions present are Na^+ and Cl^-.

At cathode
Na^+
The sodium ions accept electrons and discharge.

$$Na^+(l)+1e^- \rightarrow Na(s)$$
$$2Na^+(l)+2e^- \rightarrow 2Na(s)$$

At anode
Cl^-
The chloride ions give up electrons and discharge.

$$2Cl^-(l) \rightarrow Cl_2(g)+2e^-$$

The more reactive metals are all obtained from their salts in this way.

10.8 Extraction of metals

We saw in chapter 9 (page 102) that certain metals could not be obtained from their oxides. We can use the technique of electrolysis to extract metals from their ores.

Aluminium Aluminium is extensively used today, and yet there was a time when it was more expensive than gold. This was because aluminium ores were unreactive. It was not until 1886 that a process was invented which enabled aluminium metal to be produced easily and cheaply provided that there was a large supply of electricity. The process is based on the most common ore of aluminium, bauxite, which is an impure form of aluminium oxide. The bauxite is treated chemically to produce pure aluminium oxide (alumina), which is then dissolved in molten cryolite Na_3AlF_6, another aluminium ore, and electrolysed as shown in Figure 10.7. The molten aluminium is tapped off and cast into ingots.

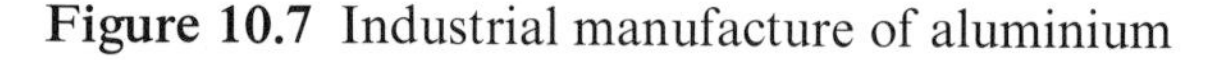

Figure 10.7 Industrial manufacture of aluminium

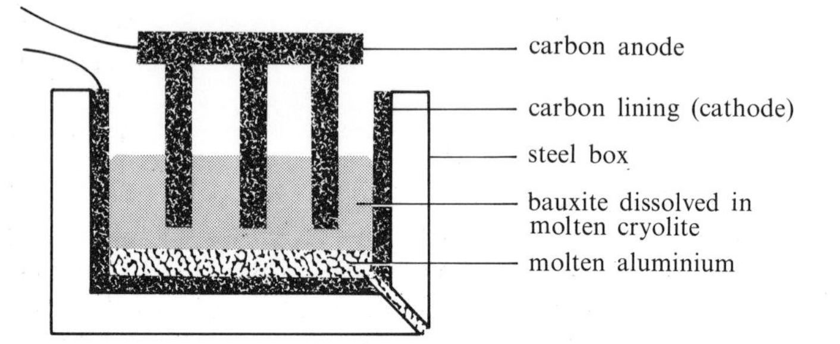

The ions present are Al^{3+}, Na^+, O^{2-}, and F^-.

At cathode	*At anode*
Al^{3+} and Na^+	O^{2-} and F^-
$Al^{3+}(l) + 3e^- \rightarrow Al(l)$	$2O^{2-}(l) \rightarrow O_2(g) + 4e^-$
$4Al^{3+}(l) + 12e^- \rightarrow 4Al(l)$	$6O^{2-}(l) \rightarrow 3O_2(g) + 12e^-$

Copper Impure copper can be refined using the apparatus shown in Figure 10.8. The plate of pure copper is made at the cathode.

Figure 10.8

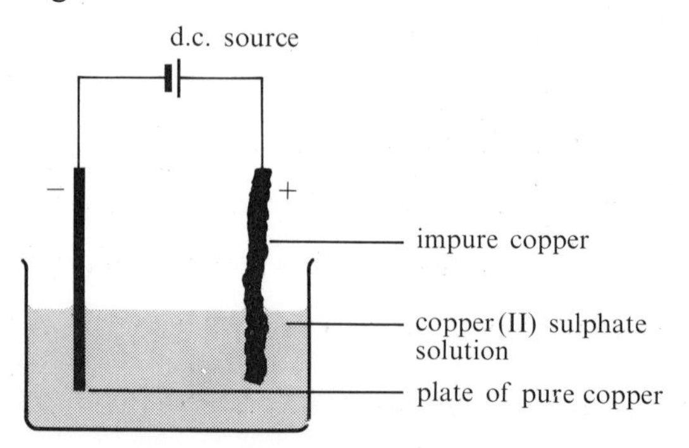

The ions present are Cu^{2+}, SO_4^{2-}, H^+, and OH^-.

At cathode

$Cu^{2+}(aq) + 2e^- \rightarrow Cu(s)$

At anode

The anode is positively charged and therefore electron seeking. There are three possible ways for the anode to obtain electrons.

1 Remove electrons from $OH^-(aq)$ ions.
2 Remove electrons from $SO_4^{2-}(aq)$ ions.
3 Remove electrons from a copper atom and release the resulting copper(II) ion into the solution.

The reaction which requires the least energy will be the one preferred, and in this case it is the third possibility.

$Cu(s) \rightarrow Cu^{2+}(aq) + 2e^-$

The copper in the impure copper is losing electrons and forming $Cu^{2+}(aq)$ ions, which are attracted to the cathode where they accept two electrons to form Cu(s). This electrolysis will continue until all the copper has been removed from the impure metal. It is a well-known way of purifying a metal. The pure metal is always made the cathode. In the case of copper, the impurities form a sludge at the bottom of the reaction vessel. This sludge contains gold and silver which, when extracted, go a considerable way to paying for the purification process.

Summary

From this chapter you should know:

1 The meaning of the terms oxidation, reduction, and redox.
2 The chemical tests which prove redox occurs.
3 How to construct a redox equation.
4 What oxidizing and reducing agents are.
5 How a voltaic cell functions.
6 The meaning of the terms anode, cathode, anion, and cation.
7 How an electrolytic cell functions.
8 The factors which control the discharge of ions in electrolysis.
9 How electrolysis affects various solutions and melts.
10 How electrolysis can be used to extract metals from their ores.

The experiments for this chapter are on pages 275–6.

Questions

1 When sulphur dioxide is passed into an aqueous solution of bromine, the red colour of the bromine water disappears. Which ion is being formed as the sulphur dioxide reacts with the water? Write the redox equation for the reaction which occurs between this ion and the bromine. *P & W*

2

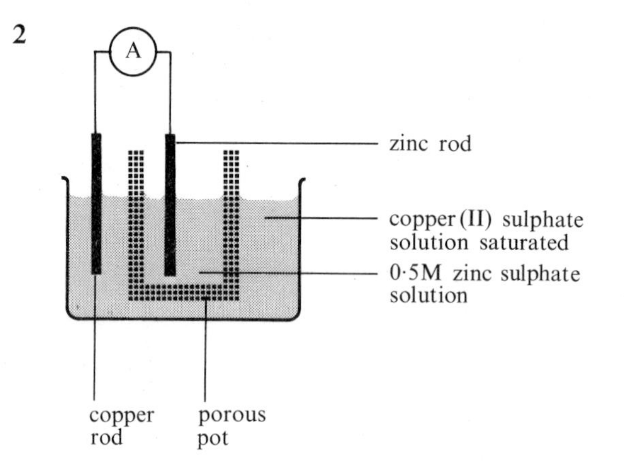

In the diagram above the ammeter shows that a current is flowing.

1 In which direction are the electrons flowing in the external circuit?
2 By making use of ionic equations, indicate how you think this external energy originates.
3 If the zinc sulphate solution was contained in a non-porous container, explain what effect this would have.
4 If some zinc powder is added to a solution of copper(II) sulphate until the blue colour disappears, there is a slight rise in temperature. Explain whether you think a chemical reaction has taken place, and write an ionic equation to represent it. *P & W*

3 During electrolysis, oxidation takes place at the anode and reduction takes place at the cathode. How would you show that this is the case during the electrolysis of a concentrated solution of the sodium chloride? *P & W*

4 Showing only those species which change during the reaction, write ionic equations for the action of dilute hydrochloric acid on:
1 Magnesium.
2 Magnesium hydroxide.
3 Magnesium carbonate.
State, with reasons, which, if any, of the above are redox reactions. *P & W*

5 Name the products at (a) the anode and (b) the cathode when the following aqueous solutions are electrolysed using inert electrodes.
1 Dilute sulphuric acid.
2 Dilute copper chloride solution.
3 Concentrated magnesium chloride solution.

For any **one** of the above solutions, write electron half-equations for the reactions occurring at the anode and cathode. At which electrode does reduction occur? *P & W*

6 State which of the following reactions involve oxidation and reduction, and, where applicable, name the oxidizing agent.

1 $Mg(s) + 2H^+(aq) \rightarrow Mg^{2+}(aq) + H_2(g)$
2 $Mg(s) + 4H^+(aq) + 2NO_3^-(aq) \rightarrow Mg^{2+}(aq) + 2NO_2(g) + 2H_2O(l)$
3 $Ba^{2+}(aq) + SO_4^{2-}(aq) \rightarrow (Ba^{2+} + SO_4^{2-})(s)$
4 $Zn(s) + Cu^{2+}(aq) \rightarrow Zn^{2+}(aq) + Cu(s)$ *P & W*

7

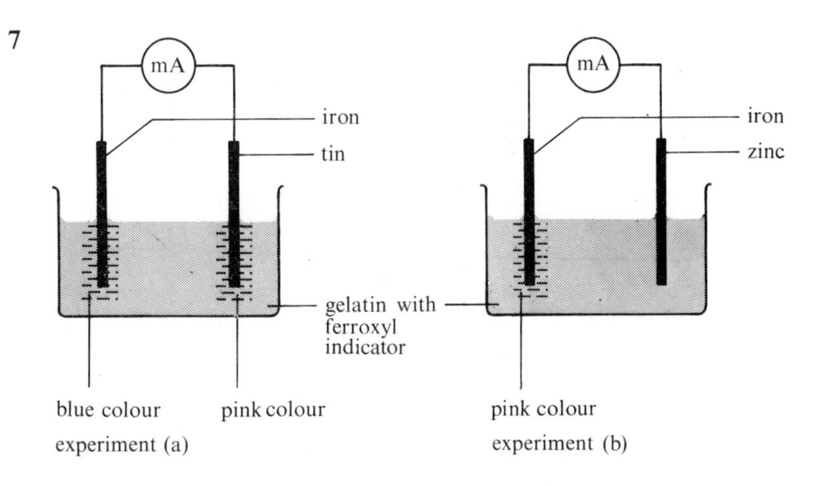

1 What ions are responsible for the blue colour and the pink colour observed in the above experiments?
2 Write electron half-equations for the reaction taking place at the iron electrode in experiment (a) and experiment (b).
3 Compare the direction of electron flow in the external circuit in the two experiments.
4 For each experiment, state at which electrodes oxidation and reduction take place.
5 Which electrode is the anode and which is the cathode in each cell? *P & W*

8 When a solution of sodium bromide was electrolysed, a brown colour was produced round one electrode.
1 Around which electrode did the colour appear?
2 What substance was produced at the other electrode and how would you identify it?
3 Which ions reacted to produce the brown substance?
4 Did the ions gain or lose electrons?
5 Was the reaction to produce the brown substance an oxidation or a reduction?
6 After the electrolysis was stopped, what could you have reacted with the brown substance to make the colour disappear? State the product or products of this reaction. *P & W*

9

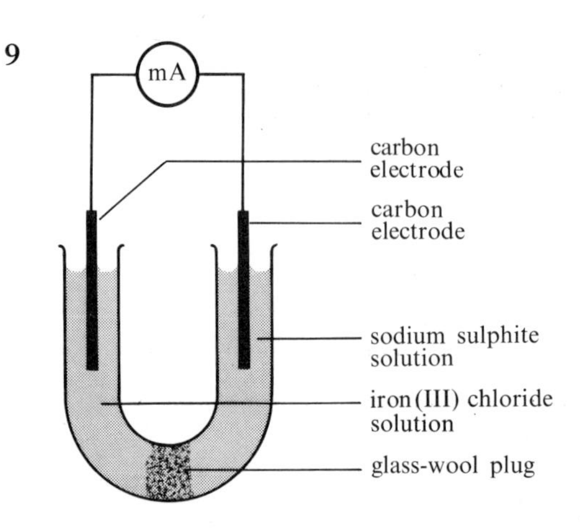

1 After some time, what additional ions would be present in each of the limbs of the U-tube?

2 How could you detect the presence of these ions?

3 Write the electron half-equations and the redox equation for the reaction taking place in the U-tube.

4 In what direction do electrons flow in the external circuit?

5 What is the reducing agent? *P & W*

10 In an electrolysis of sodium nitrate solution in water, carbon electrodes were used. Name the ions present and state which ion is discharged:

1 At the anode (positive electrode).

2 At the cathode (negative electrode).

3 When the bare ends of the two wires from the terminals of a battery are held near one another on a piece of red litmus paper, which has been moistened with sodium chloride solution, the paper is bleached at one wire and turns blue at the other. Explain these observations. *SCEEB*

11 A concentrated solution of potassium chloride in water is electrolysed using carbon electrodes.

1 What is the pH of the original solution?

2 Which element is liberated at the positive electrode?

3 Which element is liberated at the negative electrode?

4 Why does the pH at the negative electrode become greater during the electrolysis? *SCEEB*

11 Corrosion

11.1 An oxidation process

When a metal is oxidized, it loses electrons.

$Na \rightarrow Na^{+} + 1e^{-}$
$Fe \rightarrow Fe^{2+} + 2e^{-}$
$Al \rightarrow Al^{3+} + 3e^{-}$

This oxidation results in the formation of ions, which means that the metal is slowly wearing away. When this process is caused by atmospheric attack, we call it **corrosion.**

11.2 Conditions for corrosion

Two conditions are necessary for corrosion.

Oxidizing agent When oxidation occurs there is also a corresponding reduction. Therefore, for corrosion to occur, an oxidizing agent, which is an electron acceptor, must be present. The oxygen of the air is usually the oxidizing agent. The gaseous oxygen is reduced to form oxide ions.

$O_2(g) + 2e^{-} \rightarrow O^{2-}(s)$

Most metals form metal oxides when they corrode.

Transporting medium Corrosion involves electron transfer between two species. Therefore some substance must be present which will allow transfer of electrons. This is usually the moisture in the air.

Figure 11.1

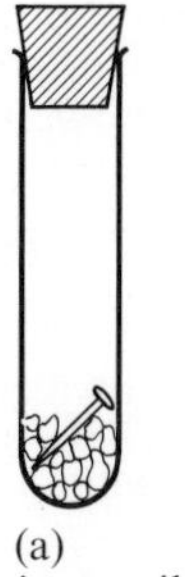

(a)
iron nail in sealed test tube containing a drying agent (anhydrous calcium chloride)

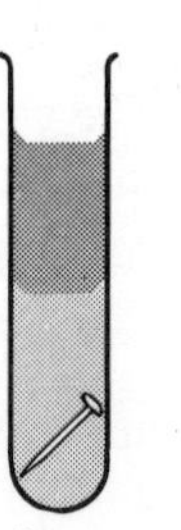

(b)
iron nail in boiled water with a layer of oil above the water

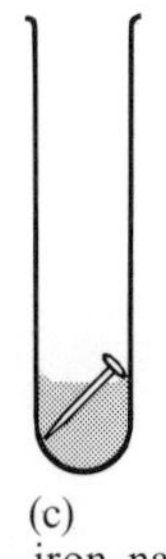

(c)
iron nail in water with the test tube open to the air

We can illustrate both of these conditions if we set up the tests shown in Figure 11.1.

Table 11.1 Results obtained from these tests

Test-tube	*Experimental conditions*	*Result*
(a)	No water	No corrosion
(b)	No air	No corrosion
(c)	Air and water	Corrosion

As you can see from Table 11.1, both oxygen and water are necessary for corrosion to occur.

Iron corrodes in the presence of air and water to form hydrated iron(III) oxide $Fe_2O_3.xH_2O$, where x is a variable. The term **rust** applies specifically to iron, for, although most metals corrode, only iron rusts. The process of rusting takes place in two steps.

$$Fe(s) \rightarrow Fe^{2+}(s) + 2e^- \quad 1$$
$$Fe^{2+}(s) \rightarrow Fe^{3+}(s) + 1e^- \quad 2$$

11.3 Factors affecting the rate of corrosion

There are several factors which can accelerate corrosion.

Salt Cars that are driven during winter or are parked near to the sea tend to corrode more quickly than cars that have not been subjected to these conditions. This is because the salt either from the roads, where it is used to keep the roads ice-free, or from the sea, dissolves in water to form a solution containing a large number of ions. This provides a much better conducting medium. As a result, the iron and steel in the bodywork of the car will rust more quickly under these conditions.

Pollutants in the air In industrial areas, especially those containing chemical plants, there are relatively high concentrations of sulphur dioxide, nitrogen dioxide, and carbon dioxide. The gases dissolve in rain water to form dilute acidic solutions which contain hydrogen ions. These dissolved gases cause the corrosion process to take place more quickly, and the gases then act as oxidizing agents.

Heat An increase in temperature will always increase the rate of a chemical reaction (see page 174). Therefore corrosion will speed up if the metal is subjected to heat. A good example of this is the corrosion of a car exhaust system. It is subjected to very high temperatures as well as attack from water and salt from the road, and this is why exhaust systems have an average life of two years.

We can illustrate some of these conditions if we set up the tests shown in Figure 11.2.

Figure 11.2

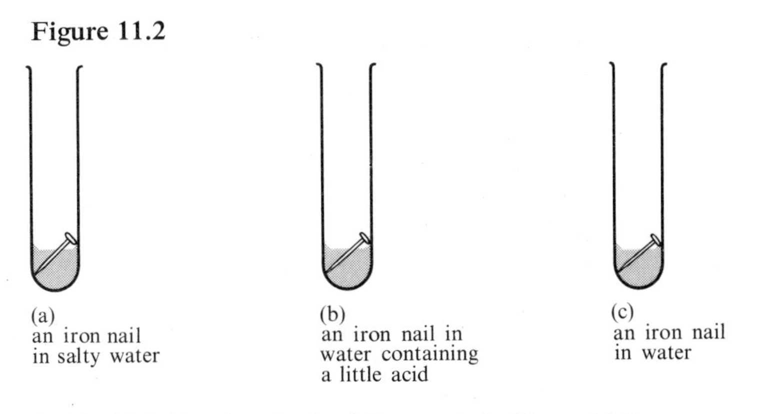

Table 11.2 Results obtained from tests in Figure 11.2

Test-tube	*Experimental conditions*	*Result*
(a)	Salty water	Extreme corrosion
(b)	Water containing acid	Extreme corrosion
(c)	Water	Corrosion

11.4 Protection of iron and steel

Iron is the most widely used metal in the world, from tin cans to steel bridges. Rusting greatly reduces the strength of iron and steel structures, and it is, therefore, a major economic and safety problem. We can reduce the rusting of iron, and in some cases eliminate it completely.

Exclusion of air One condition for iron to rust is the presence of air, so any method which will exclude air from the iron will prevent corrosion. Some examples are given below.

1. Greasing and oiling will protect the moving parts of an engine. It will also protect non-moving articles like tools.
2. Painting, plastic coating, or varnishing will protect any non-moving objects that are unlikely to be scratched.
3. Metal plating with Cr, Ag, Au, Cu, and Sn will give an attractive, corrosion-resistant, metallic finish.

Tin plating Tin cans are in fact steel cans with a thin coating of tin. Tin is used because it is resistant to attack by air and water. The inside of the can is coated with polyurethane to protect it from attack by acidic juices. A suitable arrangement for tin plating in the laboratory is shown in Figure 11.3. The tin(IV) ions are attracted to the cathode where they gain electrons, and the tin metal is deposited on the substance being plated.

Figure 11.3

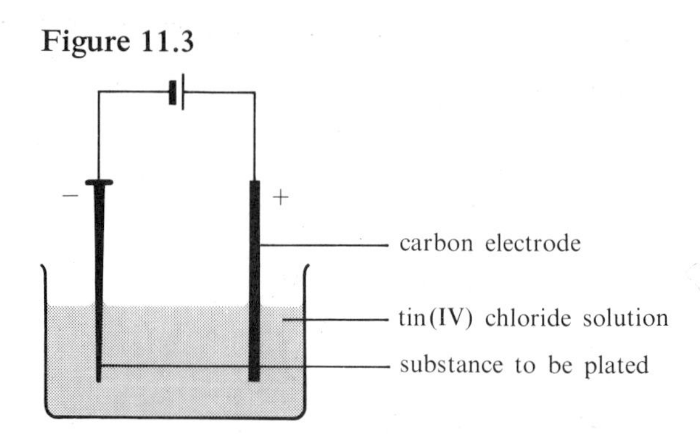

$Sn^{4+}(aq)+4e^{-} \rightarrow Sn(s)$

Industrially tin plating is either done by electrolysis or by dipping the substance to be plated in a bath of molten tin.

There is one drawback with tin-plating. If the tin is scratched a cell is set up between the tin and iron. Since tin is below iron in the electrochemical series, the electrons will flow from the iron to the tin, and the iron will rust.

Electrical (cathodic) protection

Rusting of iron is an oxidation process which involves a loss of electrons. A supply of electrons to the iron will prevent the iron from losing its electrons and, therefore, will prevent rusting. For example, many modern cars are 'negatively earthed', which means that the negative terminal of the battery is connected to the body of the car. This supplies electrons to the body and helps to prevent the iron from rusting.

Galvanizing

Iron is galvanized by dipping it into a bath of molten zinc, which places a coating of zinc on the iron. This method of protection is used for items which are subjected to rough treatment such as dustbins and corrugated iron roofing. When a zinc coating is scratched the iron is still protected since zinc is above iron in the reactivity series, and the electrons will flow from zinc to iron. This is a particular case of cathodic protection.

$Zn(s) \rightarrow Zn^{2+}(s)+2e^{-}$

The iron will not rust but the zinc will slowly corrode instead. Zinc is never used for food packaging as zinc ions are poisonous.

Alloying

Steel is produced from iron by carefully controlling the amount of carbon present. Most steels contain between 0.1 per cent and 1 per cent carbon. By mixing steel with certain metals, alloys which are resistant to corrosion can be produced. These alloys are called **stainless steels.** Steel alloyed with chromium or with nickel will produce corrosion-resistant stainless steels. They contain between 10 and 25 per cent chromium or between 8 and 20 per cent nickel.

Sacrificial protection

If we supply electrons to iron, it will not rust. We can do this by attaching a metal higher in the reactivity series to the iron. The metal will corrode preferentially. Underground pipelines are protected in this way. Bags of magnesium scrap are attached at intervals along the pipeline (Figure 11.4).

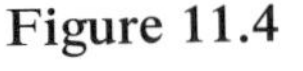

Figure 11.4

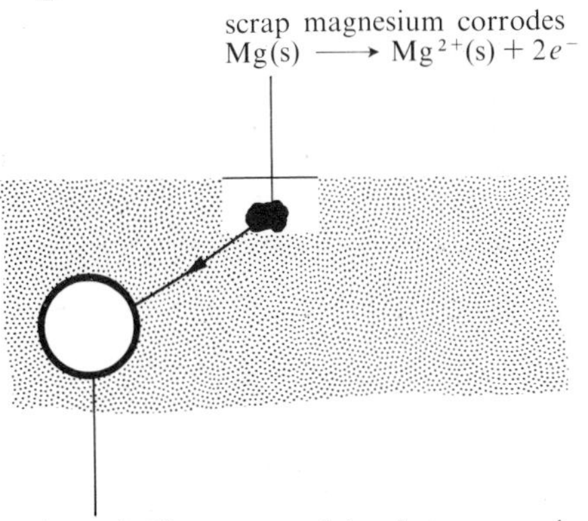

11.5 Protection of aluminium

Aluminium is high in the reactivity series and should, therefore, be a reactive metal. However if you test aluminium you will find that it is not very reactive. This is due to a layer of aluminium oxide which forms when the metal is exposed to the air. The oxide layer does not flake off, and is impervious to air and water. In other words, aluminium corrodes until the oxide layer is formed. This layer then prevents further corrosion. Aluminium for domestic utensils is further protected by thickening the oxide layer. The process is called **anodizing** (Figure 11.5).

Figure 11.5 A laboratory arrangement for anodizing aluminium

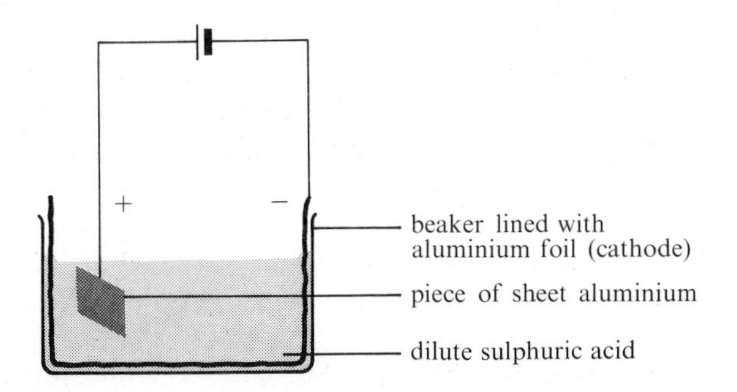

The piece of aluminium to be anodized is made at the anode. The oxygen which is released at the anode reacts with the aluminium to form aluminium oxide.

$4Al(s) + 3O_2(g) \rightarrow 2Al_2O_3(s)$

The oxide layer builds up and completely protects the aluminium. Another advantage of the layer is that it can be dyed. A metal cannot be dyed but the oxide layer can be. This means that aluminium articles can be given attractive, coloured finishes.

Summary

From this chapter you should know:

1. Corrosion is an oxidation process.
2. Oxygen and water are necessary for corrosion.
3. The factors which affect corrosion.
4. The ways in which iron and steel can be protected.
5. How to protect aluminium.

The experiments for this chapter are on pages 276–8.

Questions

1 1 What other substances besides iron are necessary for rusting to occur?
2 When iron rusts it forms iron ions. Show whether this involves a loss or gain of electrons, and state whether it is a reduction or oxidation.
What happens to the electrons lost or gained by the iron?
3 Indicate two ways by which the rate of rusting can be increased.
4 How can rusting be prevented without coating the iron with anything such as grease, paint or metal? *P & W*

2 Six clean iron nails were suspended, by thread, in corked test-tubes (a), (b), (c), (d), (e), and (f). The conditions in each tube were as shown.

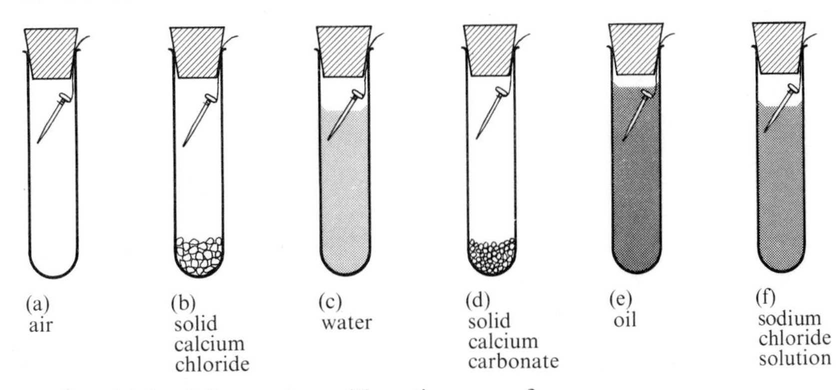

1 In which of these tubes will rusting occur?
2 In which tube will the corrosion be worst? Justify your answer.
3 What is the function of the calcium chloride in test-tube (b)? *P & W*

3 A ship, sunk during the Second World War, was raised several hundred metres from the sea-bed and towed to the shore. Its steel hull was relatively uncorroded, yet within a few weeks the steel was badly rusted. Explain the increase in the rate of corrosion and suggest a method of protecting the ship. *P & W*

4 The exhaust system of a car usually corrodes more rapidly than any other part. Give, with explanations, two reasons why you think this should be the case. *P & W*

5 **1.1** Draw a labelled diagram of the apparatus you would set up to anodize an aluminium ash tray.
1.2 What are the essential differences between anodizing and electroplating?
2 A pupil wrote: 'Corrosion is the loss of electrons in the presence of air and water'. How would you test this statement in the laboratory?
3 Give examples of the corrosion of iron being prevented by:
3.1 A metal below iron in the reactivity series.
3.2 A metal above iron in the reactivity series.
Explain how the corrosion is prevented in each case. *P & W*

6 The climate in countries such as Australia favours the rapid corrosion of steel piers. To overcome this problem, the pier is connected to the negative terminal of a d.c. generator and the positive terminal of the generator to scrap metal (old cars etc.) which is lying offshore.
1.1 Draw a labelled diagram to illustrate this arrangement.
1.2 Explain why it prevents corrosion of the pier and write an equation for the reaction taking place at the anode.
2 Draw a fully labelled diagram showing how you would tin plate an iron nail. *P & W*

7 Rowing boats used in the sea often have a brass (copper/zinc alloy) strip attached to the keel to minimize damage when launching from and landing on the beach.
1 Why would it be inadvisable to attach the brass strip with iron screws?
2 What would be the best way of attaching the strip? *P & W*

8 A pupil investigating the effect of dissolved substances on the rate of corrosion of iron carried out the following experiment. He polished three similar pieces of sheet iron with steel wool and placed one in each of three test-tubes set up as shown in the diagram.

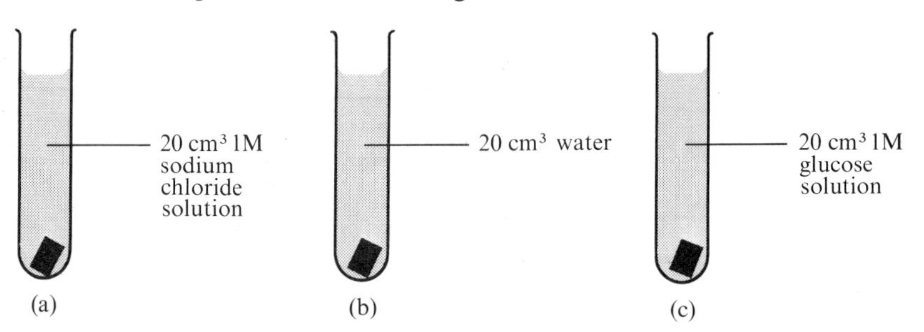

He then added 1 cm³ of a solution of potassium hexacyanoferrate(III) to each of the tubes. On inspecting the tubes a few hours later he found that corrosion was most marked in tube (a), but that there was no appreciable difference in the extent to which the iron in tubes (b) and (c) had corroded.
1 Why was it necessary to polish the pieces of iron before the experiment?
2 How did the addition of potassium hexacyanoferrate(III) help him to compare the rates of corrosion?
3 Suggest a reason why the presence of sodium chloride in the water should speed up corrosion, whereas that of glucose does not. *SCEEB*

12 Sulphur and its compounds

12.1 The element sulphur

Sulphur is a yellow, odourless solid. It has a relatively low melting point of 387 K (114 °C) and is practically insoluble in water. This would suggest that sulphur is a covalent element.

Sulphur is an element which exhibits **polymorphism.** Polymorphism occurs when two or more forms of the element exist in the same state of matter. In the solid state there are two polymorphs of sulphur, **rhombic sulphur** and **monoclinic sulphur** (Figure 12.1).

Figure 12.1 Rhombic sulphur (stable below 368.5 K) and monoclinic sulphur (stable above 368.5 K)

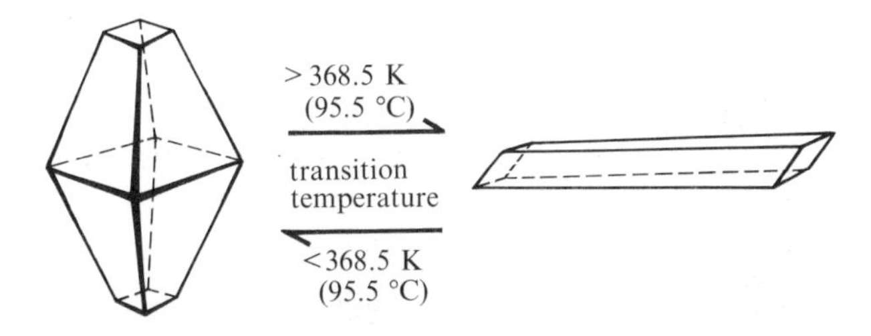

Both these forms are thought to be made up of puckered rings containing eight sulphur atoms (Figure 12.2). The packing of the atoms in the two forms is different, rhombic crystals being packed more closely than monoclinic crystals. When sulphur is heated, it melts and goes through a variety of liquid polymorphs, as shown in Figure 12.3.

Figure 12.2 Two representations of the S_8 ring

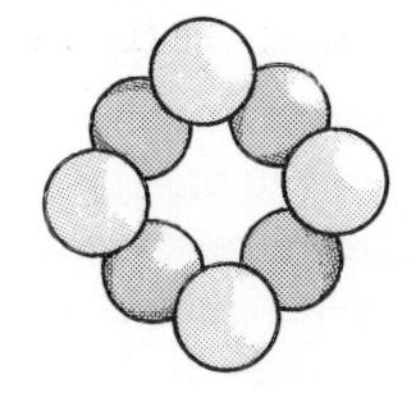

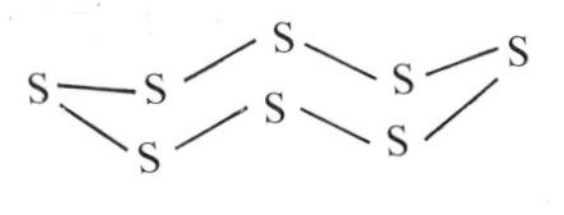

If boiling sulphur is poured into cold water, the sulphur cools down too quickly for the typical S_8 rings to form. This results in the formation of an unstable, rubber-like solid called **plastic sulphur.**

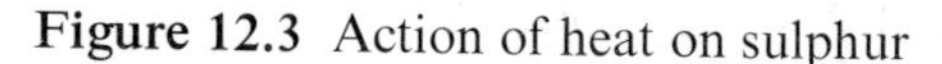
Figure 12.3 Action of heat on sulphur

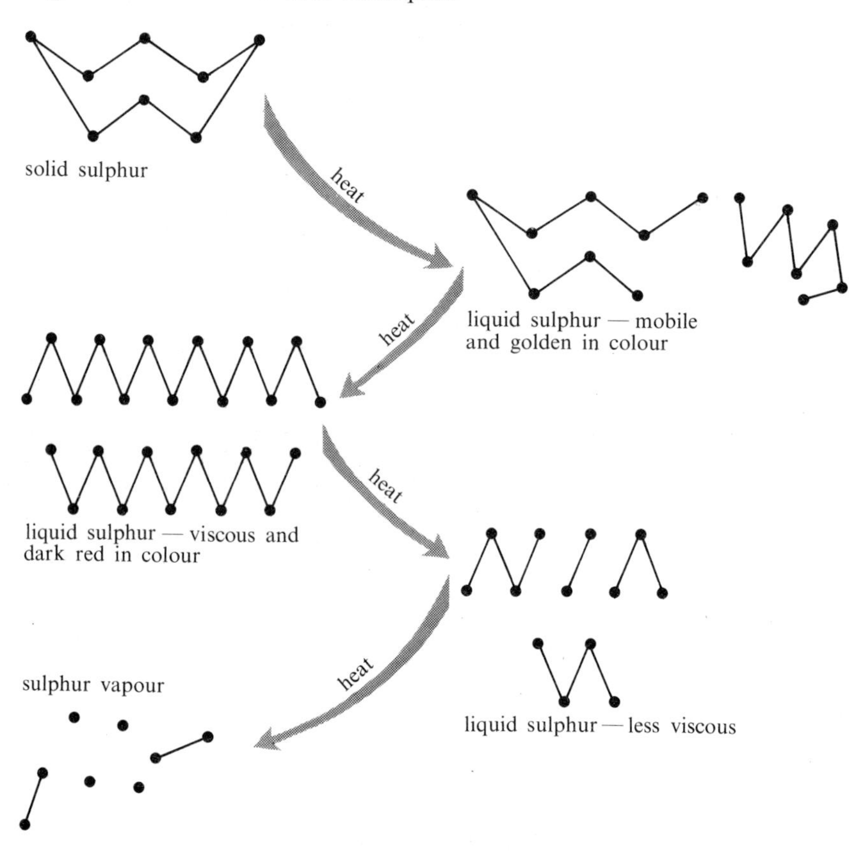

12.2 Occurence and extraction of sulphur

Sulphur occurs naturally in volcanic regions in Sicily, Japan, and Mexico. The largest deposits are found in Texas and Louisiana in America, beneath layers of quicksand. The quicksand makes traditional mining very hazardous. However, an American chemist, Herman Frasch, devised an ingenious method for extracting the sulphur which is now called the **Frasch process.**

A fairly narrow hole, about 15 cm in diameter, is drilled down into the sulphur beds, and three concentric pipes are passed down (Figure 12.4). Superheated water, that is very hot water under pressure, is passed down the outermost pipe to melt the sulphur. Hot compressed air is forced down the innermost pipe to make a froth of the molten sulphur. The sulphur froth then passes up the third pipe to the surface, where it is allowed to cool and solidify in moulds. The sulphur extracted in this way is 99.5 per cent pure, and for most purposes, requires no further purification.

Large quantities of sulphur are also found in combination with metals in the earth's crust as galena PbS; pyrites FeS_2; anhydrite $CaSO_4$; gypsum $CaSO_4.2H_2O$. Small quantities of sulphur are found in coal, oil, and natural gas, and sulphur is a by-product of their purification processes.

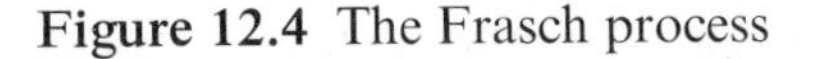

Figure 12.4 The Frasch process

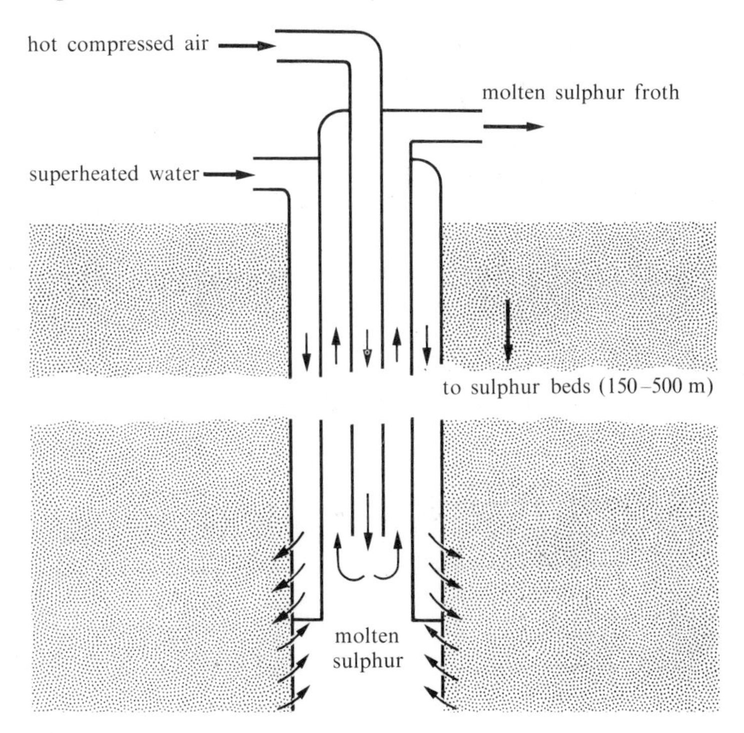

12.3 Sulphur dioxide preparation

When sulphur is burned in air, it produces sulphur dioxide:

$$S(s)+O_2(g) \rightarrow SO_2(g)$$

In industry, sulphur dioxide is manufactured by blowing air through molten sulphur.

The extraction of many metals involves the conversion of the metal sulphides to the metal oxides by roasting the sulphide ores in air. This process yields a great deal of sulphur dioxide for commercial use.

$$2FeS(s)+3O_2(g) \rightarrow 2FeO(s)+2SO_2(g)$$

In the laboratory, sulphur dioxide gas is usually obtained from a cylinder containing liquid sulphur dioxide. It can, however, be prepared chemically by the action of a dilute acid on a sulphite.

$$Na_2SO_3(s)+2HCl(aq) \rightarrow 2NaCl(aq)+H_2O(l)+SO_2(g)$$

12.4 Properties of sulphur dioxide

Sulphur dioxide is a poisonous, colourless gas with a sharp, choking smell. It is easily liquefied, and very soluble in water.

Solubility It dissolves readily in water to form sulphurous acid:

$$SO_2(g) + H_2O(l) \rightarrow H_2SO_3(aq)$$

Sulphurous acid is a weak acid, only partially ionized in aqueous solution.

$$H_2SO_3(aq) \rightleftharpoons H^+(aq) + \underset{\text{hydrogensulphite}}{HSO_3^-(aq)}$$

$$HSO_3^-(aq) \rightleftharpoons H^+(aq) + \underset{\text{sulphite}}{SO_3^{2-}(aq)}$$

Both sulphurous acid and its salts are unstable, and are readily converted into sulphuric acid and its salts when exposed to the air.

Reducing power In the presence of water, sulphur dioxide is a powerful reducing agent, or electron donor, according to the equation.

$$SO_3^{2-}(aq) + H_2O(l) \rightarrow SO_4^{2-}(aq) + 2H^+(aq) + 2e^-$$

The conversion of the sulphite ion SO_3^{2-} to the sulphate ion SO_4^{2-} can be shown by the **sulphate/sulphite test.** The addition of a solution of barium chloride to a sulphite solution will give a dense white precipitate of barium sulphite, which is soluble in dilute hydrochloric acid. The addition of a solution of barium chloride to a sulphate solution will give a white precipitate of barium sulphate, which is insoluble in dilute hydrochloric acid.

$$SO_3^{2-}(aq) + BaCl_2(aq) \rightarrow \underset{\text{soluble in dilute HCl}}{BaSO_3(s)} + 2Cl^-(aq)$$

$$SO_4^{2-}(aq) + BaCl_2(aq) \rightarrow \underset{\text{insoluble in dilute HCl}}{BaSO_4(s)} + 2Cl^-(aq)$$

Table 12.1 is a list of some of the substances which can be reduced by sulphur dioxide, along with the appropriate colour changes and equations, where appropriate. The reactions which involve a colour change can be used in the identification of sulphur dioxide.

Table 12.1 Reducing power of sulphur dioxide

Substance	*Colour change*	*Reduction half-equation*
Iron(III)	Yellow → Green	$Fe^{3+}(aq) + e^- \rightarrow Fe^{2+}(aq)$
Chlorine water	Yellow → Colourless	$Cl_2(aq) + 2e^- \rightarrow 2Cl^-(aq)$
Bromine water	Brown → Colourless	$Br_2(aq) + 2e^- \rightarrow 2Br^-(aq)$
Manganate(VII)	Purple → Colourless	
Dichromate(VI)	Orange → Green	

Any of the reduction half-equations given in Table 12.1 can be combined with the oxidation half-equation to give the overall redox equation.

$$Cl_2(aq) + 2e^- \rightarrow 2Cl^-(aq) \qquad \text{reduction}$$
$$SO_3^{2-}(aq) + H_2O(l) \rightarrow SO_4^{2-}(aq) + 2H^+(aq) + 2e^- \qquad \text{oxidation}$$

$$SO_3^{2-}(aq) + H_2O(l) + Cl_2(aq) \rightarrow SO_4^{2-}(aq) + 2H^+(aq) + 2Cl^-(aq) \quad \text{redox}$$

Oxidation to sulphur trioxide Sulphur dioxide can be converted into sulphur trioxide. Sulphur trioxide is a dense white gas that can easily be condensed to a white crystalline solid at room temperature.

$$2SO_2(g) + O_2(g) \rightleftharpoons 2SO_3(g)$$

At the high temperatures required to make sulphur dioxide and oxygen combine, sulphur trioxide decomposes. Introduction of vanadium(V) oxide to the reaction mixture brings the system to equilibrium faster. The reacting gas molecules are attracted to the surface of the vanadium(V) oxide. This attraction weakens the intramolecular bonds (those which hold the atoms in the molecule together), making the molecules more susceptible to reaction. The vanadium(V) oxide helps the reactions along but remains unchanged itself. We call such a substance a **catalyst.** Figure 12.5 illustrates a suitable laboratory set-up for the conversion of sulphur dioxide to sulphur trioxide.

Figure 12.5

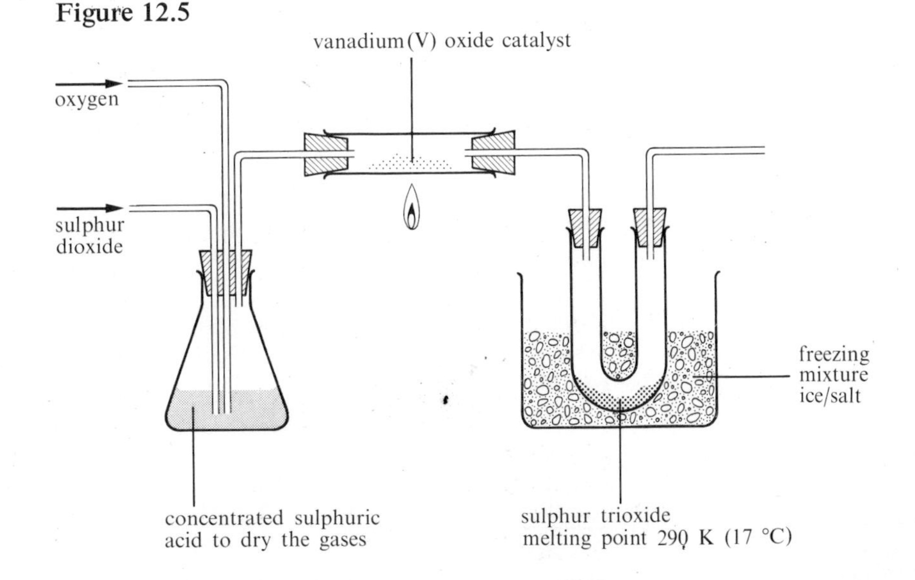

Uses Sulphur dioxide, sulphurous acid, and sulphites have many and varied uses. Their instability and ease of oxidation make them very good preservatives, particularly for dried fruits and fruit juices. Sulphurous acid does not harm the delicate fibres of natural materials such as wool and silk, so it is used to bleach them. The bleaching process is a reduction reaction. Wood pulp and straw for the manufacture of paper and cardboard are also bleached by sulphite solutions. The bleaching, however, is not permanent, and the natural yellow colour of the fibres returns in time. Perhaps the most important use of sulphur dioxide is its conversion to sulphur trioxide for the manufacture of sulphuric acid and other chemicals containing sulphur.

12.5 Le Chatelier's principle

It is appropriate at this stage to have a closer look at reversible reactions like the sulphur dioxide/sulphur trioxide system, and the conditions which govern them.

Most chemical reactions are reversible. Some, however, go so far in the forward direction that the proportion of reactants left is negligible, and we represent this by a single or one-way arrow.

$$2H_2(g) + O_2(g) \rightarrow 2H_2O(l)$$

Others go so far in the reverse direction that the products hardly exist and we say that the reaction does not go at all.

$$\underset{\text{insoluble}}{CaCO_3(s)} + H_2O(l) \rightarrow \text{no reaction}$$

In a true reversible reaction, there are appreciable quantities of both reactants and products present. The sulphur dioxide/sulphur trioxide system is a good example of a reversible reaction:

$$2SO_2(g) + O_2(g) \rightleftharpoons 2SO_3(g)$$

When this reaction has reached equilibrium, all the species, sulphur dioxide, oxygen, and sulphur trioxide, are present, and there is no apparent change in their proportions. The reaction, however, is not stationary. Sulphur dioxide and oxygen are continually reacting to form sulphur trioxide. At the same rate, the sulphur trioxide is decomposing to re-form sulphur dioxide and oxygen. This situation is called a **dynamic equilibrium.** The proportions of the species present depend very much on the external conditions which are imposed on the system. If these conditions are changed, then the proportions of the species will also change. Le Chatelier's principle states that **if the conditions of a system in equilibrium are altered, the system will attempt to reduce the effects of the imposed conditions.**

Let us apply this principle to the sulphur dioxide/sulphur trioxide system.

Effect of pressure

$$\underbrace{\underset{\text{2 moles}}{2SO_2(g)} + \underset{\text{1 mole}}{O_2(g)}}_{\text{3 moles}} \rightleftharpoons \underset{\text{2 moles}}{2SO_3(g)}$$

Pressure is the result of gas molecules bombarding the walls of the vessel in which the gas is contained. Obviously the greater the number of molecules in a given volume, the greater the pressure will be. If the pressure of the sulphur dioxide/sulphur trioxide system increases, by Le Chatelier's principle, the equilibrium will shift to try to reduce this pressure. A reduction in pressure can be achieved by reducing the number of molecules, in other words by shifting the equilibrium to the right. In this way more sulphur dioxide is converted into sulphur trioxide. We would expect increased pressure to favour the formation of sulphur trioxide, and decreased pressure to favour the formation of sulphur dioxide.

Effect of temperature

$$2SO_2(g) + O_2(g) \rightleftharpoons 2SO_3(g) \qquad \Delta H = -385\ \text{kJ}$$

The sulphur dioxide/sulphur trioxide system is one which gives out heat in the conversion of sulphur dioxide to sulphur trioxide. If the temperature of this system is increased, then by Le Chatelier's principle, the equilibrium will shift to try to reduce this temperature. A reduction in temperature can be achieved by converting sulphur trioxide into sulphur dioxide, as this reaction requires heat. We would expect high temperatures to favour the formation of sulphur dioxide and low temperatures to favour the formation of sulphur trioxide. In fact the best theoretical conditions are not always those used in industry, as we shall see when we look at the industrial processes in the next section.

12.6 Manufacture of sulphuric acid

Over 90 per cent of the sulphuric acid manufactured in the United Kingdom is made by the **contact process.** The starting point in the contact process is sulphur dioxide, obtained mostly from the oxidation of imported natural sulphur:

$$S(s) + O_2(g) \rightarrow SO_2(g)$$

Some sulphur dioxide is also obtained from sulphide ores like iron pyrites FeS_2, and in Britain, from calcium sulphate which occurs naturally as gypsum or anhydrite.

The sulphur dioxide is purified by electrostatic dust separation, similar to the dispersal of colloidal smoke particles (pages 21–2), and then washed and dried. After this the sulphur dioxide is mixed with air and passed along heated pipes containing pellets of vanadium(V) oxide catalyst. It is the close contact of the reacting gases with the vanadium(V) oxide which gives the contact process its name.

The sulphur dioxide and oxygen react according to the equation:

$$2SO_2(g) + O_2(g) \xrightleftharpoons{\text{vanadium(V) oxide}} 2SO_3(g) \qquad \Delta H = -385\ \text{kJ}$$

By Le Chatelier's principle we would expect the contact process to use high pressures which favour the conversion of sulphur dioxide to sulphur trioxide. In fact a 98 per cent yield of sulphur trioxide is obtained at atmospheric pressure, so it is not economically necessary to raise the pressure.

Also by Le Chatelier's principle we would expect the contact process to use low temperatures which favour the production of sulphur trioxide. In fact at low temperatures the reaction rate becomes very slow, and from the information shown in Table 12.2, we can see that the most economic temperature lies somewhere between 673 K (400 °C) and 773K (500 °C). The heat evolved in the reaction between sulphur dioxide and oxygen is used to preheat the entering reactants.

Table 12.2 Percentage conversion to SO_3 at various temperatures

Temperature of catalyst		*Percentage of SO_3 obtained*
K	°C	
673	400	86
707	434	99
823	550	85
913	640	60

We might expect the final step in the manufacture of sulphuric acid to be the dissolving of the sulphur trioxide in water according to the equation

$$SO_3(g)+H_2O(l) \rightarrow H_2SO_4(l)$$

In fact sulphur trioxide does not dissolve well in water, but forms a thick mist of sulphuric acid. The formation of such a mist would obviously be a great health hazard to those working in the sulphuric acid plant and would also seriously pollute the environment around the sulphuric acid plant. These dangers are overcome by taking up the sulphur trioxide gas in 97 per cent sulphuric acid. This results in the formation of oleum or fuming sulphuric acid, which can be diluted to give sulphuric acid of the required concentration.

$$SO_3(g)+H_2SO_4(l) \rightarrow H_2S_2O_7(l)$$
$$H_2S_2O_7(l)+H_2O(l) \rightarrow 2H_2SO_4(l)$$

The contact process produces sulphuric acid of an extremely high quality.

12.7 Properties of sulphuric acid

Dilute sulphuric acid exhibits all the usual properties of dilute acids: pH less than seven, reaction with metals, bases, carbonates, and so on (chapter 7.6).

Concentrated sulphuric acid, however, has more unusual properties:

Covalent It is largely covalent, and very few ions are present—hence its low conductivity in comparison with the dilute acid. When dissolved in water, it does ionize.

$$H_2SO_4(l) \xrightleftharpoons{\text{water}} H^+(aq)+HSO_4^-(aq)$$
hydrogensulphate

$$HSO_4^-(aq) \rightleftharpoons H^+(aq)+SO_4^{2-}(aq)$$
sulphate

Hygroscopic It has a high affinity for water, so much so that it will remove the elements of water from various compounds.

$$CuSO_4.5H_2O(s)-5H_2O \rightarrow CuSO_4(s)$$
copper(II) sulphate-5-water (blue) → anhydrous copper(II) sulphate (white)

$$\underset{\substack{\text{sugar}\\\text{(white)}}}{C_{12}H_{22}O_{11}(s)} - 11H_2O \rightarrow \underset{\substack{\text{carbon}\\\text{(black)}}}{12C(s)}$$

$$\underset{\substack{\text{paper}\\\text{(white)}}}{C_x(H_2O)_y(s)} - yH_2O \rightarrow \underset{\substack{\text{carbon}\\\text{(black)}}}{xC(s)}$$

Because of this 'dehydrating power', sulphuric acid is often used as a drying agent in the laboratory.

Concentrated sulphuric acid is so reactive with water that great care must be taken when handling it. When the acid is diluted or disposed of, the acid must be added slowly and carefully to the water. **Water should never be added to the acid,** because the first drops of water vapourize quickly to steam, and spit out droplets of concentrated acid.

Involatile Sulphuric acid does not vaporize easily, but it displaces more volatile acids from their salts.

$$H_2SO_4(l) + NaCl(s) \rightarrow HCl(g) + NaHSO_4(s)$$
$$H_2SO_4(l) + NaNO_3(s) \rightarrow HNO_3(g) + NaHSO_4(s)$$

The involatile nature of concentrated sulphuric acid is of great importance in the manufacture of phosphate fertilizers. Phosphate rock, an insoluble mineral, is treated with sulphuric acid to give phosphoric(V) acid, which can then be used to prepare soluble phosphate salts (chapter 13.9).

Oxidizing agent Sulphuric acid has very strong oxidizing properties, oxidizing both metals and non-metals.

Metals

$$Cu(s) + 2H_2SO_4(l) \xrightarrow{\text{heat}} CuSO_4(aq) + SO_2(g) + 2H_2O(g)$$
$$Cu(s) \longrightarrow Cu^{2+}(aq) + 2e^-$$
$$Zn(s) + 2H_2SO_4(l) \xrightarrow{\text{heat}} ZnSO_4(aq) + SO_2(g) + 2H_2O(g)$$
$$Zn(s) \longrightarrow Zn^{2+}(aq) + 2e^-$$

As you can see in each of the examples, the copper and the zinc metal have each lost electrons. They have been oxidized by the sulphuric acid.

Non-metals

$$C(s) + 2H_2SO_4(l) \xrightarrow{\text{heat}} CO_2(g) + 2SO_2(g) + 2H_2O(g)$$
$$C(s) \longrightarrow CO_2(g)$$
$$S(s) + 2H_2SO_4(l) \xrightarrow{\text{heat}} 3SO_2(g) + 2H_2O(g)$$
$$S(s) \longrightarrow SO_2(g)$$

As you can see in each of these examples the carbon and sulphur have gained oxygen. Oxidation can be considered as a gain of oxygen, and, therefore, the carbon and sulphur have been oxidized.

12.8 Uses of sulphuric acid

Over a hundred years ago it was first said that the prosperity of a country could be measured by the amount of sulphuric acid it produced. Although many changes have occured since then, sulphuric acid is still a very important chemical in many industries. Figure 12.6 gives an indication of the widespread use of sulphuric acid.

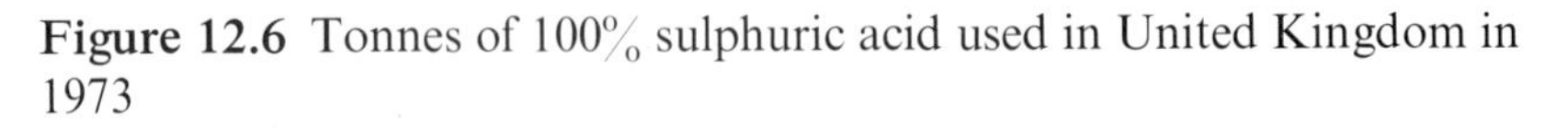

Figure 12.6 Tonnes of 100% sulphuric acid used in United Kingdom in 1973

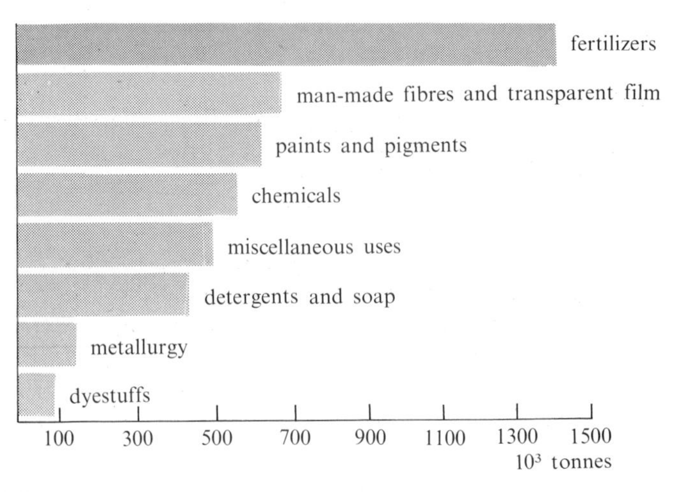

Summary

From this chapter you should know:

1. Sulphur is polymorphous.
2. How sulphur is obtained.
3. The preparation and properties of sulphur dioxide.
4. The preparation of sulphur trioxide.
5. Le Chatelier's principle and how this applies to the manufacture of sulphuric acid.
6. The properties of sulphuric acid.
7. The uses of sulphuric acid.

The experiments for this chapter are on pages 279–81.

Questions

1 1 The diagram shows a simplified flow-diagram for the production of sulphuric acid. Describe what happens at A, B, and C.

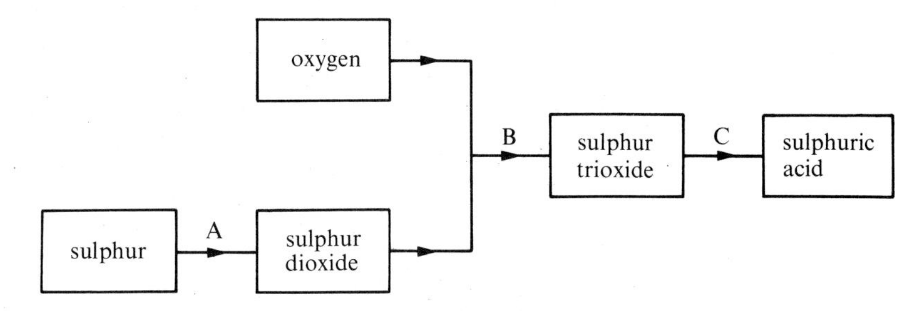

2 What is a catalyst, and how does it function?
3 When a pupil dissolved a crystal of freshly prepared sodium sulphite in water and added barium chloride solution, a white precipitate was obtained which disappeared on the addition of dilute hydrochloric acid.
When the experiment was repeated with sodium sulphite which had been in stock for some time, the white precipitate did not disappear on addition of the acid.
Offer an explanation for the difference in the results of the two experiments.
P & W

2 Explain the following statements:
1 Copper reacts with hot concentrated sulphuric acid to give sulphur dioxide whereas with dilute acid there is no reaction.
2 Zinc reacts with hot concentrated sulphuric acid to give sulphur dioxide whereas the dilute acid gives hydrogen.
3 Sodium chloride gives hydrogen chloride with hot concentrated sulphuric acid whereas sodium bromide gives bromine.
4 Concentrated sulphuric acid is a poor conductor of electricity whereas dilute sulphuric acid is a good conductor of electricity. *P & W*

3 The essential reaction in the contact process for making sulphuric acid is:

$$2SO_2 + O_2 \rightleftharpoons 2SO_3 \qquad \Delta H = -385\,\text{kJ}$$

This is a reversible reaction and a dynamic equilibrium is set up.
1 Explain what is meant by a 'reversible reaction' and 'dynamic equilibrium'.
2 Is the reaction exothermic or endothermic? Name a catalyst which can be used for this reaction.
3 Is the function of the catalyst to:
Alter the position of equilibrium to obtain a higher percentage of sulphur trioxide;
Cause equilibrium to be reached more quickly;
Ensure that sulphur trioxide is the only product of the reaction?
Explain your choice.

4 Why is the catalyst spread out, often on the surface of an inert carrier such as asbestos?
5 Why must the sulphur dioxide/air mixture be carefully purified before the reaction is carried out?
6 Why is the sulphur dioxide absorbed in concentrated sulphuric acid rather than in water? *P & W*

4 During an investigation into the properties of concentrated sulphuric acid, a pupil heated some of the acid with a few small pieces of charcoal in a test-tube, and passed the gas produced into calcium hydroxide solution (limewater). The limewater was not affected. He then repeated the experiment, using the apparatus shown below. This time he noticed that, after a few minutes, the limewater turned cloudy, and the bromine water became much lighter in colour.

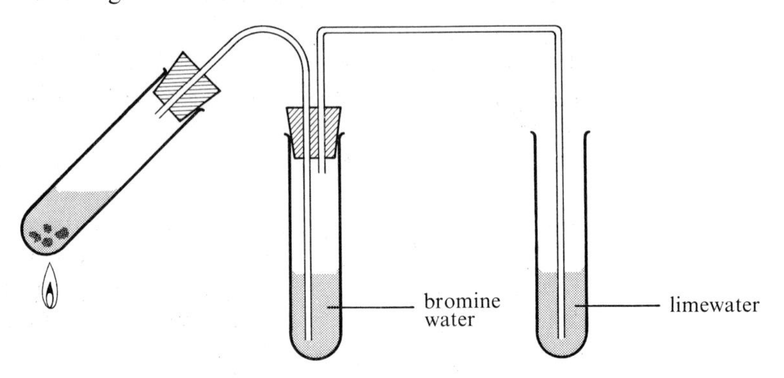

1 What gas caused the bromine water to become lighter in colour?
2 With the help of chemical equations, explain why the bromine water was discoloured.
3 Write a chemical equation for the reaction between the charcoal and the concentrated sulphuric acid.
4 Suggest a reason why the limewater did not turn cloudy in the first experiment. *P & W*

5 When sulphuric acid vapour is passed over red-hot porous chips, thermal cracking occurs and certain gases are formed. When an attempt is made to collect these gases over distilled water a colourless gas is obtained, and
(a) The water now has a pH of much less than seven and smells of burning sulphur.
(b) It now decolourizes potassium manganate(VII) solution, or changes potassium dichromate(VI) solution from orange to green.
1 Name the ion present as indicated by the pH in (a).
2 Name and give the formula of an ion present which is likely to give result (b).
3 Name the gas which has dissolved in the water to give it these new properties.
4 Name the gas which has been collected over the water.
5 Given a supply of these gases how would you reverse the process by

first making them combine and then form sulphuric acid? Draw a labelled diagram of your apparatus.
6 If the sulphuric acid formed is converted into the fertilizer, ammonium sulphate, calculate the weight of pure sulphuric acid required to make 100 tonnes of the fertilizer. *SCEEB*

6 A pupil added concentrated sulphuric acid to a substance and noted that a colourless gas was given off which decolourized bromine water. He concluded that (a) the gas was sulphur dioxide, and (b) that the sulphur dioxide had been produced by the reduction of the sulphuric acid.
1 He may have been wrong in his first conclusion. Why?
2 Name one substance which would produce sulphur dioxide when acted upon by concentrated sulphuric acid without involving the reduction of the sulphuric acid. Write a balanced equation for the reaction, and use it to show that reduction of the acid has not occured.
3.1 A solution of barium chloride was added to a solution of sodium sulphite and a white precipitate was obtained. What is this precipitate likely to be?
3.2 When dilute hydrochloric acid was added to the precipitate it reacted and a pungent smelling gas was given off. What is this gas?
3.3 A solution of sulphur dioxide in water was warmed with a little nitric acid. Barium chloride solution was added and a white precipitate was formed which did not dissolve when dilute hydrochloric acid was added. What is the precipitate? What happened to the solution of sulphur dioxide when it was acted upon by the nitric acid?
4 Name two substances which are used for the manufacture of sulphur dioxide in industry. *SCEEB*

7 $2SO_2(g) + O_2(g) \rightleftharpoons 2SO_3(g)$

This equation represents the conversion of sulphur dioxide to sulphur trioxide in the contact process.
1 How can sulphur dioxide be obtained on the industrial scale?
2 Why is the sign $\rightleftharpoons$ used in preference to $\rightarrow$?
3 The reaction releases heat. Why is this useful?
4 Why is sulphur trioxide important?
5 Give a chemical name for the solution made by bubbling sulphur dioxide through water.
6 Why does this solution conduct electricity better than water does?
7 Why is the solution able to act as a bleach?
8 Assuming 100 per cent efficiency, what weight of sulphur trioxide could be produced from a million (10^6) kilograms of sulphur dioxide? *SCEEB*

13 Nitrogen and its compounds

13.1 The element nitrogen

About 80 per cent of the earth's atmosphere is composed of the element nitrogen, a colourless, odourless, tasteless gas, characterized by its extremely unreactive nature. Elementary nitrogen is often referred to as **free** nitrogen. **Fixed** nitrogen, that is nitrogen in combination with other elements, is also fairly abundant. It is found in the protein material of plants and animals, and also in the earth's crust as metal nitrates, such as Chile saltpetre $NaNO_3$.

Figure 13.1 The fractional distillation of liquid air

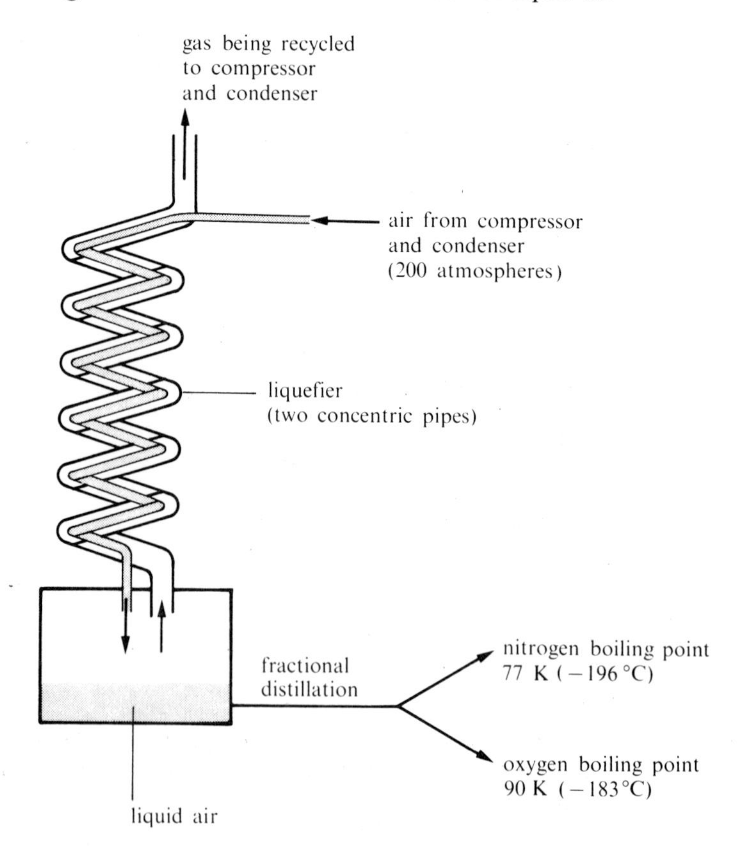

Nitrogen is obtained by the fractional distillation of liquid air. Dust particles are first removed from the air. Then carbon dioxide and water are removed because at low temperatures they would become solid and block the pipes. Finally the air is liquefied by subjecting it to low temperatures and high pressures. The components of liquid air, that is nitrogen, oxygen, and the noble gases, all have different boiling points, and so can be collected at different levels in the fractionating column (Figure 13.1).

Nitrogen does not react easily because the element is composed of diatomic molecules, the atoms of which are held together very strongly by three covalent bonds. Only when sufficient energy is supplied to break these bonds does nitrogen react.

Burning magnesium provides sufficient energy. A piece of burning magnesium will continue to burn when lowered into a gas jar containing nitrogen. The magnesium burns in the nitrogen to produce magnesium nitride.

$$3Mg(s) + N_2(g) \rightarrow Mg_3N_2(s)$$

The electrical discharge in a thunder storm also provides sufficient energy. In thunder storms, a small amount of nitrogen reacts with the oxygen in the air to form nitric oxide and nitrogen dioxide.

$$N_2(g) + O_2(g) \rightarrow 2NO(g)$$
$$2NO(g) + O_2(g) \rightarrow 2NO_2(g)$$

Nitrogen gas can be converted into nitrogen dioxide gas in the laboratory using the apparatus shown in Figure 13.2.

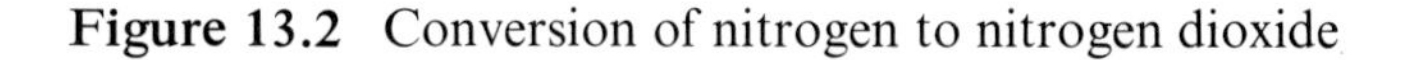

Figure 13.2 Conversion of nitrogen to nitrogen dioxide

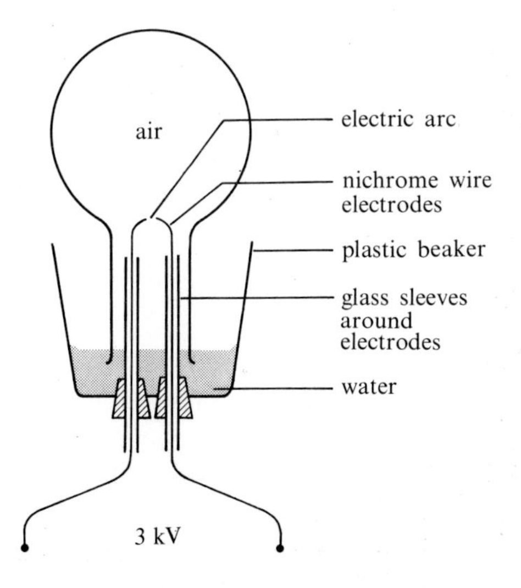

In the presence of a catalyst, nitrogen gas can be made to combine with hydrogen gas to form ammonia, one of the most important nitrogen compounds.

13.2 Ammonia

Ammonia gas has a characteristic, pungent smell. Small traces of ammonia are found in the air because of the breakdown of plant and animal protein by bacteria. The odour of ammonia is noticable in stables and cow-sheds.

Because of its plant and animal origins, coal yields a certain amount of ammonia when it is heated in the absence of air. However, by far the most important source of ammonia is the direct combination of nitrogen and hydrogen in the presence of a catalyst. Industrially this is done by the **Haber process** (Figure 13.3). Nitrogen gas is obtained by the fractional distillation of liquid air. Hydrogen gas is obtained either by the electrolysis of brine, or from the coal or oil industries.

$$N_2(g) + 3H_2(g) \underset{}{\overset{\text{catalyst}}{\rightleftharpoons}} 2NH_3(g)$$

The catalyst used in the Haber Process consists of small pieces of iron.

Figure 13.3 The Haber process

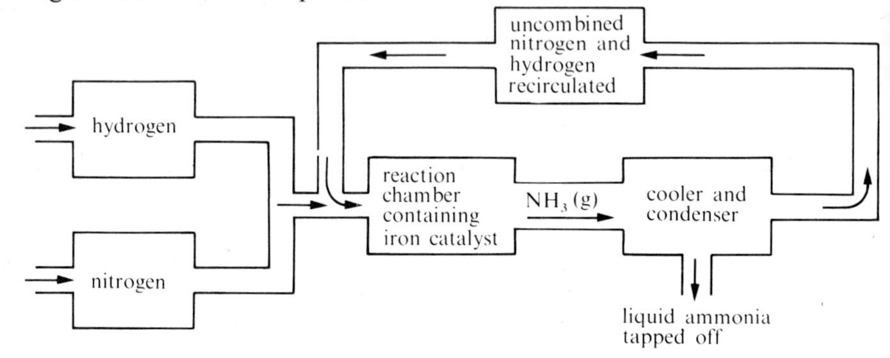

As shown by the equation, the reaction between nitrogen and hydrogen is reversible. In fact, under normal conditions, the equilibrium lies very much to the left, which means that the yield of ammonia is very small. The yield can, of course, be improved by changing the conditions. Let us apply Le Chatelier's principle.

Effect of pressure

$$\underbrace{N_2(g) + 3H_2(g)}_{\text{4 moles}} \rightleftharpoons \underbrace{2NH_3(g)}_{\text{2 moles}}$$

An increase in pressure will tend to make the equilibrium move in the direction which causes a decrease in pressure, that is from left to right. This means that nitrogen and hydrogen will combine to form ammonia. The Haber process uses high pressures of up to 1000 times atmospheric pressure to increase the yield of ammonia.

Effect of temperature

$$N_2(g) + 3H_2(g) \rightleftharpoons 2NH_3(g) \qquad \Delta H = -91\ \text{kJ}$$

The reaction between nitrogen and hydrogen is exothermic. A decrease in temperature will tend to make the equilibrium move in the direction which causes an increase in temperature, that is from left to right. This favours the formation of ammonia.

In practice, low temperatures slow up the rate of the reaction too much, so the Haber process uses temperatures in the region of 770 K (500 °C) to

870 K (600 °C). Temperatures of this order result in a 40 per cent yield of ammonia. However, any unreacted gases can be recirculated into the reaction chamber, so that there is no wastage of the reactants.

In the Haber process, the ammonia is continually removed as it is formed by liquefying it with a freezing mixture. The reasons for this are twofold. Firstly, removal of the ammonia will stop it from decomposing. Secondly, constant removal of the ammonia means that more ammonia is always being formed in an attempt to establish equilibrium.

For laboratory use, ammonia is prepared either by warming concentrated aqueous ammonia:

$$NH_4^+(aq) + OH^-(aq) \xrightarrow{heat} NH_3(g) + H_2O(l)$$

or by heating an ammonium salt with a strong alkali:

$$(NH_4^+ + Cl^-)(s) + Na^+(aq) + OH^-(aq) \longrightarrow NH_4^+(aq) + OH^-(aq) + Na^+(aq) + Cl^-(aq)$$
$$NH_4^+(aq) + OH^-(aq) \xrightarrow{heat} NH_3(g) + H_2O(l)$$

13.3 Properties of ammonia

Smell Perhaps the most distinctive characteristic of ammonia is its smell, which can always be used as a means of identifying it.

Basic nature Another characteristic which can assist in identifying ammonia is its basic nature. If a glass rod, which has been dipped in concentrated hydrochloric acid, is held in ammonia gas, the ammonia neutralizes the acid, and gives clouds of white ammonium chloride:

$$NH_3(g) + HCl(g) \rightarrow NH_4Cl(s)$$

Solubility Because it is polar, ammonia is soluble in water. It is so soluble that the fountain experiment can be carried out (chapter 4.8). When a solution of aqueous ammonia is to be prepared a funnel has to be used to prevent the water from being 'sucked back' into the reaction flask (Figure 13.4).

Figure 13.4 Making aqueous ammonia

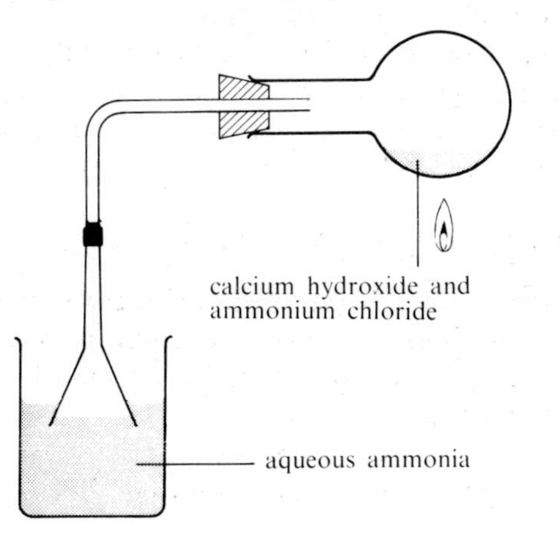

When ammonia dissolves in water, aqueous ammonia, a weak alkali, is produced.

$$NH_3(g) + H_2O(l) \rightleftharpoons NH_4^+(aq) + OH^-(aq)$$

Reducing power Ammonia gas is a good reducing agent, which means it can be fairly easily oxidized. It burns in oxygen to give nitrogen (Figure 13.5).

$$4NH_3(g) + 3O_2(g) \rightarrow 2N_2(g) + 6H_2O(g)$$

Figure 13.5 Oxidation of ammonia by oxygen

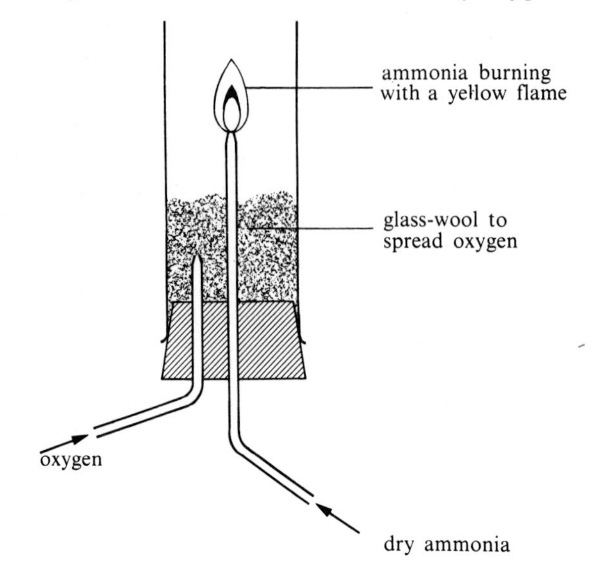

It reduces copper oxide to give nitrogen (Figure 13.6).

$$2NH_3(g) + 3CuO(s) \rightarrow N_2(g) + 3Cu(s) + 3H_2O(g)$$

Figure 13.6 Oxidation of ammonia by copper(II) oxide

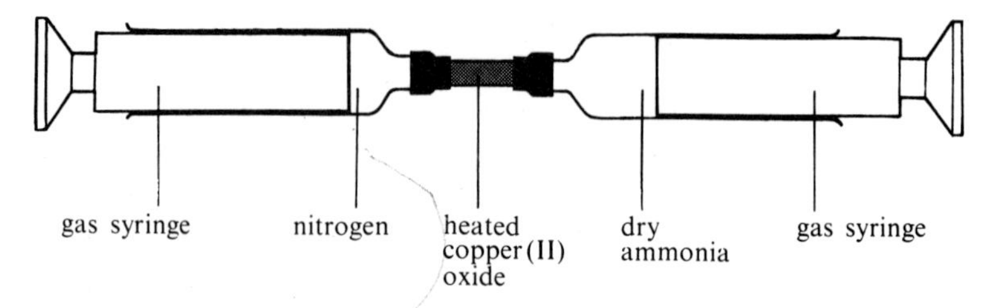

It can also be oxidized by air in the presence of a platinum catalyst to give nitric oxide, which is then oxidized to nitrogen dioxide (Figure 13.7).

$$4NH_3(g) + 5O_2(g) \xrightarrow{\text{Pt catalyst}} 4NO(g) + 6H_2O(g)$$
$$2NO(g) + O_2(g) \longrightarrow 2NO_2(g)$$

This reaction is an extremely important step in the manufacture of nitric acid (see section 13.5).

Figure 13.7

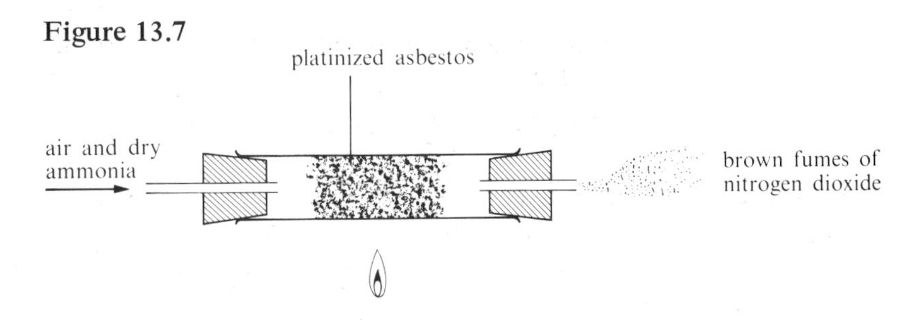

13.4 Uses of ammonia and its salts

We noted in section 13.1 that ammonia was one of the most important compounds of nitrogen. This is because of the widespread use of both ammonia and its salts. The most important use of ammonia is in the production of fertilizers (section 13.9). It is also used in the production of nitric acid by the Ostwald process (section 13.5) and as a refrigerant. It can be used as a refrigerant because it evaporates readily, removing heat from the surroundings as it does so, and then can be easily liquefied by compression. Table 13.1 shows some common uses of ammonium compounds.

Table 13.1 Uses of ammonium compounds

Compounds	*Uses*
Aqueous ammonia	Domestic cleaner, grease remover
Ammonium bromide	Photography
Ammonium carbonate	Smelling salts
Ammonium chloride	Dry-cell batteries
Ammonium nitrate	Explosives, fertilizer
Ammonium phosphate	Fertilizer
Ammonium sulphate	Fertilizer

13.5 Manufacture of nitric acid

It is very difficult to oxidize nitrogen to give the oxides necessary for the production of nitric acid, so the **Ostwald process** uses ammonia as its starting point. A mixture of air and ammonia is heated to a temperature of 870 K (600 °C), and passed through a reacting vessel containing layers of platinum gauzes. On the surface of the platinum the ammonia is oxidized by the oxygen in the air to produce nitric oxide.

$$4NH_3(g)+5O_2(g) \xrightarrow{\text{Pt catalyst}} 4NO(g)+6H_2O(g)$$

The reaction is exothermic, and enough heat is generated to keep the platinum gauzes at the correct temperature. When the nitric oxide is rapidly cooled, it combines with more oxygen to form nitrogen dioxide which is then dissolved in water to form nitric acid.

$$2NO(g)+O_2 \rightarrow 2NO_2(g)$$
$$3NO_2(g)+H_2O(l) \rightarrow 2HNO_3(aq)+NO(g)$$

The nitric oxide produced is then oxidized to nitrogen dioxide, and absorbed in water.

13.6 Properties of nitric acid

Dilute nitric acid exhibits all the usual characteristics of dilute acids (chapter 7.5). As the acid becomes more concentrated, however, some further characteristics emerge which are thought to be due to the nitrate ion.

Very dilute nitric acid

Very dilute nitric acid is reduced by metals to give hydrogen gas:

$$Mg(s) + 2HNO_3(aq) \rightarrow Mg(NO_3)_2(aq) + H_2(g)$$

Dilute nitric acid

Dilute nitric acid supplied by most chemistry laboratories (of the order of 2M) is reduced by metals to give nitric oxide. It is easier to write an equation for this reaction if we identify the oxidation and reduction steps:

$$NO_3^-(aq) + 4H^+(aq) + 3e^- \rightarrow NO(g) + 2H_2O(l) \quad \text{reduction}$$
$$Mg(s) \rightarrow Mg^{2+}(aq) + 2e^- \quad \text{oxidation}$$

Multiplying the reduction equation by 2 and the oxidation equation by 3, and adding:

$$2NO_3^-(aq) + 8H^+(aq) + 6e^- \rightarrow 2NO(g) + 4H_2O(l)$$
$$3Mg(s) \rightarrow 3Mg^{2+}(aq) + 6e^-$$

$$3Mg(s) + 2NO_3^-(aq) + 8H^+(aq) \rightarrow 3Mg^{2+}(aq) + 2NO(g) + 4H_2O(l) \quad \text{redox}$$

This reaction is not limited to those metals which are above hydrogen in the electrochemical series. Provided that the acid is sufficiently concentrated, most metals will react with it. Aqua regia, a mixture of nitric and hydrochloric acids, is used to dissolve gold and platinum.

Concentrated nitric acid

Concentrated nitric acid is reduced by metals to give nitrogen dioxide gas. Once again, the more complex reaction is better split up into the oxidation and reduction steps

$$NO_3^-(aq) + 2H^+(aq) + e^- \rightarrow NO_2(g) + H_2O(l) \quad \text{reduction}$$
$$Cu(s) \rightarrow Cu^{2+}(aq) + 2e^- \quad \text{oxidation}$$

Multiplying the reduction step by 2, and adding:

$$2NO_3^-(aq) + 4H^+(aq) + 2e^- \rightarrow 2NO_2(g) + 2H_2O(l)$$
$$Cu(s) \rightarrow Cu^{2+}(aq) + 2e^-$$

$$Cu(s) + 2NO_3^-(aq) + 4H^+(aq) \rightarrow Cu^{2+}(aq) + 2NO_2(g) + 2H_2O(l) \quad \text{redox}$$

It has been very easy here to divide the reactions up into those producing hydrogen, those producing nitric oxide, and those producing nitrogen dioxide. In fact it is never quite so simple—there is often a mixture of products obtained, depending on the concentration of the acid.

13.7 Nitrate salts

When nitric acid reacts with bases, or metals, one of the products is always a nitrate salt. Is there a way of distinguishing a nitrate salt from any other salt? We have already met (page 142) a test for the sulphate ion. It involves the precipitation of an insoluble sulphate, barium sulphate. A similar technique cannot be used for the nitrate ion because all nitrates are soluble. The test used for identifying the nitrate ion is the **brown ring test.** A few drops of freshly prepared iron(II) sulphate solution are added to the suspected nitrate solution. The test-tube is tilted to an angle of 45°, and concentrated sulphuric acid is poured carefully down the side of the tube to form a separate layer (Figure 13.8). The formation of a brown ring between the two layers indicates the presence of the nitrate ion.

Figure 13.8 The nitrate or brown test

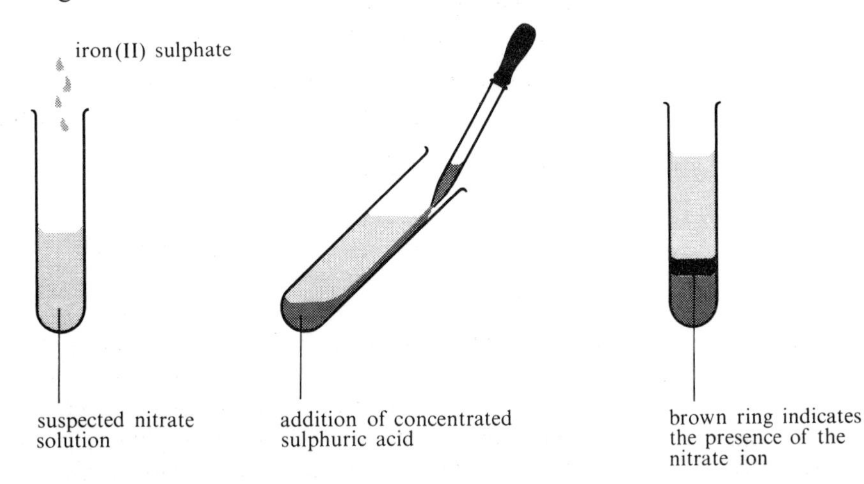

It is interesting to heat a series of metal nitrates and see how well they 'obey' the reactivity series of the metals. The nitrates of the most active metals (sodium and potassium) decompose with difficulty to yield the metal nitrites:

$$2NaNO_3(s) \xrightarrow{heat} 2NaNO_2(s) + O_2(g)$$

The nitrates of metals lower down in the series (zinc, lead, and copper) decompose a little more easily to yield the metal oxide:

$$2Zn(NO_3)_2(s) \xrightarrow{heat} 2ZnO(s) + 4NO_2(g) + O_2(g)$$

The nitrates of metals at the bottom of the series (silver and mercury) decompose readily to yield the metals themselves:

$$2AgNO_3(s) \xrightarrow{heat} 2Ag(s) + 2NO_2(g) + O_2(g)$$

13.8 The nitrogen cycle

Nitrogen is an essential consistituent of protein, and a vital material required by both plants and animals for their growth and repair. Animals are able to obtain their protein by eating plants, or by eating other animals which have themselves eaten plants (Figure 13.9). Plants, however, have to make their own protein from its constituents.

Figure 13.9 A food web

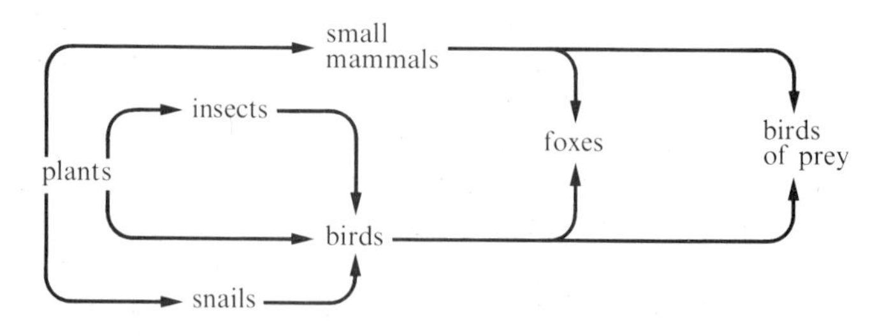

Some plants, including peas, clover, and beans, are able to convert free nitrogen from the air to make their protein. Such plants are called **leguminous plants.** They have special nodules on their roots which contain **nitrifying bacteria,** that is, bacteria which will convert free nitrogen directly into nitrates that the plant can use (Figure 13.10).

Figure 13.10 Root nodules on a field bean

John Day and Peter Dart, Rothamsted Experimental Station

Other plants are unable to do this. They require fixed nitrogen, in the form of nitrates or ammonium salts, which can then be taken up in solution by their roots and used to make protein.

A particular patch of ground cannot go on providing fixed nitrogen for its plant life for an indefinite period of time. Unless it is replaced by some means or other, the fixed nitrogen content will gradually diminish and eventually disappear, leaving the ground barren.

Nature replaces fixed nitrogen by ammonium compounds produced by decomposing plant and animal remains. Where land is being farmed intensively, and the plant material harvested, man must ensure that the fixed nitrogen is replaced. At one time, farmers used to leave a field fallow (that is without crops) for a year, and at the end of the year plough in the plant growth to replace the nitrogen. With the increasing demands on the land, however, methods such as crop rotation had to be used.

With crop rotation, the land could not be allowed to lie fallow. Instead, every two or three years, a leguminous crop would be planted to replace the nitrogen which had been removed. Natural fertilizers, such as plant compost, animal manure, guano, and naturally occurring nitrates, have always been, and still are, used for replacing the valuable nitrogen supplies in the soil. Figure 13.11 summarizes the ways in which nitrogen is removed from and replaced in the soil.

Figure 13.11 The nitrogen cycle

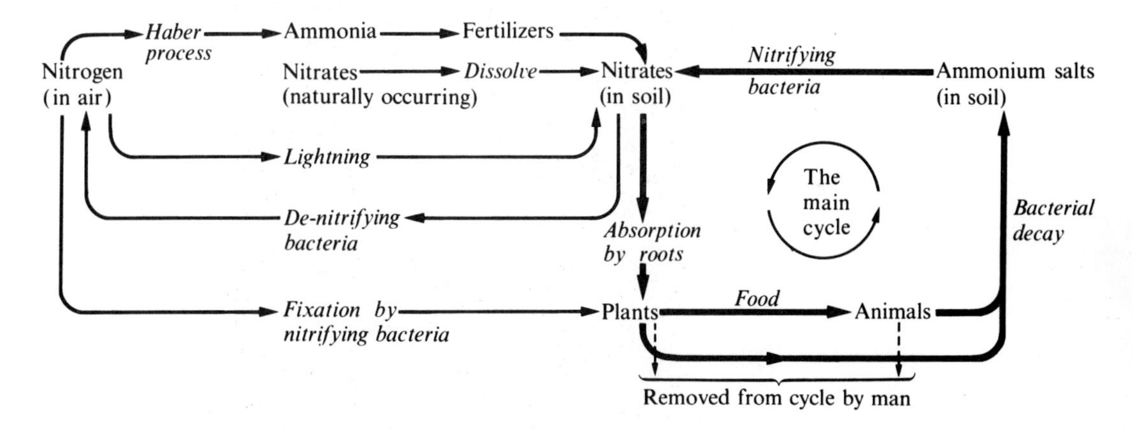

13.9 Fertilizers

Nowadays even greater demands are being made on the land to produce maximum crop yields, and the manufacture and use of artificial fertilizers is essential to achieve greater production.

Ammonium phosphate This is gradually replacing calcium superphosphate $Ca(H_2PO_4)_2$ as a fertilizer mainly because superphosphate gives off acidic fumes and produces low concentrations of phosphate. Calcium phosphate is treated with concentrated sulphuric acid and a mixture of phosphoric(V) acid and calcium sulphate are produced:

$$Ca_3(PO_4)_2(s) + 3H_2SO_4(l) \rightarrow 2H_3PO_4(l) + 3CaSO_4(s)$$

The mixture is separated and the phosphoric(V) acid is treated with gaseous ammonia to produce ammonium phosphate:

$$H_3PO_4(l) + 3NH_3(g) \rightarrow (NH_4)_3PO_4(s)$$

Phosphates are required for plant growth. Ammonium phosphate is soluble in water and can be accepted easily by plants.

Nitrates A large proportion of the nitric acid produced is used in the production of nitrate fertilizers. Ammonium nitrate is produced by the neutralization of aqueous ammonia with nitric acid.

$$NH_3(aq) + HNO_3(aq) \rightarrow NH_4NO_3(aq)$$

Sodium nitrate is produced by neutralizing sodium hydroxide with nitric acid.

$$NaOH(aq) + HNO_3(aq) \rightarrow NaNO_3(aq) + H_2O(l)$$

Ammonium sulphate Ammonia gas will react directly with sulphuric acid to produce ammonium sulphate, a fertilizer of great importance.

$$2NH_3(g) + H_2SO_4(aq) \rightarrow (NH_4)_2SO_4(aq)$$

All the substances we have discussed are used as fertilizers. However, bags of fertilizer contain mixtures of these substances, and the content of the mixture varies depending on the condition of the soil and the crop being grown.

Summary

From this chapter you should know:

1. Nitrogen is unreactive but not inert.
2. How nitrogen is obtained from the air.
3. How ammonia is produced.
4. The factors which govern the production of ammonia.
5. The properties and uses of ammonia.
6. How to prepare nitric acid.
7. The properties and uses of nitric acid.
8. How to test for the presence of the nitrate ion.
9. The properties of nitrates.
10. The nitrogen cycle.
11. The importance of fertilizers.

The experiments for this chapter are on pages 282–3.

Questions

1 1 Two gases, A and B, combine to form another gas C according to the following equation:

$$A(g) + B(g) \rightleftharpoons C(g) \qquad \Delta H \text{ negative}$$

Explain what conditions of temperature and pressure favour the production of compound C.

2 Outline the several steps involved in the conversion of a mixture of nitrogen and hydrogen gases to a solution of nitric acid.

3 Describe briefly how dry crystals of ammonium sulphate may be prepared in the laboratory.

4 What weight of ammonium phosphate could be obtained from 60 cm^3 of 5 molar aqueous ammonia? *P & W*

2 1 What are the sources of the hydrogen and nitrogen used in the manufacture of ammonia? What is done to speed up the reaction.

2 Name a substance which can be reacted with ammonia to make a fertilizer, and give the formula for the compound produced.

3 Say briefly why fertilizers have to be made today, but did not have to be made 200 years ago.

4 It is said that Haber's discovery of the ammonia synthesis prolonged the First World War. What compounds apart from fertilizers did the Germans make from ammonia? *P & W*

3 1.1 In the experiment illustrated, what gas, other than displaced air, would be collected in the gas jar?

1.2 Describe the solubility and colour of the gas collected.

1.3 How would you show that you had prepared this gas?

2 Name the catalyst involved in the oxidation of ammonia and describe briefly the consequences for mankind if this industrial process had to be discontinued because of the pollution it causes. *P & W*

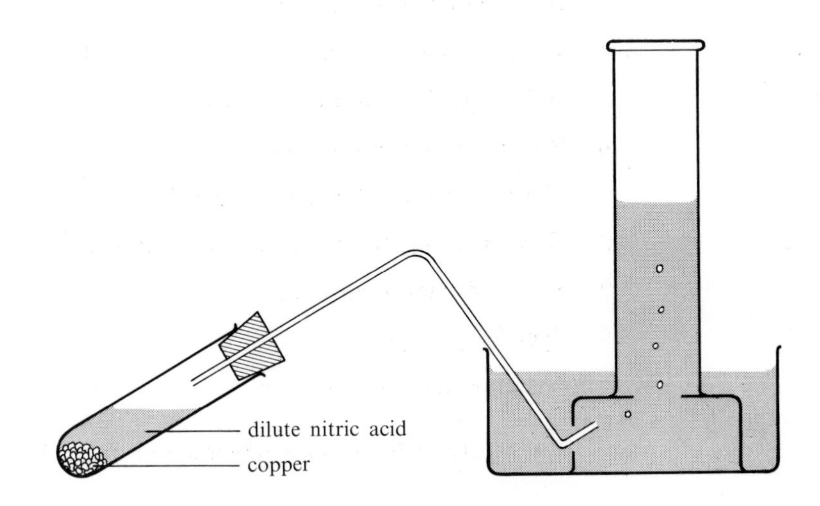

4 A stream of dry ammonia was passed over black copper(II) oxide in a combustion tube. The combustion tube was strongly heated. The gas issuing from the tube was passed first through a U-tube immersed in a beaker of cold water, and then collected over water. A colourless neutral gas was collected, and the water over which it was collected became alkaline. Moisture condensed in the U-tube.
1 What happened to the copper(II) oxide?
2 What was the gas collected? Give two tests you could carry out to confirm your answer.
3 Why was the water over which the gas was collected alkaline?
4 Where did the moisture come from?
5 Deduce what elements are present in ammonia, and explain your reasoning.
6 What property of ammonia was being demonstrated?
7 What would happen if calcium oxide was used instead of copper(II) oxide? *P & W*

5 1 Why is the Haber synthesis of ammonia operated at 773 K (500 °C) rather than 273 K (0 °C) or 1273 K (1000 °C)?
2 Describe briefly how:
2.1 You would make a fertilizer from ammonia.
2.2 You could get a sample of nitrogen from ammonia.
2.3 An acid can be made from ammonia.
3 Why is it wasteful and harmful for sewage from a city to be put directly into a river or the sea? *P & W*

6 1 Explain briefly the difference between 'fixed' and 'free' nitrogen.
2 The reaction taking place in the Haber process can be represented by the following equation.

$$N_2 + 3H_2 \rightleftharpoons 2NH_3 \qquad \Delta H = -91\ \text{kJ}$$

2.1 Name the catalyst used in this reaction.
2.2 With the aid of the equation above, explain what conditions are necessary in order to obtain the maximum yield of ammonia.
3 When copper turnings are dropped into three separate test tubes containing (a) very dilute nitric acid, (b) dilute nitric acid and (c) concentrated nitric acid, what gas would you expect to be evolved from each? *P & W*

7 1 The apparatus on the opposite page shows the arrangement required to determine the formula of an oxide of nitrogen.
1.1 What compound is formed as the oxide of nitrogen passes over the heated copper?
1.2 What gas will be collected in the gas jar?
1.3 When the results were recorded it was found that 1.4 g of nitrogen combined with 0.8 g of oxygen. Suggest a formula for the oxide of nitrogen.
1.4 Write a possible equation for the reaction which occurs in the combustion tube.
2 The fixation of atmospheric nitrogen is effected by means of the Haber process, which produces ammonia.

2.1 Write the balanced equation for the reaction.
2.2 What catalyst is used in the process?
2.3 When ammonia is passed into water, an alkaline solution is formed. Write the equation and explain why the reaction occurs. *P & W*

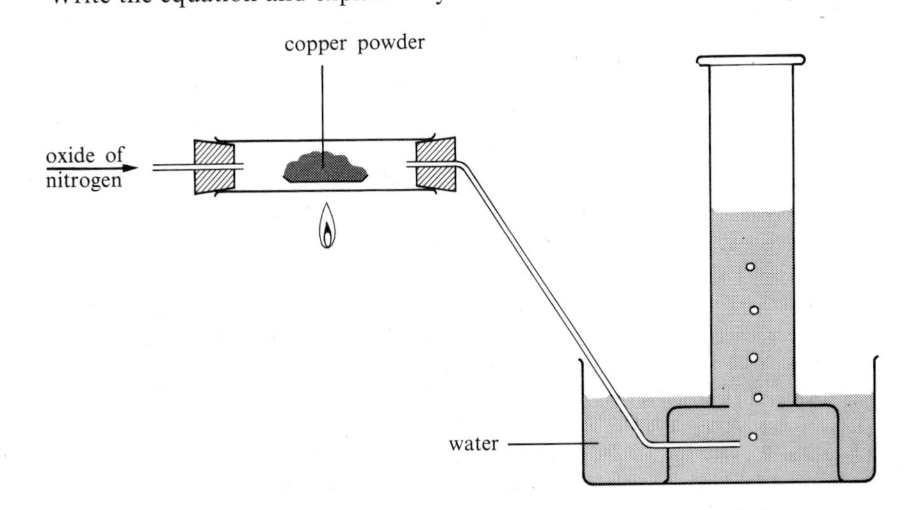

8 **1** After passing a spark for a long time through a mixture of nitrogen and oxygen contained in a flask, what visible evidence is there that a chemical change has taken place? Name a new substance now present in the flask, and write a balanced equation for its formation.
2 If some water is now added to the contents of the flask, what effect would the liquid have on a neutral pH indicator paper?
3 When do the reactions in **1** and **2** occur in nature, and why are they important for plant life?
4 In the production of ammonium nitrate, ammonia gas is acted upon by nitric acid. What is the theoretical mass of ammonium nitrate formed by passing excess ammonia gas into 500 cm^3 of 1M nitric acid? *SCEEB*

9 **1** Name a substance which in industry is reacted with ammonia to make a fertilizer, and give the formula of the fertilizer.
Nitric acid is manufactured according to the simplified flow-diagram below.

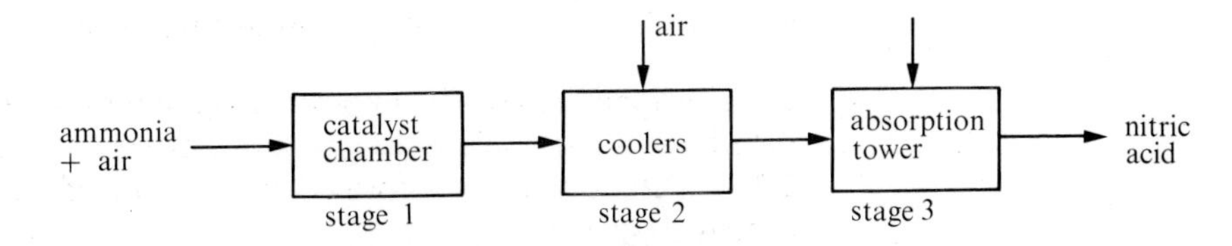

2 What catalyst is used in the process?
3 Would it be necessary to continue heating the catalyst chamber throughout the process? Explain your answer.
4 What would be added at stage 3?
5 What products would you expect to obtain in stages 1 and 2?
6 Write the half-reaction (ion-electron) equations (electron half-equations) for the reaction between copper and concentrated nitric acid. *SCEEB*

14 Carbon

14.1 Polymorphism

'Diamonds are a girl's best friend' may be a somewhat cynical reflection of our modern society and its materialistic value judgements. Nevertheless it emphasizes the hardness and durability of the diamond, as well as its beauty as a gem stone.

It is quite surprising to find that a diamond is made of pure carbon, since we tend to associate carbon with black substances. This is because of our familiarity with diamond's poorer cousin graphite, which is also pure carbon. Diamond and graphite are **polymorphs.** Polymorphism occurs when a substance exists in two different crystalline forms.

Let us compare the properties of diamond and graphite, and see if their properties can be related to the crystal shape and the type of bonding in each case. Diamonds are very hard and do not conduct an electric current, whereas graphite is soft to touch and is a good conductor.

An atom of carbon has six electrons with an electron arrangement of 2.4. Therefore it should exhibit a valency of four. Indeed this is so in a great number of compounds like methane CH_4 and tetrachloromethane CCl_4, for which we have already drawn electron cloud overlap diagrams (pages 46–7). Diamond simply consists of carbon atoms bonded to each other in this way, and the crystal structure is not difficult to envisage (Figure 14.1). If the model is built with balls and rods, the resulting structure is found to be very rigid indeed. This rigid structure accounts for the hardness of diamond, and since all the valency electrons are used in bonding, the structure contains no 'free' electrons. This means that it cannot conduct an electric current.

X-ray analysis of graphite shows that the crystal is made up of hexagonal plates, and that the C—C bonds are planar and at 120° to each other (Figure 14.2). In this type of bonding only three of the valency electrons are being used in bond formation. The fourth electron from each atom is free to move between the plates. The structure must always contain the correct number of electrons compatible with elemental carbon. However, if electrons are forced in at one end of the structure, the same number of electrons will be forced out at the other end, and this explains why graphite is a conductor. Since the structure is made up of a 'pile of plates' held together by small intermolecular forces, called Van der Waals' forces, it is easy to see how the plates slip over one another. This property makes it suitable as a lubricant and as 'lead' in a pencil.

It has possibly occurred to you by this time that the conversion of graphite into diamond might be a lucrative hobby in your spare time. First, the good news—it can be done! Now the bad news—you can't do it! The conversion was first done in 1955 by subjecting graphite to an enormous pressure of about 100 000 atmospheres at a temperature of about 3300 K (3000 °C) in the presence of a catalyst. Small, industrial-grade diamonds were obtained at about the same cost as natural ones.

Figure 14.1 The structure of diamond

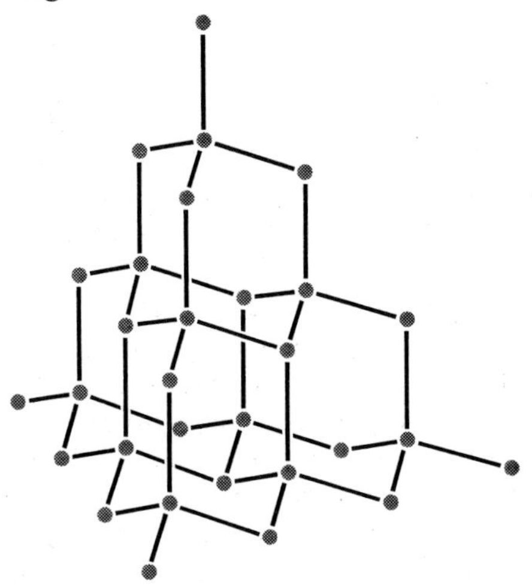

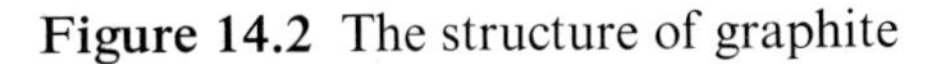

Figure 14.2 The structure of graphite

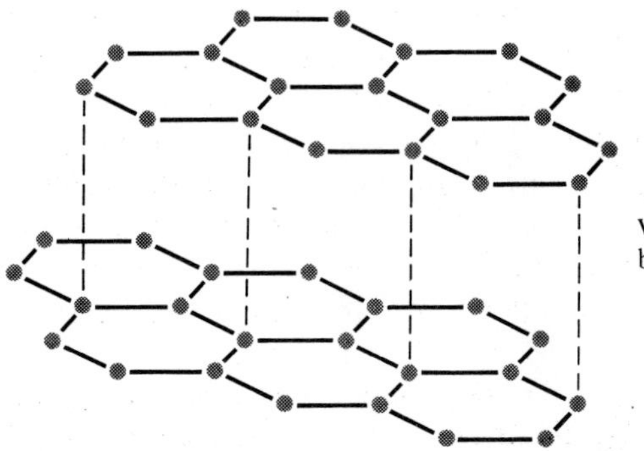

14.2 Combustion of carbon

When carbon is burned in a good supply of oxygen, it forms carbon dioxide gas:

$$C(s) + O_2(g) \rightarrow CO_2(g) \qquad \Delta H = -394\,\text{kJ}$$

However, if the oxygen supply is inadequate for combustion to take place easily, carbon monoxide gas is formed. If a slow stream of carbon dioxide is passed over red hot charcoal, carbon monoxide can be collected over water. Carbon monoxide burns with a characteristic licking blue flame to form carbon dioxide. This reaction will be considered in more detail in chapter 15 (page 183) when fuel gases are being discussed.

$$CO_2(g) + C(s) \rightarrow 2CO(g) \qquad \Delta H = +172\,kJ$$
$$2CO(g) + O_2(g) \rightarrow 2CO_2(g) \qquad \Delta H = -566\,kJ$$

14.3 Carbon monoxide

Carbon monoxide is poisonous. It is formed during the incomplete combustion of petrol and diesel, and this is what makes the exhaust fumes from internal combustion engines so dangerous, although the concentration of carbon monoxide may be less than 1 per cent in air. The haemoglobin in the blood, which is normally the oxygen carrier, combines with carbon monoxide to form carboxyhaemoglobin, and the victim dies of oxygen starvation.

Some metal oxides can be reduced to the metal by carbon monoxide. Iron(III) oxide is reduced to iron in the blast furnace by this method (Figure 14.3).

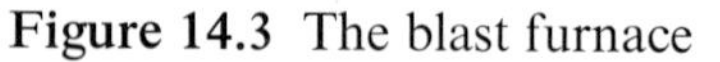

Figure 14.3 The blast furnace

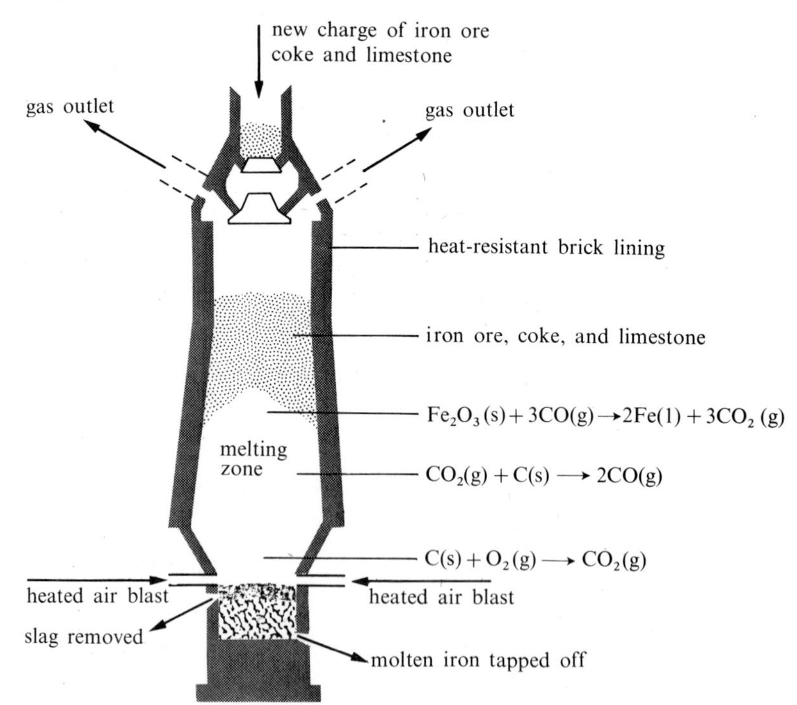

14.4 Carbon dioxide

Carbon dioxide is obtained in the laboratory by the action of hydrochloric acid on marble chips (calcium carbonate):

$$CaCO_3(s) + 2HCl(aq) \rightarrow CaCl_2(aq) + H_2O(l) + CO_2(g)$$

In industry carbon dioxide is obtained as a by-product of fermentation of sugars to alcohol, and from the manufacture of cement.

$$C_6H_{12}O_6(aq) \xrightarrow{yeast} 2C_2H_5OH(aq) + 2CO_2(g)$$
glucose ethanol

$$CaCO_3(s) \xrightarrow{heat} CaO(s) + CO_2(g)$$
limestone cement

Solid carbon dioxide sublimes at atmospheric pressure at a temperature of 195 K (−78 °C):

$$CO_2(s) \rightleftharpoons CO_2(g)$$
dry ice

Carbon dioxide is a stable molecule which resists further oxidation. This means that it will deprive a fire of oxygen and put it out, as can be illustrated by pouring carbon dioxide on to a candle flame. If the burning material is hot enough, however, it may supply enough energy to break the carbon to oxygen bonds, and the material will continue to burn. A piece of burning magnesium ribbon when plunged into a jar of carbon dioxide does just this:

$$2Mg(s) + CO_2(g) \rightarrow 2MgO(s) + C(s)$$

Test for carbon dioxide

Add some calcium hydroxide solution (limewater) to a jar of carbon dioxide and the solution turns cloudy. When carbon dioxide is bubbled into limewater, the solution turns cloudy because a white precipitate of calcium carbonate is formed:

$$CO_2(g) + Ca(OH)_2(aq) \rightarrow CaCO_3(s) + H_2O(l)$$
insoluble calcium carbonate

If the gas is bubbled for a longer time, the white precipitate gradually disappears again, because the acid salt calcium hydrogencarbonate is formed, and it is a soluble salt:

$$CaCO_3(s) + H_2O(l) + CO_2(g) \rightarrow Ca(HCO_3)_2(aq)$$
soluble calcium hydrogencarbonate

Calcium hydrogencarbonate solution decomposes when boiled, and reprecipitates the calcium carbonate:

$$Ca(HCO_3)_2(aq) \rightarrow CaCO_3(s) + H_2O(l) + CO_2(g)$$

The chemistry of this process is very important since it explains the formation of stalactites and stalagmites, and also the hardness of water (page 160). Rain falling through the air dissolves carbon dioxide, forming a small amount of the weak acid, carbonic acid:

$$H_2O(l) + CO_2(g) \rightleftharpoons H_2CO_3(aq)$$

This small amount of carbonic acid is sufficient to react with chalk and limestone to form calcium hydrogencarbonate solution.

$$CaCO_3(s) + H_2CO_3(aq) \rightarrow Ca(HCO_3)_2(aq)$$

This reaction causes the limestone to dissolve, and over a considerable length of time, underground caves are formed. The calcium hydrocarbonate solution then drips from the roofs of the caves. Evaporation takes place and small amounts of calcium carbonate are deposited on the roofs and floors of the caves.

$Ca(HCO_3)_2(aq) \rightarrow CaCO_3(s) + CO_2(g) + H_2O(l)$

These deposits grow to form stalagmites and stalactites (Figure 14.4).

Figure 14.4

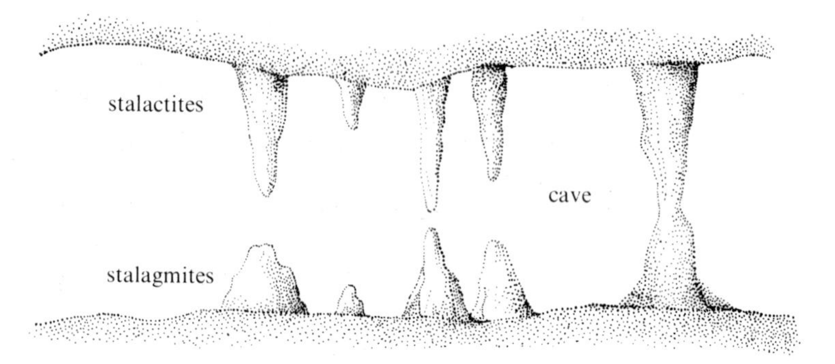

Water in limestone regions contains dissolved calcium hydrogencarbonate, and this makes the water **hard.** It is the decomposition of this salt which causes 'scaling' of boilers and 'furring' of kettles. The dissolved calcium ions in the water also cause a scum to form with soap (chapter 20.3). Hardness due to calcium hydrogencarbonate is known as **temporary hardness** since the water can be easily made **soft** by boiling it:

$Ca(HCO_3)_2(aq) \rightarrow CaCO_3(s) + H_2O(l) + CO_2(g)$

14.5 Carbonates

A large number of metals occur in nature as their carbonates. Some of them are listed in Table 14.1.

Table 14.1

Natural ore	*Metal carbonate contained in ore*
Limestone	$CaCO_3$
Chalk	$CaCO_3$
Marble	$CaCO_3$
Dolomite	$CaCO_3$, $MgCO_3$
Malachite	$CuCO_3$
Spathic iron ore	$FeCO_3$
Calamine	$ZnCO_3$

Cement is made by heating limestone with some sand and silicates to form impure calcium oxide:

$$CaCO_3(s) \rightarrow CaO(s) + CO_2(g)$$

To make mortar for building, the cement is mixed with sand and water. The mixture hardens over a long period of time. Many reactions occur, and the carbon dioxide from the air reacts with the mortar to form calcium carbonate again.

14.6 Washing soda and baking soda

Soluble carbonates can be prepared in the laboratory by saturating a solution of the appropriate alkali with carbon dioxide, and then adding the same volume again of the alkali to produce a 'half-saturated' solution.

$$NaOH(aq) + CO_2(g) \rightarrow NaHCO_3(aq)$$

1 mole   1 mole

$$NaHCO_3(aq) + NaOH(aq) \rightarrow Na_2CO_3(aq) + H_2O(l)$$

$$2NaOH(aq) + CO_2(g) \rightarrow Na_2CO_3(aq) + H_2O(l)$$

---

2 moles   1 mole

Sodium carbonate is used to soften water, and it is sold as washing soda $Na_2CO_3.10H_2O$. This is a white crystalline solid which gives off its water of crystallization **(effloresces)** on standing to form the monohydrate:

$$Na_2CO_3.10H_2O(s) \rightarrow Na_2CO_3.H_2O(s) + 9H_2O(g)$$

Washing soda softens the water by precipitating the calcium ions from the solution as calcium carbonate:

$$Ca^{2+}(aq) + CO_3^{2-}(aq) \rightarrow CaCO_3(s)$$

Sodium hydrogencarbonate is called baking soda or bicarbonate of soda since it is used as a raising agent along with tartaric acid (cream of tartar):

$$HCO_3^-(s) + H^+(aq) \rightarrow H_2O(l) + CO_2(g)$$

During the baking the carbon dioxide bubbles expand and cause the dough to rise. It is important that the sodium hydrogencarbonate is not in excess in the mixture, because sodium carbonate, which has an unpleasant taste, is formed:

$$2NaHCO_3(aq) \rightarrow Na_2CO_3(aq) + H_2O(l) + CO_2(g)$$

To avoid this happening manufacturers sell the flour as 'self-raising flour', or they provide 'baking powder' to add to the 'plain flour'. Baking powder consists of bicarbonate of soda, cream of tartar, and rice flour. The rice flour slows down the formation of carbon dioxide until the dough is made.

'Washing soda' and 'baking soda' are manufactured by the **Solvay process.** Brine, saturated with ammonia, is sprayed down a tower, which has carbon dioxide passing up it:

$$NH_3(g) + H_2O(l) + NaCl(aq) + CO_2(g) \rightarrow NaHCO_3(s) + NH_4Cl(aq).$$
$$2NaHCO_3(s) \rightarrow Na_2CO_3(s) + H_2O(g) + CO_2(g)$$

Summary

From this chapter you should know:

1 Diamond and graphite are polymorphs.

2 The physical properties of the polymorphs are due to the crystal shapes, and the nature of the bonds.

3 There are two oxides of carbon.

4 The test for carbon dioxide.

5 Stalactites and stalagmites are formed in limestone regions.

6 Temporary hardness of water is due to calcium hydrogencarbonate.

7 Cement hardens as well as 'dries out'.

8 Washing soda and baking soda are made by the Solvay process.

The experiments for this chapter are on pages 283–4.

Questions

1 1 Give one example of where carbon monoxide is commonly met outside the laboratory and explain how it arises.
2 Describe an experiment which shows that it is a reducing agent.
3 Explain what happens when carbon dioxide is passed for a long time into limewater.
4 Burning carbon on a deflagrating spoon is placed in a jar of air. Water is then added and shaken up with litmus paper. The litmus turns red. Explain what has happened and deduce whether carbon is a metal or a non-metal. *P & W*

2 Limestone is insoluble in water. How do you explain the presence of calcium ions in drinking water in limestone areas?

3 1 Name two crystalline forms of the element carbon and give a use for each.
2 If you were given a piece of material and told that it was one of these forms of carbon, describe any two tests you would carry out to find out which was which. *SCEEB*

4 Carbon monoxide can be prepared as shown below.

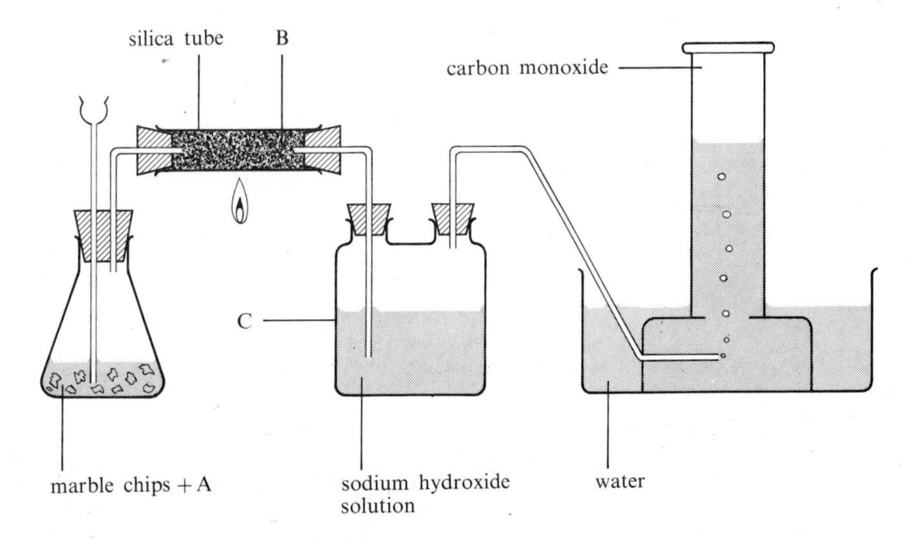

1 Name a suitable reagent for A.
What is the solid B?
What is the purpose of the sodium hydroxide solution?
2 Write equations for the reactions in (a) the flask, (b) the silica tube, and (c) the two-neck bottle C.
3 How would you show that the wax of a candle contains carbon and hydrogen? *SCEEB*

15 Fuels

15.1 Exothermic reactions.

A fuel is a substance which burns giving out a great deal of heat energy. Where does this heat energy come from?

Burning is an example of a reaction in which chemical bonds are broken and made. To break the bonds, heat is required. To make the bonds, heat is given out. When a fuel is burnt, the heat energy required to break the bonds is obviously much less than the heat given out by making the bonds. The net effect of this is that heat energy is evolved. Such a reaction is called an **exothermic reaction.** The heat energy change involved in a reaction is given the symbol ΔH. For exothermic reactions ΔH has a negative sign, indicating that heat has been lost, or given out, by the system.

$$C(s)+O_2(g) \rightarrow CO_2(g) \qquad \Delta H = -394\,kJ$$

$$CH_4(g)+2O_2(g) \rightarrow CO_2(g)+2H_2O(g) \qquad \Delta H = -890\,kJ$$

methane
(natural gas)

There are, of course, reactions in which the heat energy required for the bond-breaking steps exceeds the heat energy liberated in the bond-making steps. Such reactions are called **endothermic** reactions, and they only take place when sufficient heat energy is supplied.

$$C(s)+2S(s) \rightarrow CS_2 \qquad \Delta H= +107\,kJ$$

As fuels have different chemical constituents, they undergo different bond-breaking and bond-making steps when they burn. As a result, their ΔH values can vary widely. Figure 15.1 gives some idea of the heat values of various fuels.

Figure 15.1 Heat values of fuels

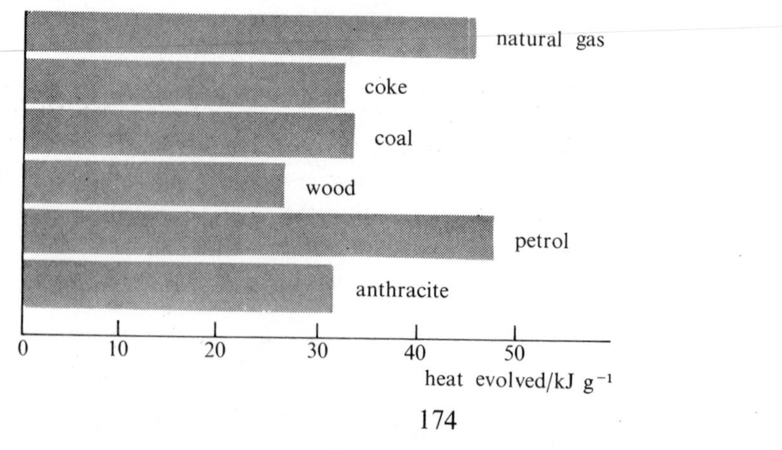

It is interesting to note that the heat value of fuels used to be referred to as the 'calorific value' when heat energy was measured in calories rather than joules. Even today various foods, or body fuels, are assigned calorific values so that would-be slimmers can count up their calories before they eat.

Most common fuels contain fairly high percentages of carbon, so it is obviously very important to burn them efficiently. Inefficient combustion, in other words, an insufficient supply of oxygen, leads to formation of carbon monoxide, which is extremely poisonous, and to unburnt carbon in the form of soot, which blocks chimneys and pollutes the atmosphere.

15.2 Solid fuels

Wood is probably the most widely distributed fuel in the world, and certainly the oldest known to man. Compared with other fuels, wood does not have a high heat value, so it is only used in areas where it is abundant and where there is no suitable alternative.

The wood and other forest vegetation of 500–600 million years ago has been the foundation of our fuel supplies today.

In the warm, wet climate of the carboniferous period, vegetation, in the form of huge trees, giant ferns, club mosses, and sedges, flourished. When this lush vegetation died, it formed thick decaying deposits which became **peat.** Peat is still present in many parts of the British Isles, but it is not an efficient fuel owing to high moisture content and low heat value. In other areas, upheaval of the earth's crust led to the burial of the deposits of vegetation, and their subjection to increased temperatures and pressures. This led to the formation of a soft brown coal called **lignite.** Further extremes of temperature and pressure converted lignite into **bituminous coal,** the hard black coal that we know today. This coal is often found thousands of metres beneath the surface of the earth, firmly sandwiched between layers of sandstone and shale from which it has to be mined. Bituminous coal has a higher percentage of carbon and a greater heat value than the fuels which are intermediates in its formation. In certain areas an extremely hard coal with a 95 per cent carbon content is found. It is called **anthracite.** Anthracite is the last 'step' in the coal formation process, being formed only under the greatest extremes of temperature and pressure.

Because of its vegetable origin, coal contains significant percentages of nitrogen and sulphur as well as carbon. It is, therefore, inefficient to burn coal on an open fire where these valuable constituents would be lost. If coal is heated in the absence of air, a process called **destructive distillation** of coal or carbonization, it yields the constituents which would otherwise be lost, and also provides coke and coal gas, themselves valuable fuels. Figure 15.2 illustrates the destructive distillation of coal, and Figure 15.3 the products which can be obtained.

Figure 15.2 Destructive distillation of coal

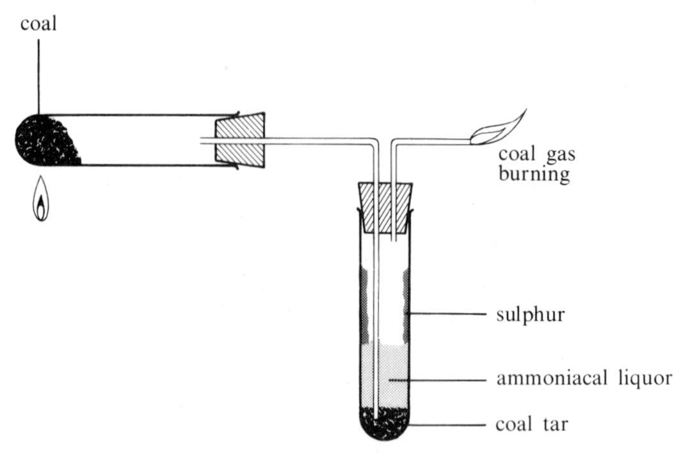

Figure 15.3 Products from destructive distillation of coal

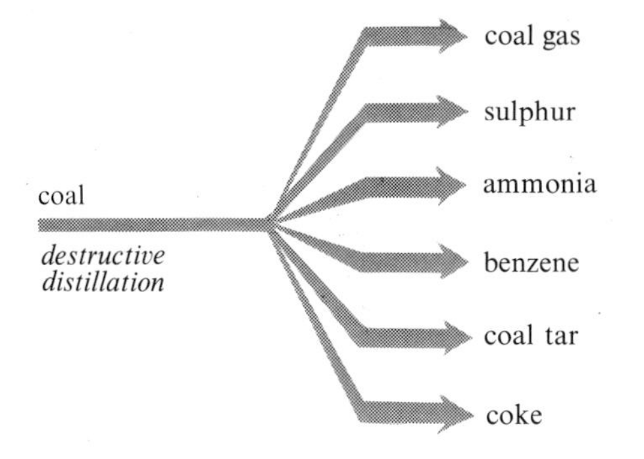

15.3 Liquid fuels

Crude oil is the source of most of our liquid fuels. It is formed in much the same way as coal from the partial decay of plant and animal life, followed by sedimentation and upheaval, heat, and pressure. The fact that crude oil is always found with salt water (Figure 15.4) suggests that it originated from marine plant and animal life.

Crude oil is found with natural gas, which may collect under such high pressures that, when a drill penetrates the oil-bearing layers, the pressure of the gas forces the oil to gush out. Locating crude oil can be a very costly business, involving aerial and ground surveys, magnetic and seismic measurements, and trial drilling. As a result, oil is a very costly but extremely valuable commodity. The richest oil deposits in the world are located in the Middle East especially in Saudia Arabia and Iran. There are also fairly extensive oil fields in other parts of the world (Figure 15.5). The most recent oil finds, of course, have been those in the North Sea off the coast of Scotland. Oil found under the sea bed is very costly to extract, because a completely new kind of oil technology is required to bring the oil ashore. Also a completely new breed of oil men are needed, who are prepared to work for several months away from home in the most difficult of conditions.

Figure 15.4 Location of crude oil

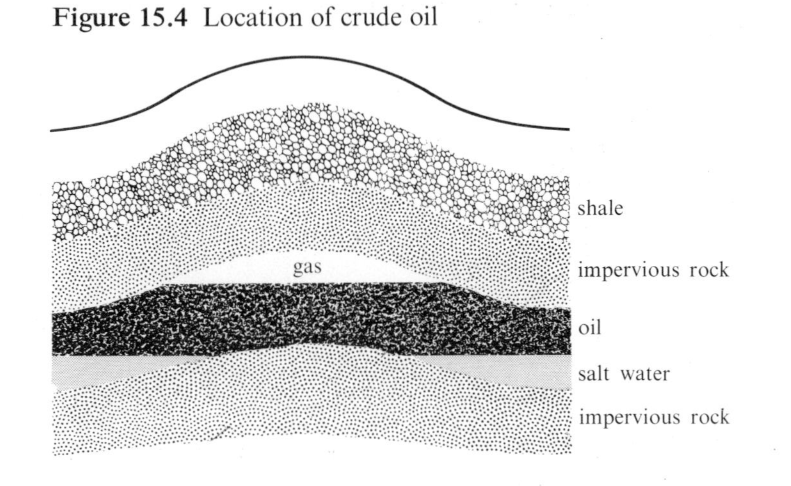

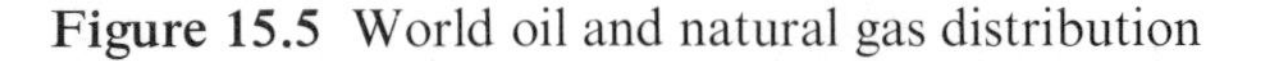
Figure 15.5 World oil and natural gas distribution

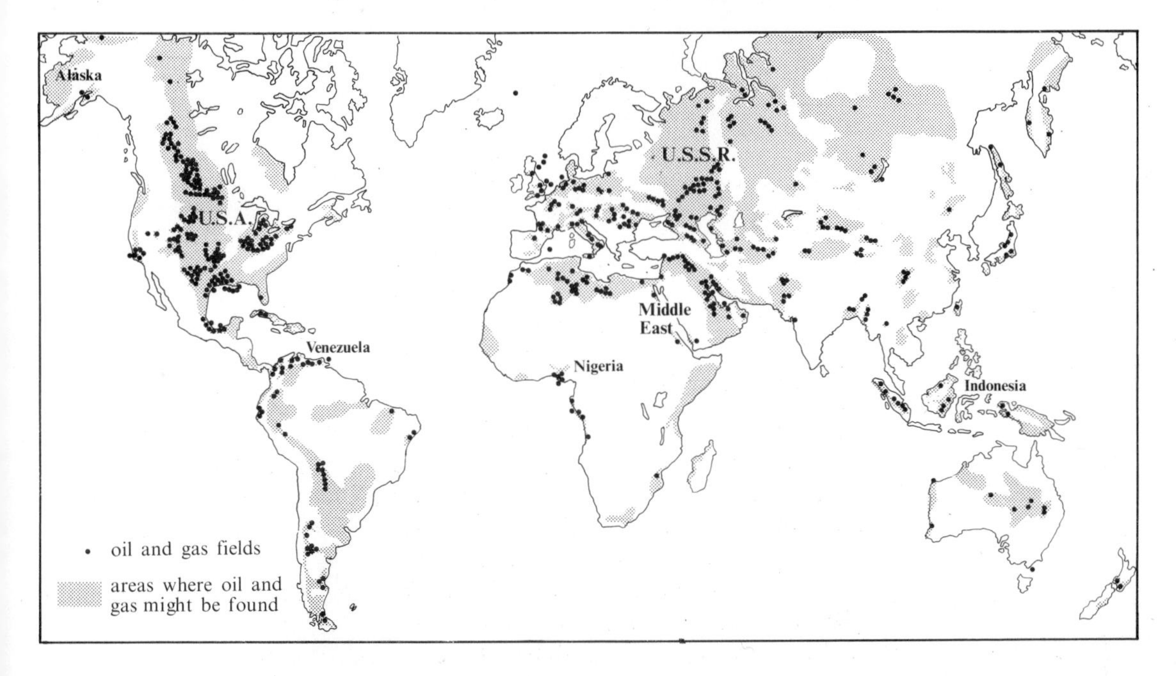

Oil is the most important fuel in use today. The demand for oil has more than doubled over the last ten years. Figure 15.7 shows how this demand compares with world oil production.

As more and more uses are found for oil and the demand continues to increase, the question arises as to whether or not oil production can cope with this demand. We do not know how much oil remains undiscovered, but it is certain that unless sensible measures are taken to conserve what oil we have, we could, in the very near future, run out of oil.

Crude oil is largely a mixture of hydrocarbons, that is compounds containing only carbon and hydrogen. There are, however, other elements

Figure 15.6 British Petroleum's drilling platform Sea Quest 177 km off Aberdeen. It discovered oil at a depth of 3423 m

Figure 15.7 World oil production and consumption from 1958

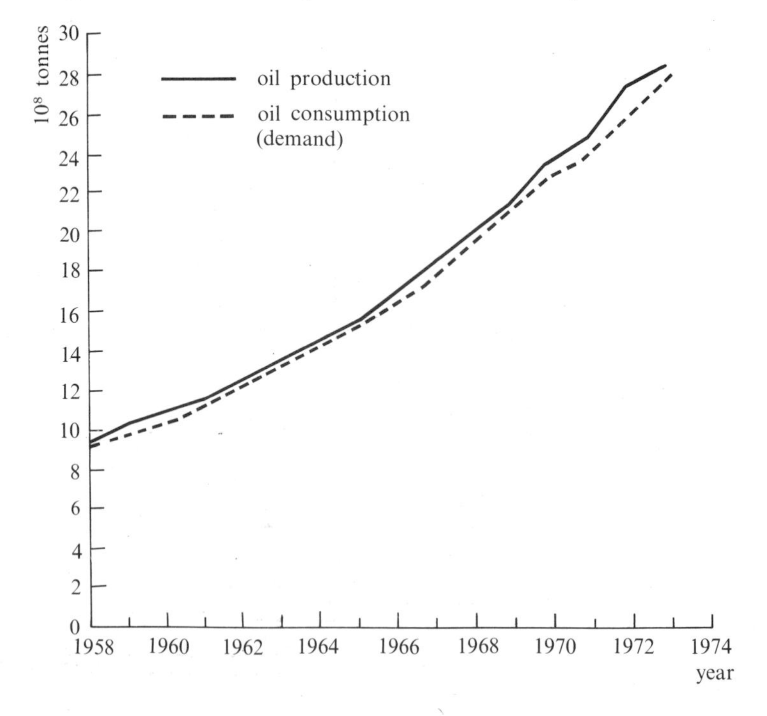

found in significant quantities, namely sulphur, nitrogen, and oxygen. These elements are usually found in combination with carbon and hydrogen. The component molecules of crude oil vary greatly in size and structure from those with one or two carbon atoms to those with over seventy, and from those with a simple straight-chain structure to those with complex branches or ring structures. It is obvious that these various components must be separated if they are to be of use.

15.4 Fractional distillation of crude oil

Crude oil is separated into a series of **fractions,** that is groups of compounds of similar size, by fractional distillation. The oil is pumped under pressure through a furnace, where it boils at a very high temperature. The vapour is then released into a fractionating tower where the least volatile fractions sink to the bottom and the most volatile fractions rise to the top (Figure 15.8).

Figure 15.8 A fractionating tower

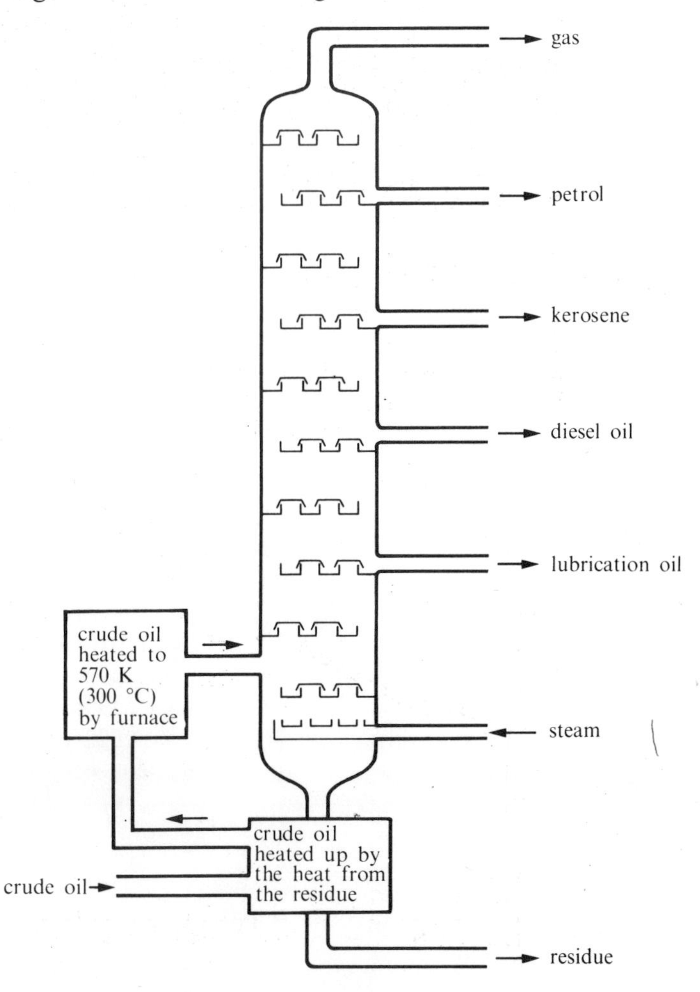

The fractionating tower is composed of a series of trays, each containing bubble caps (Figure 15.9), which are used to give an effective separation of the substances in the vapour.

Figure 15.9 A bubble cap

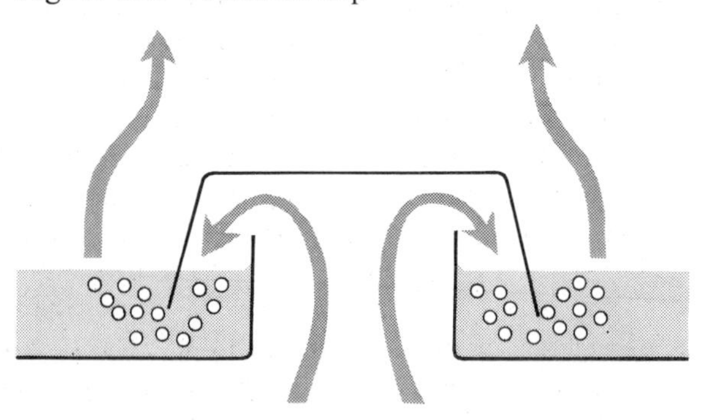

The vapour passes up the tower, and as it does so, the temperature decreases. The highest point in the tower will be at the lowest temperature. There is a temperature gradient in the tower. Just as steam will condense below 373 K (100 °C), the different substances in the vapour condense at particular temperatures. The vapour passes from tray to tray via the bubble caps. Some of the vapour will condense and the liquid will form on the tray, while the more volatile vapour bubbles through this liquid and carries on up the tower until it reaches a point where it will also condense. The vapour which does not condense is removed as a gas. This process separates the crude oil into different fractions, which are drawn off at various points up the tower.

Table 15.1 Products from fractional distillation of crude oil

Product	*Number of carbon atoms*	*Boiling range* K	*Boiling range* °C
Gas	1–4	<310	<40
Petrol	4–12	310–345	40–75
Kerosene	9–16	420–510	150–240
Diesel oil	15–25	490–520	220–250
Lubrication oil	20–70	520–620	250–350
Bitumen residue	>70	>620	>350

Obviously the separation at this stage is not very sophisticated. Further fractional distillation of the fractions can lead to a much more accurate separation.

15.5 Petrol

The demand for the petrol fraction far outweighs the supply which is available. It is possible however, to convert the less useful fractions into petrol by **polymerizing** short-chain carbon compounds into longer ones, and by **cracking** long-chain carbon compounds into shorter ones. The terms in heavy type will be dealt with in more detail in the next chapter.

Petrol should be free from gummy residues which cause pistons to stick, and it should not 'knock' or 'pink'. 'Knocking' in a car engine is caused by the petrol and air mixture burning too rapidly in the cylinders, giving a sudden blow or knock to the piston, which is obviously not good for the engine. Certain fuels have a greater tendency to cause knocking than others. There is an arbitrary scale, called the octane rating, which gives a measure of the tendency to cause knocking. The range of the scale is from zero, for fuels which knock badly, to one hundred, for fuels with antiknock properties. Good petrols have an octane rating of ninety-five or higher.

It has been shown that hydrocarbons with a branched or ring structure tend to burn more smoothly than those with a straight-chain formation. Hence it is possible to increase the antiknock properties of a petrol by introducing into it a large proportion of compounds with branched or ring structures. Straight-chain hydrocarbons can be converted into rings by heating them with hydrogen in the presence of a catalyst. This process is called **hydroforming.** Simple hydrocarbons can be given a more complex, branched structure by uniting them with unsaturated hydrocarbons such as ethene C_2H_4, a process called **alkylation.**

Another method for improving the octane rating of a petrol is to add a compound which slows down the combustion process. The best known of these is tetraethyl lead(IV) $Pb(C_2H_5)_4$. Although tetraethyl lead(IV) is probably the most widely used antiknock, it causes both technical and environmental problems. A second compound, 1,2-dibromoethene $C_2H_2Br_2$, is also added to ensure that the lead is converted to the volatile lead bromide during the combustion, and blown out of the cylinder in the exhaust gases. The technical problem of removing the lead from the engine is solved by discharging it into the atmosphere for us to inhale. Since lead compounds are toxic, the huge increase in the number of cars in the last ten years has made the pollution factor acute. Much more emphasis is now being put on the processes of hydroforming and alkylation in an effort to reduce the lead content of petrol.

15.6 Products from oil

Although the petrol fraction is the one which is in the greatest demand, there are many uses for the other fractions obtained in the fractional distillation of oil. The more volatile gas fractions include propane and butane, the constituents of bottled gas and lighter fuels. The less volatile fractions include:

Kerosene (paraffin): a fuel for aircraft and oil stoves.
Fuel oil: a fuel used in factories and ships.

Diesel oil: a fuel for diesel engines.
Lubrication oils of various grades.
Greases and jellies for lubricating purposes.
Paraffin wax.
Bitumen for road-making.

Perhaps one of the most significant factors to emerge from oil technology is the synthesis of protein. We all require at least 50 g of protein daily to survive, but in many areas of the world, people are eating less than this minimum, so any new source of protein is of great importance.

Straight-chain alkanes (chapter 16.2), obtained from the fractional distillation of crude oil, are purified and mixed with an aqueous solution of yeast. The yeast acts on the alkanes and converts them into proteins, which are separated out and dried. The end-product is a powder which, at the moment, is used as animal feedstuff. However, the time will surely come when this protein, or one manufactured in a similar way, will be used as a valuable addition to all our diets.

Important products from the refining process include commercially pure hydrocarbons which can be used as starting points for the production of a whole range of organic compounds. In the following chapters we shall see how these hydrocarbons are used in the manufacture of alcohols, detergents, plastics, textiles, and many other products.

15.7 Gaseous fuels

The gas which we use in our homes, town gas, is not one particular gas, but rather a mixture of gases of fixed heat value. The components of town gas, which vary from place to place depending on which gases are available, may include coal gas, water gas, producer gas, oil gas and, of course, natural gas. In the period 1970 to 1975 the production of gas in the United Kingdom has trebled, and this is entirely made up of natural gas from the North Sea. The abundance of natural gas has made all the other processes obsolete for the time being.

It may well be that at some time in the future, as natural gas supplies diminish, we shall again need to manufacture gas from coal. Even so, the supply of coal if finite and the development of nuclear power, despite the radiation hazards associated with it, is of utmost importance.

Natural gas Natural gas consists mainly of methane CH_4, the gas produced when vegetable matter decomposes under water. Tremendous volumes of natural gas have been found in many places—the Sahara, the North Sea, Holland, and many areas in the USA. Natural gas has a very high heat value and, like other oil-based gases, it can be used to enrich the town gas supplies. In many areas, natural gas is used as the main supply of gas for domestic use. To maintain the heat value of ordinary town gas, a non-flammable gas such as nitrogen or carbon dioxide has to be added as ballast.

Oil gas The most volatile fractions obtained from the fractional distillation of crude oil have very high heat values. These gases are often added to enrich 'lean' gases of poorer heat content to maintain the quality required for town gas. A gas can also be produced from oil in a similar way to the way in which water gas is produced from coal or coke. The gas produced in this way is often used directly as town gas, and as a commercial source of hydrogen for the Haber process.

Coal gas Coal gas is the gas obtained by the destructive distillation of coal. It is largely composed of hydrogen (50 per cent), the other components being methane, carbon monoxide, and ethene. At one time all town gas was derived from coal, but with the rising cost of coal and the use of natural gas and oil gas, town gas, is no longer derived from coal.

Water gas and producer gas Water gas is produced when steam is passed over white-hot coke:

$$C(s) + H_2O(g) \rightarrow CO(g) + H_2(g) \qquad \Delta H = +118\,\text{kJ}$$

As you can see from the equation, water gas is a mixture of carbon monoxide and hydrogen. Both these gases burn, so water gas is a good fuel.

Producer gas is produced when air is passed over red-hot coke.

$$2C(s) + \underbrace{O_2(g) + 4N_2(g)}_{\text{air}} \rightarrow 2CO(g) + 4N_2(g) \qquad \Delta H = -223\,\text{kJ}$$

Producer gas is not such a good fuel as water gas because it contains nitrogen, which does not burn.

It is common procedure for an industrial plant to make both water gas and producer gas, or a mixture of the two. Producer gas is made first, blowing air over red hot coke until the coke becomes white hot. This process is exothermic. Then water gas is made by passing steam over the white hot coke until the coke cools to red heat again. This process is endothermic.

15.8 Nature of the flame

Figure 15.10 The bunsen burner flame

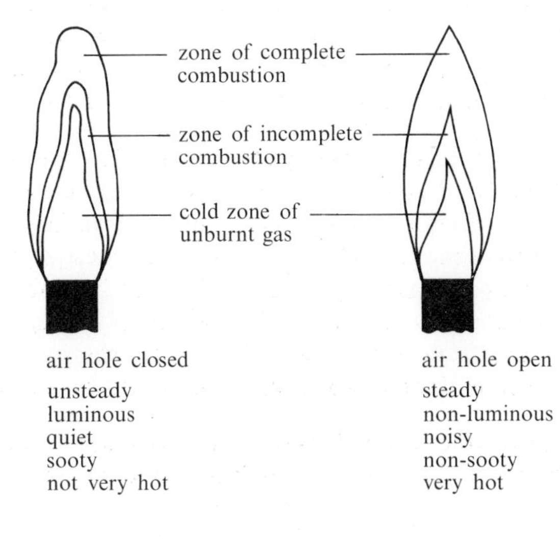

When gases burn, the type of flame produced is very dependent on the proportion of air which is mixed with the gas. Figure 15.10 is an illustration of the types of flame produced with the bunsen burner.

Summary

From this chapter you should know:

1. Exothermic reactions involve heat loss (ΔH negative) and endothermic reactions involve heat gain (ΔH positive).
2. A fuel is a substance which burns.
3. All fuels originated from plant and animal life.
4. Destructive distillation of coal yields coal gas, sulphur, ammonia, benzene, coal tar, and coke.
5. Fractional distillation of crude oil yields gas, petrol, kerosene, diesel oil, lubrication oil, and bitumen.
6. Hydrocarbons can be made larger by polymerization, or smaller by cracking.
7. The antiknock property, or octane rating, of petrol can be increased by alkylation, hydroforming, or adding tetraethyl lead(IV).
8. Town gas is composed mainly of natural gas.
9. Other fuel gases are oil gas, coal gas, water gas, and producer gas.

The experiments for this chapter are on pages 284–5.

Questions

1 1 Name three elements present in coal and describe how coal was formed in the earth.
2 Name two main products obtained as a result of the destructive distillation of coal, and describe one use made of each.
3 One of the by-products of the above process gives rise to a valuable fertilizer. What is the by-product, and how is it converted into a fertilizer? *P & W*

2 Here is a quotation from a book about Britain:

'The coals which provide her manufacturing power were made out of decomposing jungle. From their seams, it has been said, we draw the heat and energy of the primeval sun.'

Explain carefully the second sentence of the quotation. *P & W*

3 Semi-water gas is a mixture of producer gas and water gas. What gases will be present in the mixture?
Considering the energy changes involved in the preparation of producer gas and water gas, what advantage does the preparation of semi-water gas have over the preparation of water gas by itself? *P & W*

4 1 Describe briefly how oil is thought to have been formed.
2 Petrol obtained by the straight fractional distillation of oil is not sufficient to meet demand. How can petrol be obtained from other distillation fractions? *P & W*

5 Mention three characteristics which a good fuel should have and compare coal and oil under these headings. *P & W*

16 Hydrocarbons

16.1 Organic Chemistry

Organic chemistry is the study of carbon compounds. It is an extensive subject, because there is an almost unlimited number of carbon compounds. The main reason for the existence of so many carbon compounds is that carbon atoms are able to link together by means of covalent bonds. This means that there are compounds containing long chains of carbon atoms, branched chains, rings, and linked rings. Carbon atoms can also be linked together by double or triple covalent bonds. Figure 16.1 illustrates a variety of organic compounds.

Figure 16.1 The variety of organic compounds

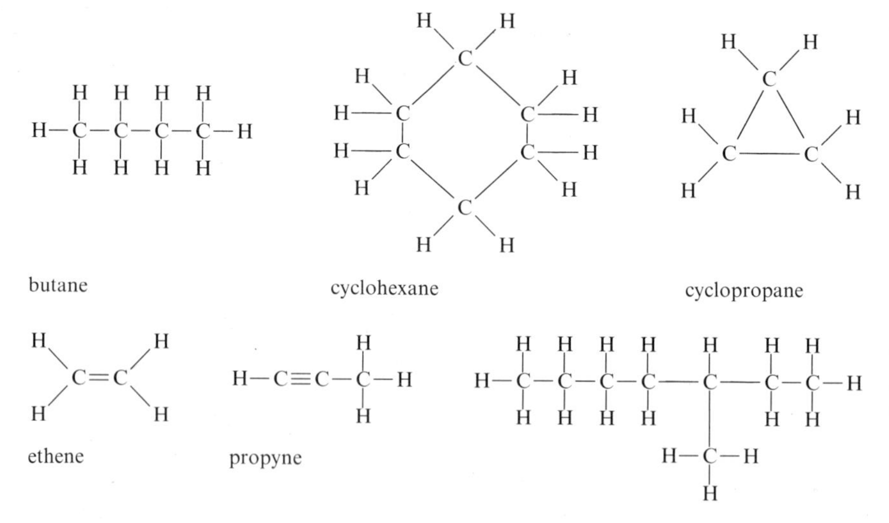

At this stage we have limited ourselves to the **hydrocarbons** which are compounds containing carbon and hydrogen only. There is, of course, a great variety of organic compounds which contain atoms of other elements, particularly nitrogen, sulphur, and oxygen. We will meet some of these compounds in later chapters.

It should be pointed out at this stage that the compounds shown in Figure 16.1 are diagrammatic representations. You should remember from chapter 2 (page 37) that the covalent bonds around a carbon atom are not planar, but are directed to the four corners of a tetrahedron as shown in the methane atom in Figure 16.2.

Figure 16.2

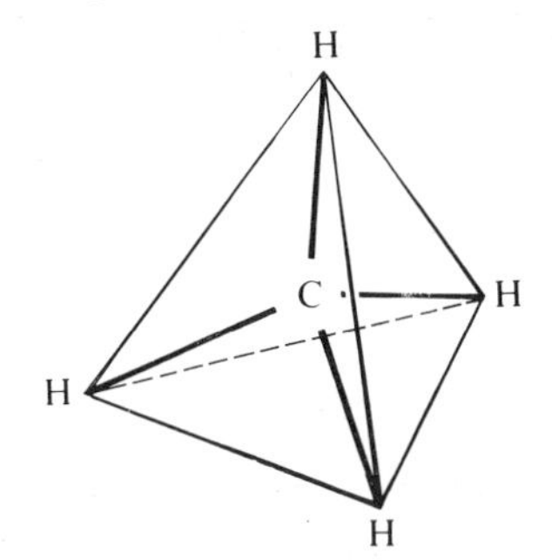

In the same way that there are groups of similar elements—for example, the alkali metals: lithium, sodium, potassium, caesium, francium; and the halogens: fluorine, chlorine, bromine, iodine—so there are groups of similar compounds in organic chemistry. These groups are called **homologous series,** and their existence simplifies the study of organic chemistry.

16.2 Alkanes

The simplest homologous series is the alkanes. The alkanes are hydrocarbons in which the constituent atoms are linked by single covalent bonds. Table 16.1 gives some information about the alkanes.

Table 16.1 The alkanes

Name	*Molecular formula*	*Boiling point* K	°C	*State at* 293 K (20°C)
Methane	CH_4	109	−164	Gas
Ethane	C_2H_6	186	−87	Gas
Propane	C_3H_8	231	−42	Gas
Butane	C_4H_{10}	272.5	−0.5	Gas
Pentane	C_5H_{12}	309	36	Liquid
Hexane	C_6H_{14}	342	69	Liquid
Heptane	C_7H_{16}	371	98	Liquid
Octane	C_8H_{18}	399	126	Liquid
Nonane	C_9H_{20}	424	151	Liquid
Decane	$C_{10}H_{22}$	447	174	Liquid
Eicosane	$C_{20}H_{42}$	616	343	Solid

If we look at the molecular formulae of the alkanes we can see that there is a distinct relationship between the number of carbon atoms and the number of hydrogen atoms. This relationship, which is called the **general formula,** is C_nH_{2n+2}, where n is the number of carbon atoms. The members of a homologous series can always be represented by a general formula.

If we look at the boiling points of the alkanes we can see that there is an increase in boiling point as the molecules increase in size. This can be accounted for in terms of the Van der Waals' forces. Obviously, as the molecular size increases so the Van der Waals' forces increase, and so more energy is required to boil the compound. We can also see that the increase in boiling point is regular. This is because each member differs from the preceding one by a constant factor, the addition of one methylene group:

$$\begin{array}{c} \mathrm{H} \\ | \\ -\mathrm{C}- \\ | \\ \mathrm{H} \end{array} \quad \text{or} \quad -\mathrm{CH_2}-$$

The members of a homologous series always display a regular gradation of physical properties.

Although the main source of methane is natural gas, all the alkanes can be obtained commercially by the fractional distillation of crude oil. They can also be prepared in the laboratory by **decarboxylation** (removal of CO_2) of the appropriate carboxylic acid. For example, methane is prepared by heating soda lime (calcium hydroxide slaked with sodium hydroxide) with ethanoic acid, as shown in Figure 16.3.

$$CH_3COOH(l) \rightarrow CH_4(g) + CO_2(g)$$
$$CO_2(g) + 2NaOH(aq) \rightarrow Na_2CO_3(aq) + H_2O(l)$$

Figure 16.3 Laboratory preparation of methane

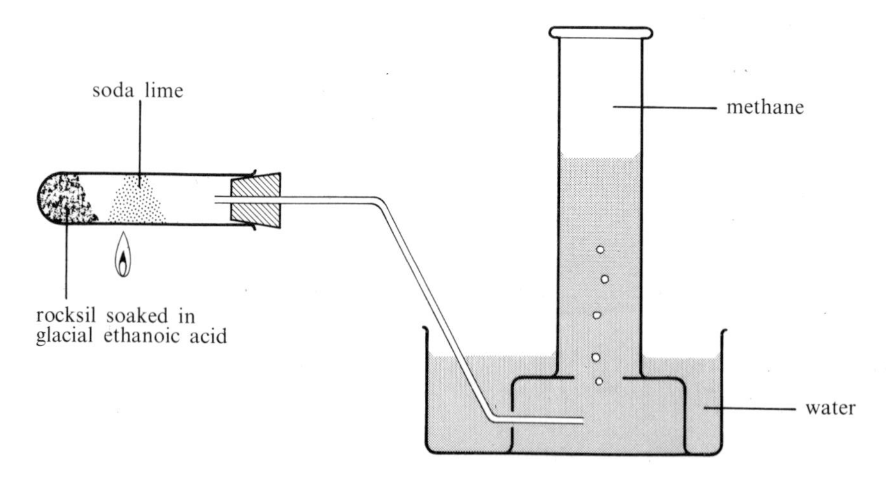

16.3 Properties of alkanes

It is a characteristic of homologous series that all the members have similar properties.

Solubility The alkanes are non-polar molecules, since they are insoluble in polar solvents such as water. They do dissolve in non-polar solvents such as tetrachloromethane.

Combustion The alkanes burn, and they are used as fuels. As they are composed of carbon and hydrogen only, the products of complete combustion are carbon dioxide and water.

$$CH_4(g)+2O_2(g) \rightarrow CO_2(g)+2H_2O(g) \qquad \Delta H = -890\,\text{kJ mol}^{-1}$$

Reactivity The alkanes are characterized by their comparative lack of reactivity with other chemicals, hence their original name 'paraffins' which means 'little affinity'. They are unreactive because their molecules are non-polar and contain single covalent bonds. Such molecules are said to be **saturated.**

Substitution In the reaction between methane and chlorine, an atom of chlorine is substituted for a hydrogen atom in the methane molecule.

$$CH_4(g)+Cl_2(g) \rightarrow \underset{\text{chloromethane}}{CH_3Cl(l)}+HCl(g)$$

By supplying additional molecules of chlorine it is possible to replace all the hydrogen atoms.

$$CH_3Cl(g)+Cl_2(g) \rightarrow \underset{\text{dichloromethane}}{CH_2Cl_2(l)}+HCl(g)$$

$$CH_2Cl_2(g)+Cl_2(g) \rightarrow CHCl_3(l)+HCl(g)$$
trichloromethane
(chloroform)

$$CHCl_3(g)+Cl_2(g) \rightarrow CCl_4(l)+HCl(g)$$
tetrachloromethane
(carbon tetrachloride)

16.4 Nomenclature and isomerism

If we draw out the structural formulae of the first few members of the alkane series we arrive at the interesting situation shown in Table 16.2.

Table 16.2 Structural formulae of alkanes

Name	*Molecular formula*	*Structural formula*
Methane	CH_4	H–C(H)(H)–H
Ethane	C_2H_6	H–C(H)(H)–C(H)(H)–H
Propane	C_3H_8	H–C(H)(H)–C(H)(H)–C(H)(H)–H

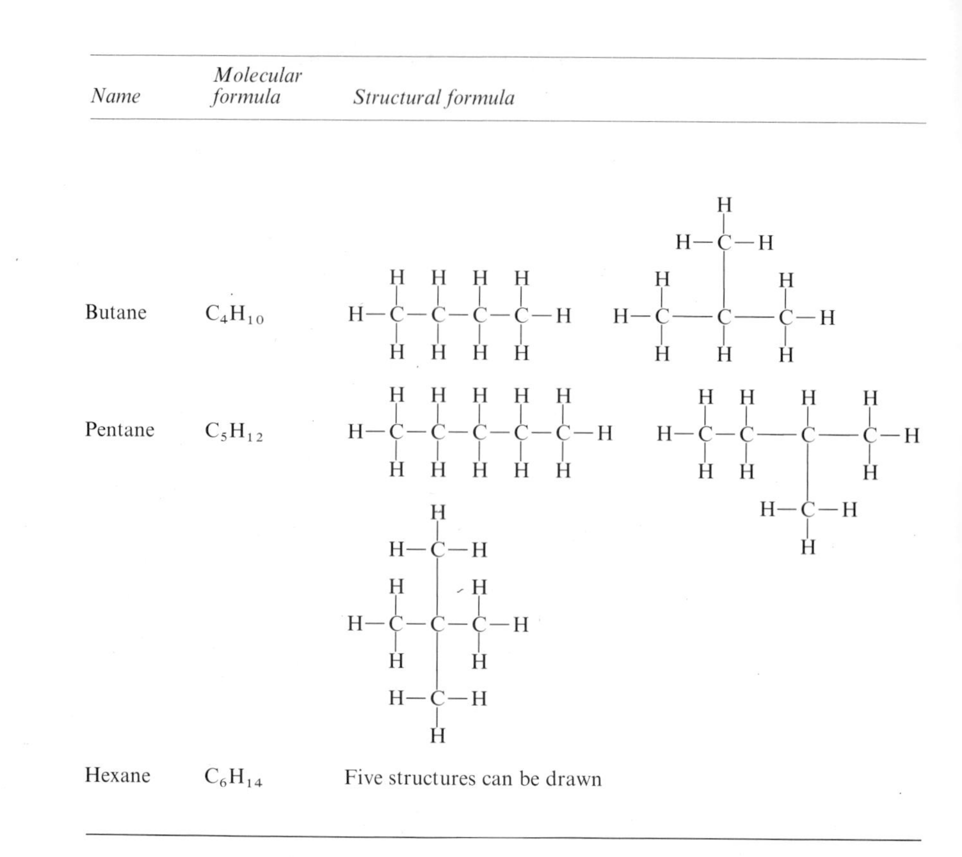

Name	*Molecular formula*	*Structural formula*
Butane	C_4H_{10}	
Pentane	C_5H_{12}	
Hexane	C_6H_{14}	Five structures can be drawn

When we get to butane, we can draw two structural formulae for the one molecular formula. When we reach pentane three structural formulae can be drawn, and by the time we reach hexane, five different structures exist. Compounds with the same molecular formula but different structural formulae are called **isomers,** and we say that butane shows isomerism. To avoid confusion between isomers, organic compounds are named very carefully and systematically. The rules for naming the alkanes are very simple. In order to show the carbon chain clearly we have omitted all the H symbols in the structural formulae.

1 Take the longest unbranched carbon chain as the parent:

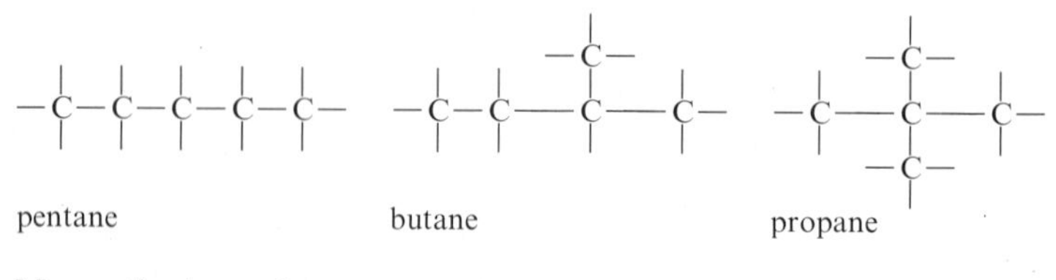

2 Name the branches:

$—CH_3$ methyl
$—C_2H_5$ ethyl
$—C_3H_7$ propyl

3 Indicate the number of branches:

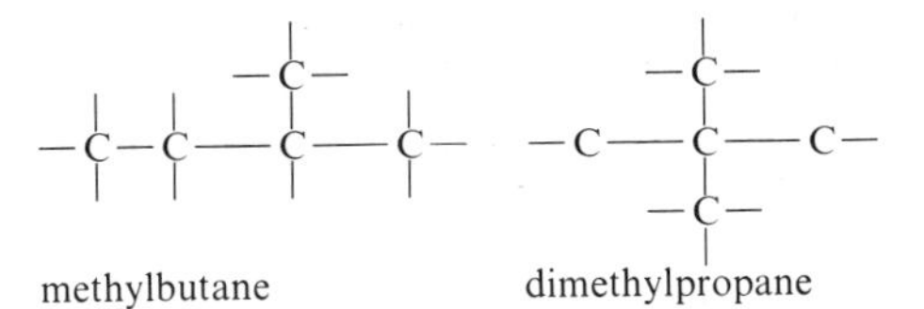

methylbutane dimethylpropane

4 Indicate the position of the branches by a number (always numbering the parent chain from the end nearest the branches):

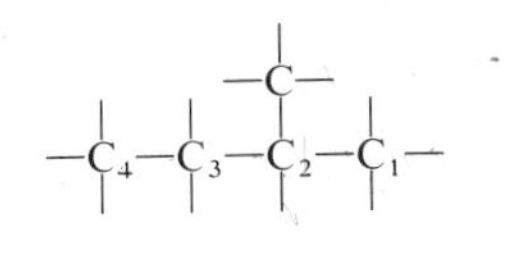

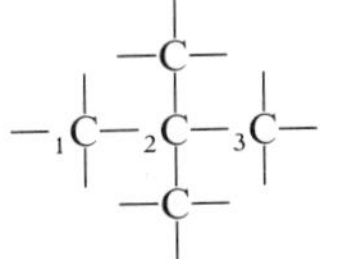

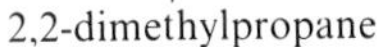

2-methylbutane 2,2-dimethylpropane

Some further examples of the systematic naming of alkanes are show below:

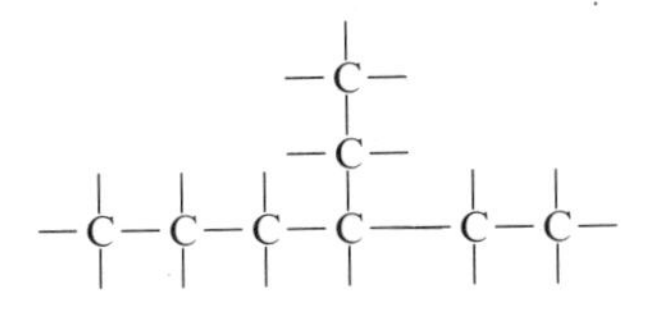

3-ethylhexane

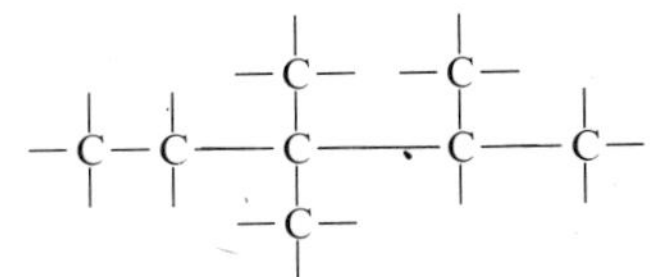

2, 3, 3-trimethylpentane

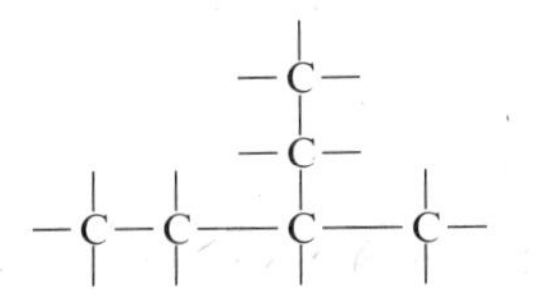

3-methylpentane

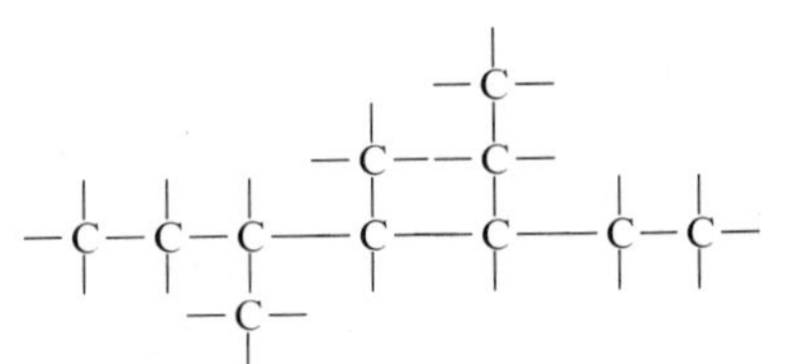

3-ethyl-4, 5-dimethylheptane

16.5 Alkenes

The alkenes are hydrocarbons which contain double bonds as well as single bonds. Table 16.3 gives some information about the alkenes.

Table 16.3 The alkenes

		Boiling point		
Name	*Formula*	K	°C	*State at* 293 K (20°C)
Ethene	C_2H_4	169	−104	Gas
Propene	C_3H_6	226	−47	Gas
Butene	C_4H_8	267	−6	Gas
Pentene	C_5H_{10}	303	30	Liquid

We can see from Table 16.3 that the general formula for the alkenes is C_nH_{2n}, where n is the number of carbon atoms. The alkenes exhibit a gradation of boiling point in the same way as other homologous series.

The main commercial source of the alkenes is from the thermal or catalytic cracking of larger alkane molecules:

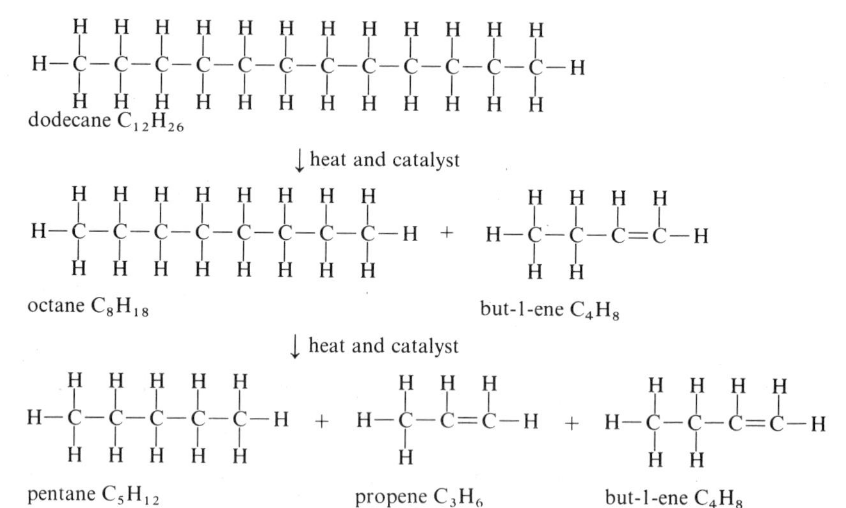

In the industrial process, mixtures of alkenes are obtained, and these have to be separated by fractional distillation. It is possible to crack hydrocarbons in the laboratory. Figure 16.4 illustrates a suitable method.

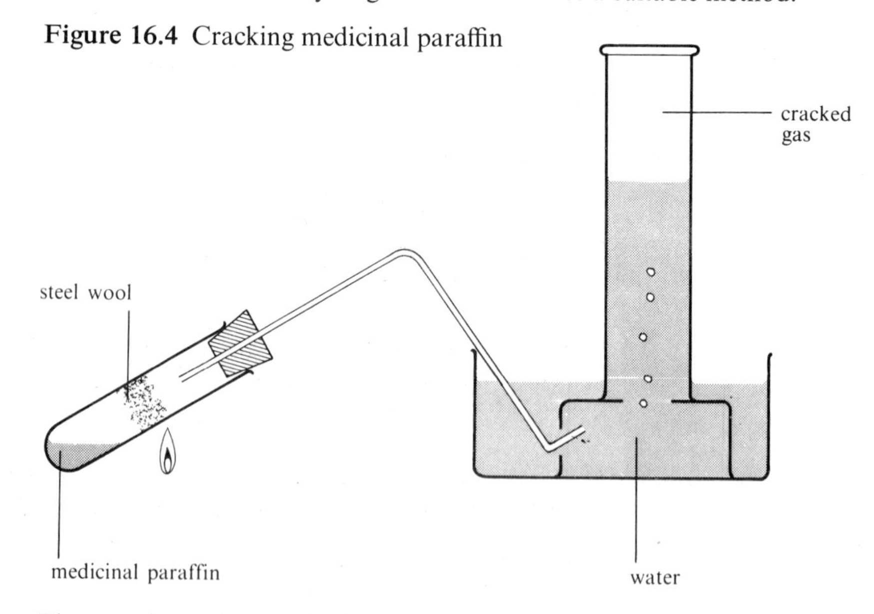

Figure 16.4 Cracking medicinal paraffin

The experiment illustrated in Figure 16.4 is not suitable for preparing pure samples of alkenes in the laboratory. The chemical method, which involves dehydration of the appropriate alcohol, is much better. For example, ethene can be prepared by heating ethanol with twice its volume of concentrated sulphuric acid at 180°C (Figure 16.5).

$$C_2H_5OH(l) - H_2O(l) \rightarrow C_2H_4(g)$$

Figure 16.5 Laboratory preparation of ethene

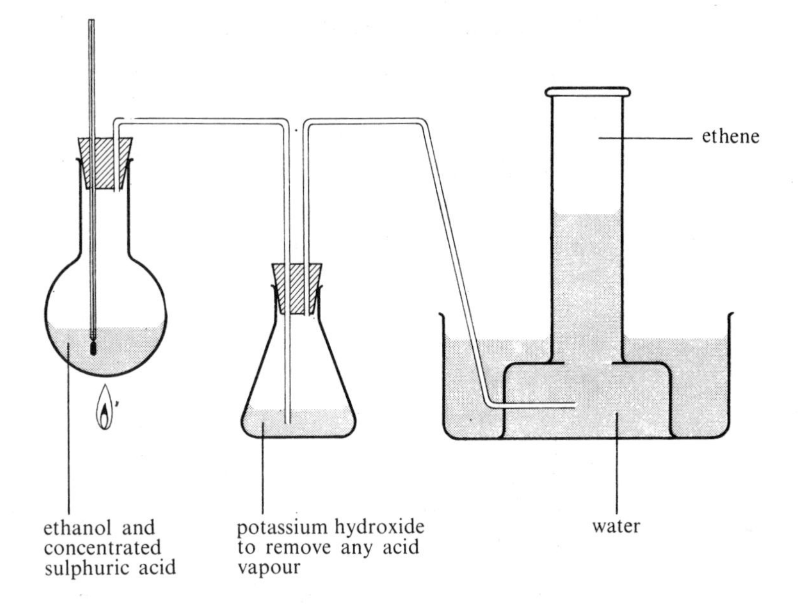

16.6 Properties of the alkenes

Solubility Like the alkanes, the alkenes are insoluble in water, but soluble in tetrachloromethane.

Combustion The alkenes burn to give carbon dioxide and water:

$$C_2H_4(g) + 3O_2(g) \rightarrow 2CO_2(g) + 2H_2O(g) \qquad \Delta H = -1410\,kJ$$

Because of the higher proportion of carbon in the alkenes, they burn with a sootier flame than the alkanes.

Reactivity The alkenes are generally a lot more reactive than the alkanes. This can be accounted for by their **unsaturated** nature, that is the existence of double bonds in their structure.

Addition Due to their unsaturated nature, the alkenes react by addition, which means another species is simply added on, as shown in the following examples.

$$C_2H_4(g) + Cl_2(g) \rightarrow \underset{\text{dichloroethane}}{C_2H_4Cl_2(g)}$$

$$C_2H_4(g) + H_2(g) \rightarrow \underset{\text{ethane}}{C_2H_6(g)}$$

The decolourization of bromine water is a typical test for an unsaturated compound:

$$C_2H_4(g) + Br_2(aq) \rightarrow \underset{\text{dibromoethane}}{C_2H_4Br_2(l)}$$

In all these reactions we can consider that the addition takes place as shown below:

```
    H               H
    |               |
H — C   Cl      H — C — Cl
    ||  |    →      |
H — C   Cl      H — C — Cl
    |               |
    H               H
```

In other words, the atoms of the molecule which is adding on become attached to the two adjacent carbon atoms. This means that the correct name for the product above is 1, 2-dichloroethane.

Polymerization Due to their unsaturated nature, alkenes will add to each other, or **polymerize:**

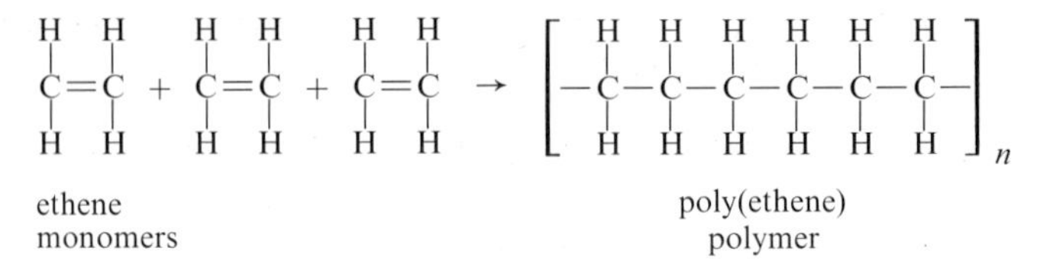

This is a reaction of great industrial importance, as it is the whole foundation of the plastics industry. It is discussed further in chapter 17.

16.7 Other homologous series

At this stage it might be of interest to look at some other hydrocarbons.

Propyne C_3H_4 is a member of the homologous series called the alkynes. The structural formula is:

```
            H
            |
H — C ≡ C — C — H
            |
            H
```

The general formula for the alkynes is C_nH_{2n-2}.

Cyclopentane C_5H_{10} is a member of the cycloalkane series. Its structural formula is:

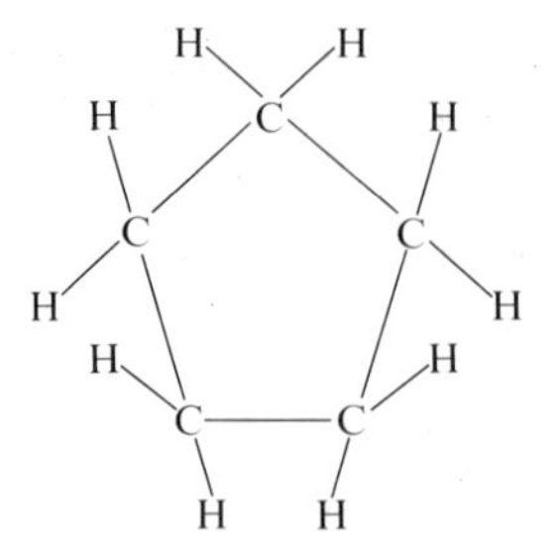

The general formula for the cycloalkanes is C_nH_{2n}. The substances in this series behave in a similar way to the alkanes. Although the cycloalkanes have the same general formula as the alkenes, they are saturated while the alkenes are unsaturated.

Summary

From this chapter you should know:

1 Carbon atoms join together to form a great variety of carbon compounds.

2 Members of a homologous series:
Can be represented by a general formula
Can be prepared by similar methods
Exhibit a gradation of physical properties
Exhibit similar chemical properties

3 The alkanes, C_nH_{2n+2}, are saturated, and react by substitution.

4 The alkenes, C_nH_{2n}, are unsaturated, and react by addition.

5 Isomers of a compound have the same molecular formula but different structural formulae.

The experiments for this chapter are on page 286.

Questions

1 Natural gas consists mainly of methane and ethane. Name the homologous series of which these compounds are members, giving the general formula. Is 10 g oxygen sufficient for the complete combustion of 4 g methane? Show how you reach your conclusion. *P & W*

2 **1** Write a brief account of the formation of oil from decaying matter indicating why an oil well 'gushes' when first tapped.
2 How would you show that crude oil contains at least three liquid constituents?
3 Liquid paraffin is known to be a hydrocarbon. How would you show that it is a saturated hydrocarbon? How would you obtain a sample of an unsaturated hydrocarbon from liquid paraffin? Why is the process of obtaining unsaturated hydrocarbons from saturated ones of great importance to the oil industry? *P & W*

3 Rewrite the following, filling in the blanks.
A hydrocarbon is a substance containing ______ and ______ only.
A series of hydrocarbons in which all the members have the same general formula is called a ______ series.
A hydrocarbon which contains no ______ to ______ double bonds is said to be ______.
______ water, when added to ______ hydrocarbons, is decolourized. *P & W*

4 1 What unique property does the element carbon possess which gives rise to the very large number (over one million) of carbon compounds?
2 Write down the name, molecular formula, and structural formula of:
2.1 A saturated hydrocarbon.
2.2 An unsaturated hydrocarbon. *P & W*

5 Butane is a **hydrocarbon,** with **molecular formula** C_4H_{10}, which has two **isomers.**
1 Explain clearly the terms in heavy type.
2 Write structural formulae for the isomers of butane.
3 What weight of oxygen would be required for the complete combustion of 116 g of butane? *P & W*

6 **1.1** What does the term unsaturated mean?
1.2 How could you show that a vegetable oil like olive oil is unsaturated?
1.3 How are oils similar to olive oil treated industrially to make solid fats?
2 A sample of a gaseous compound was burned in air to produce equal numbers of moles of carbon dioxide and water. Was the gas methane, ethane or ethene? Give reasons for your answer. *P & W*

7 1 In the purification of crude oil, the oil is **fractionally distilled,** and some of the distillation products are **cracked** to produce **unsaturated** hydrocarbons.
1.1 Explain the meaning of the words in heavy type.
1.2 Why is cracking important?
2 Write equations for:
2.1 The combustion of carbon in excess air.
2.2 The combustion of carbon in a limited supply of air.
Explain why the product of this combustion is dangerous.
3 Draw structural formulae for the isomers with a molecular formula of C_5H_{12}. *P & W*

8 To make efficient use of the products of the fractional distillation of petroleum some fractions are subjected to **thermal cracking.** One of the products at least is **unsaturated.**
1 Explain what is meant by the terms in heavy type.
2 How would you test a sample of petrol for suspected unsaturation?
3 Write the structural formula for butane.
4 Cracking of butane can take place to form principally propene (propylene) C_3H_6 and **one** other compound. What is the name and formula of that compound likely to be? *SCEEB*

9 Crude oil is fractionally distilled and seven fractions are obtained as shown in the table opposite.
1 In what ways are fractions 1 and 7 different from each other?
2 What use is made of fraction 2?
3 There is a great demand for some of the early fractions like 2, but crude oil on distillation yields about 50 per cent of fractions 6 and 7.

3.1 Tell briefly what is done to get more of the earlier fractions.
3.2 This process yields hydrocarbons which can decolourize bromine water. Explain what this indicates about the hydrocarbons.
3.3 Why are short chain hydrocarbons of this type particularly useful as starting materials in the petrochemical industry?

Fraction number	*Approximate number of carbon atoms per molecule*
1	1–4
2	5–8
3	9–11
4	10–14
5	13–19
6	19–35
7	>35

P & W

17 Macromolecules

17.1 Giant molecules

The majority of molecules which we have come across do not contain large numbers of atoms: oxygen O_2; water H_2O; methane CH_4; ethanol C_2H_5OH. There is, however, an important group of substances whose molecules can contain thousands of atoms. These are giant molecules and are known as **macromolecules** or **polymers.** We can divide these giant molecules into natural polymers and synthetic polymers.

17.2 Natural polymers

Living organisms contain complex molecules, many of which are polymers of simple molecules.

Starch Most plants contain the polymer starch, which has the formula $(C_6H_{10}O_5)_n$. The significance of the '*n*' in the formula is that the number of $C_6H_{10}O_5$ units is not accurately known. There are thousands of these units linked together in the molecule to form long chains.

$$----C_6H_{10}O_5-C_6H_{10}O_5-C_6H_{10}O_5-C_6H_{10}O_5----$$

Cellulose Cotton and flax are almost pure cellulose, and the fibrous material in wood is about 40 per cent cellulose. The molecule has the formula $(C_6H_{10}O_5)_x$. The basic unit is $-C_6H_{10}O_5-$, the same as that in starch. We differentiate between starch and cellulose by indicating in the formulae that they contain different numbers of base units. The long chain-like molecules in cellulose are responsible for the fibrous nature of cotton, flax, and wood.

Protein fibres Proteins will be examined in detail in chapter 19, but we must mention them here as they are macromolecules. The structure shown below is characteristic of proteins.

$$----CH_2.CO.NH.-CH_2.CO.NH.-CH_2.CO.NH.----$$

Like cellulose and starch, it is a long chain-like molecule. This is the cause of the fibrous nature of wool and silk.

Rubber Rubber is perhaps the best known of all natural polymers. It is similar to other polymers in that it contains long chain-like molecules, and that these molecules contain many similar units. A simple formula for rubber is $(C_5H_8)_n$.

The elasticity of rubber is caused by the coiling of the molecules. When rubber is stretched the molecules straighten out and when it is released the molecules coil up again

Figure 17.1

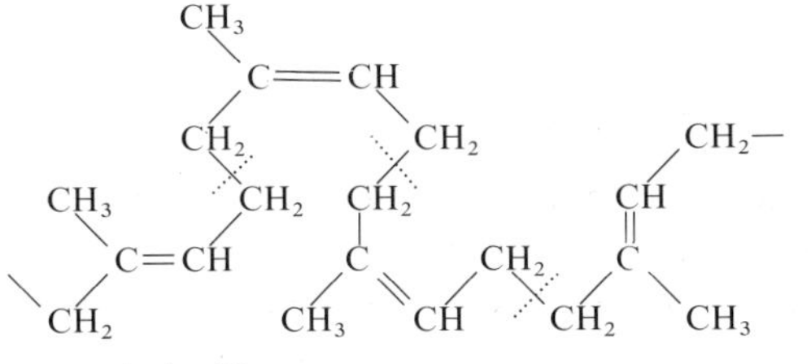

unstretched rubber

$$-CH_2.\overset{CH_3}{\overset{|}{C}}.CH\,CH_2.\ \vdots\ CH_2.\overset{CH_3}{\overset{|}{C}}.CH\,CH_2.\ \vdots\ CH_2\overset{CH_3}{\overset{|}{C}}.CH\,CH_2.\ \vdots\ CH_2\overset{CH_3}{\overset{|}{C}}.CH\,CH_2-$$

stretched rubber

Rayon Cellulose can be converted into a continuous fibre capable of being spun and woven. This fibre is called rayon. Cellulose, in the form of wood pulp, is treated with sodium hydroxide solution and carbon disulphide. This converts the celluose into a syrupy substance called viscose, which is then forced through small holes in a metal plate into a bath of dilute sulphuric acid. The acid converts the viscose solution into glossy transparent filaments which can be twisted to form rayon thread. This conversion of a natural substance to a man-made material can be regarded as the bridge between natural polymers and synthetic polymers.

17.3 Synthetic polymers

Natural polymers have properties which make them useful to man—the uses of silk and wool are well-known. The fact that the fibres in these materials are made of long molecules containing many similar units provided the key to the production of synthetic polymers. Man-made fibres are made by copying the natural process of linking small units, called **monomers,** together to make polymers. We call this process **polymerization,** which can occur by means of **condensation** or **addition** reactions.

Condensation polymerization Condensation involves the elimination of a simple molecule between each pair of monomers. Let us consider the following monomers:

$H{-}\boxed{A}{-}OH$ and $H{-}\boxed{B}{-}Cl$

where $\boxed{A}$ and $\boxed{B}$ represent hydrocarbon chains.

When monomers of the type $H{-}\boxed{A}{-}OH$ are polymerized, a molecule of water is eliminated between each pair of monomers, and a long chain-like molecule is produced:

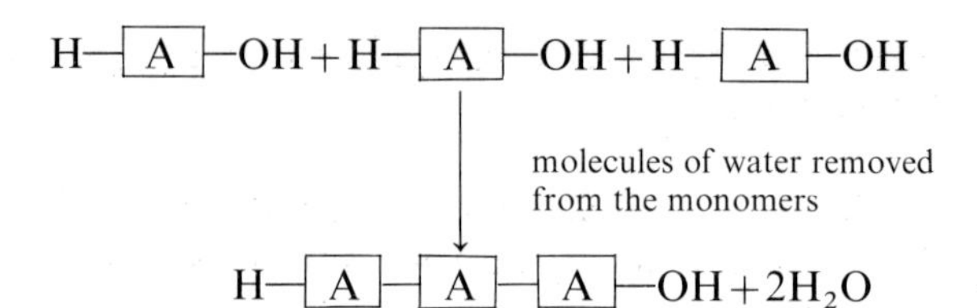

When monomers of the type H—B—Cl are polymerized, a molecule of hydrogen chloride is eliminated between each pair of monomers, and a long chain-like molecule is produced:

H—B—Cl + H—B—Cl + H—B—Cl

↓ molecules of hydrogen chloride removed from the monomers

H—B—B—B—Cl + 2HCl

Some of the natural polymers which we have already considered are condensation polymers, for example, wool, silk, and cellulose.

Bakelite This was the first synthetic polymer to be manufactured industrially. It is formed by a condensation reaction between phenol and methanal.

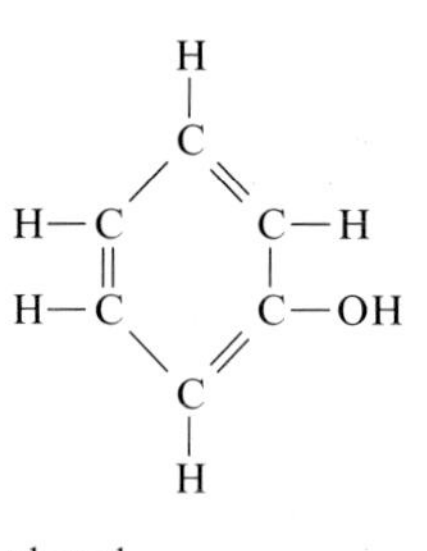

phenol

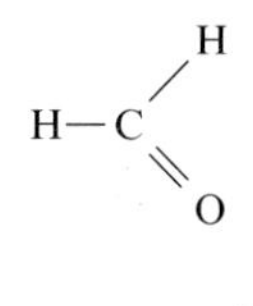

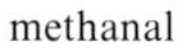

methanal

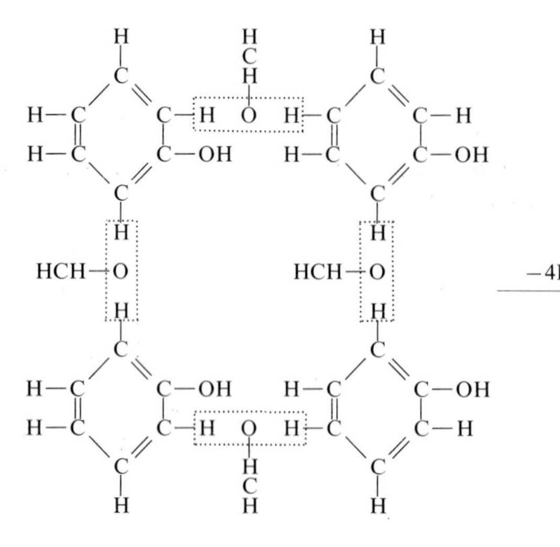

$-4H_2O$ →

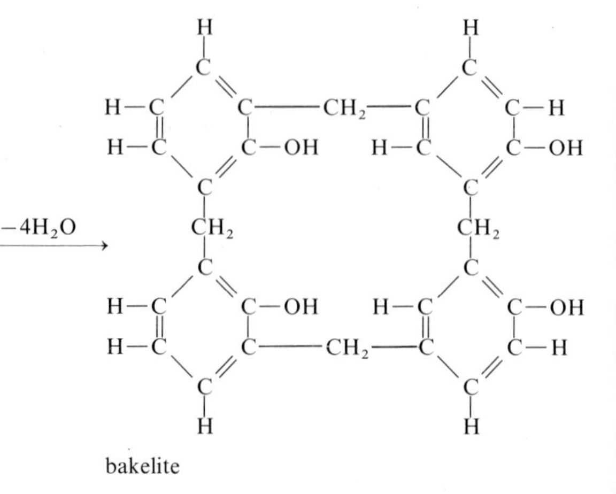

bakelite

Uses: electric plugs; electrical insulators; all types of electrical fittings; distributor caps.

Urea–formaldehyde resin

Bakelite has one disadvantage in that it is always brown. This is because of a reaction of phenol with air. If the phenol is replaced by urea, a clear polymer is obtained which can be dyed if this is required. The monomers are urea and methanal. (formaldehyde).

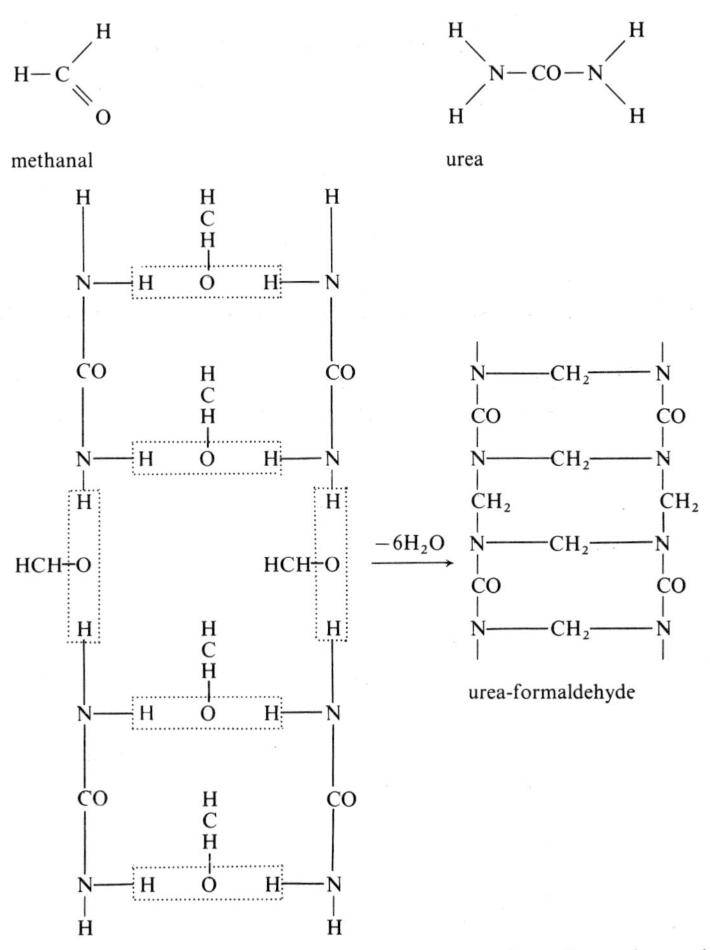

Uses: similar to bakelite, but now replacing bakelite as it can be dyed to whatever colour is required.

Nylon There is a variety of nylon polymers. We will consider one. Nylon 6.6 is a condensation polymer produced from the monomers 1,6-diaminohexane and hexanedioyl dichloride (adipyl chloride).

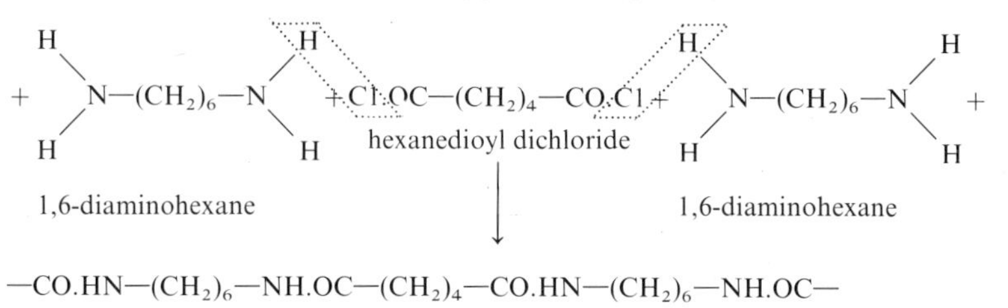

nylon 6.6

Uses: production of clothing; ladies tights; climbing ropes; parachute fabric; gear wheels; curtain runners.

Terylene Terylene is produced from the monomers ethane-1,2-diol and dimethyl benzene-1,2-dicarboxylate by means of a condensation reaction.

$$HO.CH_2.CH_2.OH + CH_3.O.CO.C_6H_4.COO.CH_3 \rightarrow HO.CH_2.CH_2.O.CO.C_6H_4.COO.CH_3$$

ethane-1,2-diol; dimethyl benzene-1,2-dicarboxylate

This process is repeated many times in the polymerization to give:

$$(-O.CH_2.CH_2.O.CO.C_6H_4.CO-)_n$$

terylene

Addition polymerization Addition polymerization occurs between monomers containing double bonds. One of the bonds is broken and the free electrons form bonds with the neighbouring monomers. The only natural addition polymer is rubber.

Poly(ethene) Consider the formation of poly(ethene) from ethene.

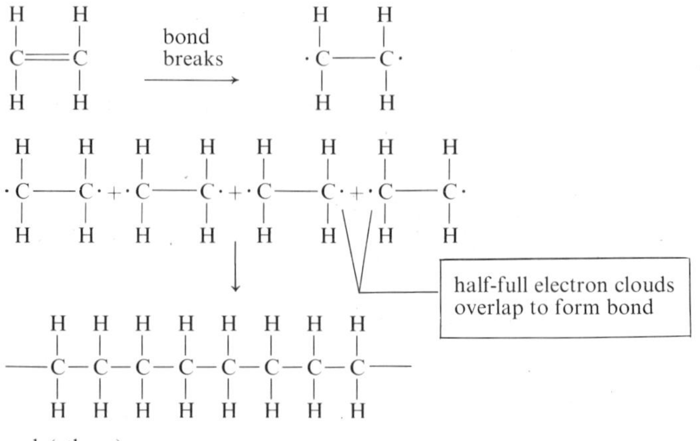

poly(ethene)

Uses: detergent bottles; washing-up bowls; water-storage tanks; aircraft construction kits; artificial ski slopes.

Poly(chloroethene)

PVC (polyvinyl chloride) is an addition polymer and is obtained by polymerizing chloroethene (vinyl chloride).

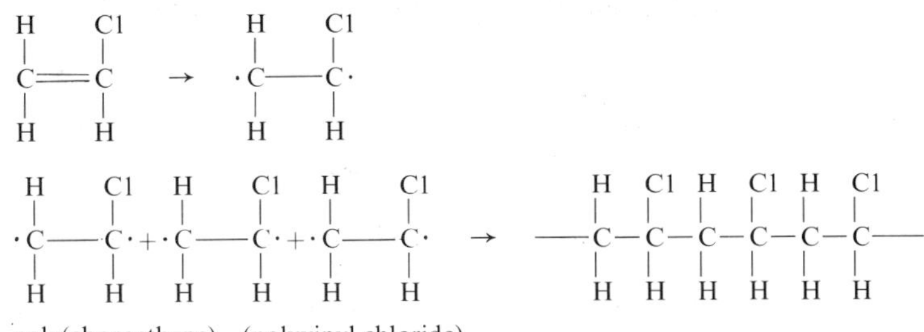

poly(choroethene) (polyvinyl chloride)

Uses: gramophone records; electric cable coverings; hose pipes; baby pants; floor tiles; wall-paper; curtain rails; raincoats; roofing; handle-bar grips; guttering; film; insulators; shoes; coated fabrics.

PTFE

Poly(tetrafluoroethene) is an addition polymer obtained by polymerizing tetrafluoroethene. The mechanism is similar to that in the formation of PVC.

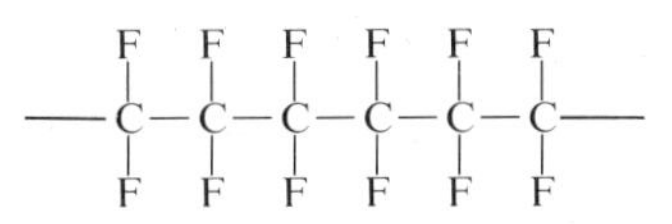

poly(tetrafluoroethene) (PTFE)

Uses: the teflon 'non-stick' in frying pans.

Perspex

Perspex is poly(methyl 2-methylpropenoate). It is obtained in similar way to PVC by polymerizing methyl 2-methylpropenoate (methyl methacrylate).

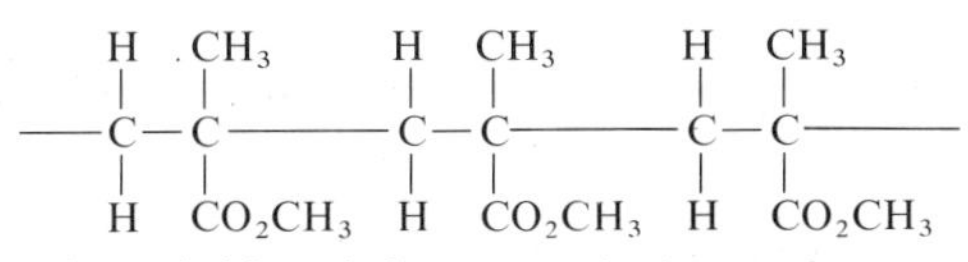

poly(methyl 2-methylpropenoate) (perspex)

Uses: telephone parts; windows in aircraft; dentures; artificial eyes; lighting fittings; glass-clear mouldings.

Polystyrene

Polystyrene is poly(phenylethene) and is obtained by the addition polymerization of phenylethene (styrene). The mechanism is similar to that in the formation of PVC.

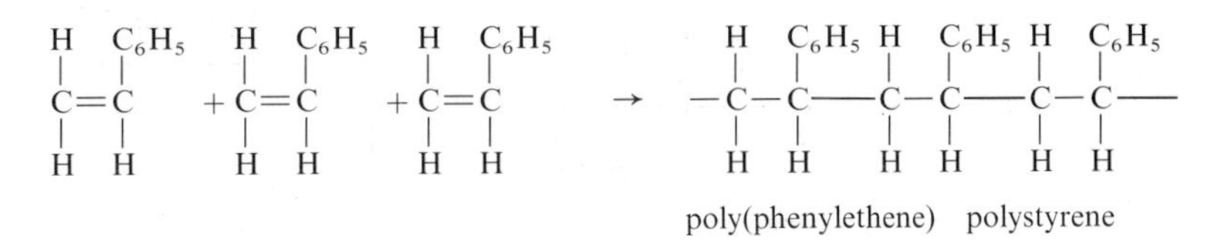

poly(phenylethene) polystyrene

Uses: food containers and packaging; cosmetic bottles; television cabinets; 'plastic' cups; ceiling tiles; apple trays.

Thermoplastic or Thermosetting?

If synthetic polymers are heated, some will soften and some will not. Those which soften, yet return to their original form are said to be **thermoplastic** polymers. Those which do not soften are said to be **thermosetting** polymers. Poly(ethene) consists of long, unbranched chains, whereas bakelite has a three-dimensional rigid structure. The rigid arrangement of bakelite prevents it from melting. On heating it will decompose instead. A selection of thermosetting and thermoplastic polymers are given below:

1 Thermosetting polymers: bakelite; urea–formaldehyde resin.
2 Thermoplastic polymers: poly(ethene); nylon; PVC; PTFE; perspex; polystyrene.

17.4 Silicones

Silicon is in Group 4 of the Periodic Table. From this we would expect it to form tetravalent compounds in a similar way to carbon. These compounds are called silanes, the simplest being SiH_4:

$$\begin{array}{ccc} & \text{H} & \\ & | & \\ \text{H}- & \text{Si} & -\text{H} \\ & | & \\ & \text{H} & \end{array}$$

Silicones are substances containing silicon and oxygen. We can compare the production of silicones with that of condensation polymers.

Silicon does not form long chains like carbon, but it can form chains with alternating silicon and oxygen atoms. A possible method of preparing silicones is shown below.

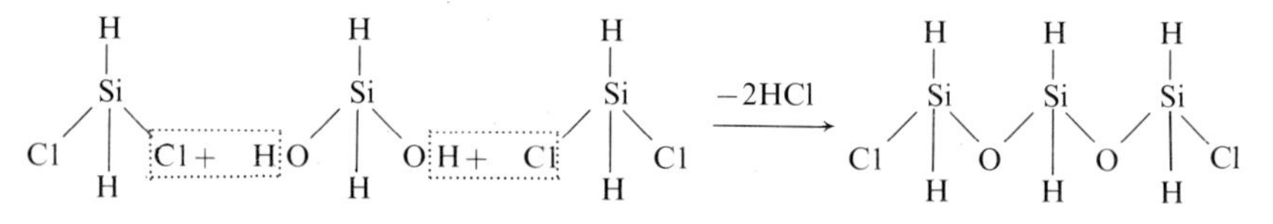

dichlorosilane dihydroxysilane

When this reaction is repeated many times, a siloxy chain is formed:

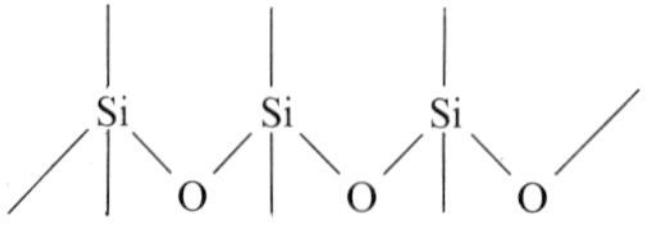

These chains are the basis of all silicones. Silicones are used as water repellants, polishes, and greases.

Summary

From this chapter you should know:

1 What a polymer is.

2 There are many naturally occuring polymers.

3 The meaning of the terms monomer, polymerization, condensation, and addition.

4 How synthetic polymers are formed.

5 The difference between thermoplastic and thermosetting polymers.

6 The significance of the silicones.

The experiments for this chapter are on page 287.

Questions

1 Explain the difference between a condensation polymer and an addition polymer and give an example of each type. *P & W*

2 1 What does the term 'polymer' mean?
2 Explain each of the following terms associated with the process of polymerization:
Addition, condensation, monomer, thermosetting.
3 What is the essential difference between the processes for the preparation of nylon and the preparation of rayon?
4 Describe the laboratory preparation of either nylon or rayon.
5 Explain why, on burning, nylon smells of burning hair and rayon smells of burning paper. *P & W*

3 1 Explain briefly the difference between addition polymerization and condensation polymerization.
2 By which of these processes is each of the following polymers formed:
Nylon, polythene, PVC, bakelite? *P & W*

4 1 Which of the following are polymers:
Olive oil, nylon, rubber, glucose, sugar, paper, margarine, starch.
2 Why are silicones water-repellent? *P & W*

5 1 Explain the difference between condensation and addition reactions giving an example of each type.
2 Polymers can be classified other than as condensation and addition. Name the other forms of classification and describe the properties of each type. *P & W*

6 The polymer, polytetrafluoroethene, can be represented as follows:

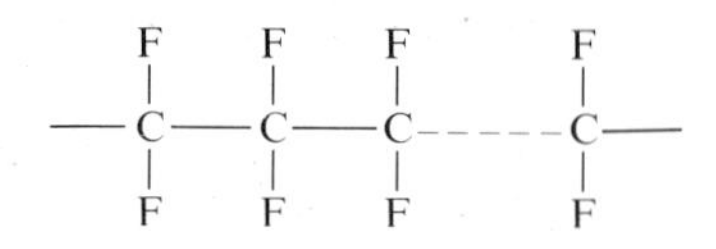

1 Draw the structure of the **monomer** from which this **thermoplastic** polymer is made.
2 What are the meanings of the words in heavy type?
3 What type of polymerization occurs in the formation of this polymer?
P & W

7 What is meant by the word 'polymer'?
Here is a list of substances: terylene, styrene, cellulose, ethane, perspex, ammonia. From this list, name:
1 A naturally occurring polymer.
2 A man-made polymer.
3 A substance which is not a polymer but can readily be converted into one.
4 A substance which is not a polymer and which could not polymerize.
SCEEB

8

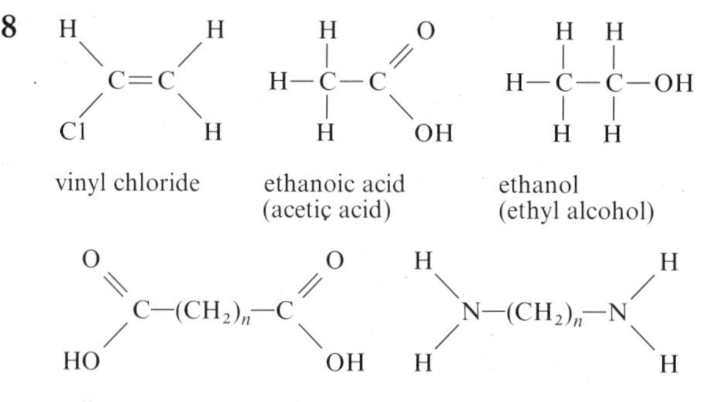

Which of the above substances would you use to prepare:
1 An addition polymer?
2 A condensation polymer?
Draw diagrams to indicate the structures of these two polymers, in each case showing three monomer molecules linked. *SCEEB*

9 1 Polythene is a **thermoplastic addition polymer.** Bakelite is a **thermosetting condensation** polymer.
Explain the meaning of each of the five words in heavy type.
2 From what monomer is poly(ethene) made?
What is the usual source of this monomer in industry?
3

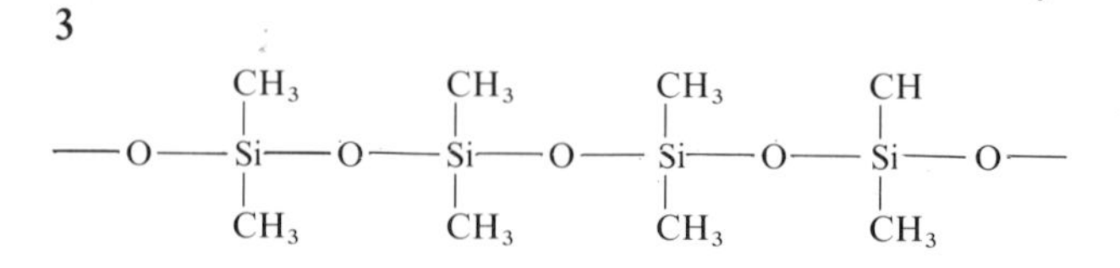

What are polymers of the type shown called?
State *two* properties associated with this type of polymer. *SCEEB*

10 Polymers consist of units repeated throughout the chain. These units are derived from the monomers from which the polymers are made.

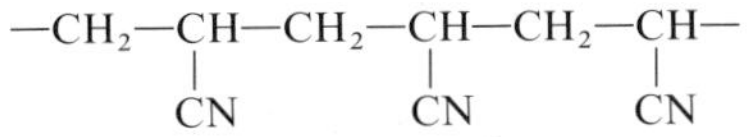

$$-CH_2-\underset{\displaystyle CN}{\underset{|}{CH}}-CH_2-\underset{\displaystyle CN}{\underset{|}{CH}}-CH_2-\underset{\displaystyle CN}{\underset{|}{CH}}-$$

Orlon

$$-\underset{\displaystyle O}{\underset{\|}{C}}(CH_2)_4\underset{\displaystyle O}{\underset{\|}{C}}.NH(CH_2)_6.NH.\underset{\displaystyle O}{\underset{\|}{C}}(CH_2)_4\underset{\displaystyle O}{\underset{\|}{C}}.NH(CH_2)_6.NH-$$

nylon

1.1 Draw the structural formula of the repeating unit in Orlon.
1.2 Draw the structural formula of the monomer from which Orlon is made.
1.3 State whether Orlon is made by addition or condensation.
2.1 Draw the structural formula of the repeating unit in nylon.
2.2 Draw the structural formulae of the monomers from which nylon is made.
2.3 State whether nylon is made by addition or condensation.
3 Polymers are found in everyday use. What is the purpose of:
3.1 The teflon coating on some frying pans?
3.2 The vinyl skin on some wall-papers?
3.3 The PVC covering of electrical connecting wire? *SCEEB*

11 Chloroethene (vinyl chloride) C_2H_3Cl is used to make the plastic poly(chloroethene) (polyvinyl chloride).
1 Draw the structural formula of chloroethene.
2 Draw part of the poly(chloroethene) molecule showing how three of the chloroethene molecules are linked.
3 What is the name for this kind of polymerization? *SCEEB*

18 Alcohols, acids, and esters

18.1 Fermentation

Alcohol can be obtained from fermentation in various ways.

1 The fermentation of grape juice to make wine has given pleasure to man since ever he learned to jump on the grapes instead of eating them. Grape juice contains a sugar, glucose, which is converted to alcohol by an enzyme, zymase, contained in the skin of the grape. An **enzyme** is a naturally occurring compound which acts as a catalyst in a living organism, but the enzyme itself is not living.

$$\underset{\text{glucose}}{C_6H_{12}O_6(aq)} \xrightarrow{\text{zymase}} \underset{\text{alcohol}}{2C_2H_5OH(aq)} + 2CO_2(g)$$

The wine contains about 10 per cent alcohol, the 'strength' at which it is consumed as table-wine. Fractional distillation of the wine yields a distillate containing 95 per cent alcohol, which is then used to 'fortify' other wines.

2 Brewers allow barley to sprout, then they dry it and grind it with water to form a solution which contains the enzyme diastase. The starch in the grain is converted to a sweet, sugary solution of maltose. Yeast is then added to provide the enzyme maltase, which converts the maltose into glucose, and also the enzyme zymase, which converts the glucose to alcohol.

3 Distillers use the yeast grown in the brewery to convert the sugars in the solution to alcohol. Since the solution is boiled in the distillation process, the yeast is killed. Malt whisky is made from barley, while grain whisky is made from maize. Most of the popular brands of whisky are blended from 'malts' and grain.

In every fermentation, the growing yeast is converting glucose to carbon dioxide and energy. The alcohol is a by-product of this process. Animals convert glucose to carbon dioxide and energy by respiration. The yeast is using the fermentation process as an incomplete respiration process:

$$C_6H_{12}O_6 \rightarrow 2C_2H_5OH + 2CO_2 + \text{energy} \qquad \textbf{fermentation}$$
$$C_6H_{12}O_6 + 6O_2 \rightarrow 6H_2O + 6\,CO_2 + \text{energy} \qquad \textbf{respiration}$$

18.2 Alcohols

The alcohol in drinks, ethanol, is one of a homologous series of alcohols.

CH_3OH	methanol
CH_3CH_2OH	ethanol
$CH_3CH_2CH_2OH$	propanol
$CH_3CH_2CH_2CH_2OH$	butanol

Industrial alcohols are now produced by the petrochemical industry. Ethene (ethylene) C_2H_4 can be converted to ethanol by steam in the presence of a catalyst:

$$CH_2{=}CH_2(g) + H_2O(g) \rightarrow CH_3CH_3OH(l)$$

Ethanol produced industrially is used as rectified spirit, as a solvent, and in toilet preparations. Methylated spirits, in spite of the name, contains about 90 per cent ethanol and 5 per cent methanol, and small amounts of chemicals, which cannot be removed by distillation, to stop people drinking it. Ethane-1,2-diol is sold as antifreeze for car radiators and it is still called ethylene glycol in the car trade. Propane-1, 2, 3-triol is treated with nitric acid to make the high explosive nitroglycerine.

CH_2OH — CH_2OH ethane-1, 2-diol (ethylene glycol)

CH_2OH — $CHOH$ — CH_2OH propane-1, 2, 3-triol (glyercol)

Properties of alcohols

All the alcohols which are liquids dissolve in water. This is what we might expect from their bonding, and the possibility of hydrogen bonding within the compound and in the water mixture.

Let us consider several molecules of water:

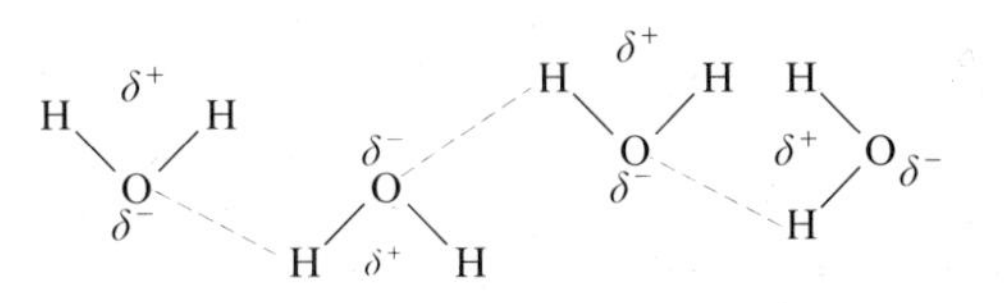

We know that water molecules are polar (chapter 3.) This polarity causes attractions between oxygen and hydrogen atoms of adjacent molecules, as shown by the dashed lines. These attractions are called **hydrogen bonds.** The hydrogen bonds are the reason for water being a liquid.

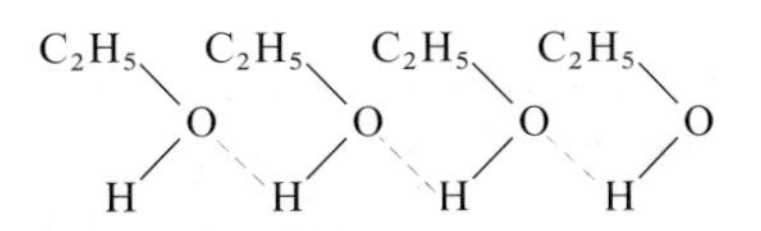

hydrogen bonding in ethanol

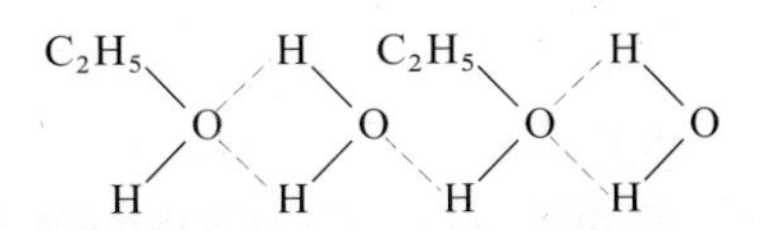

hydrogen bonding in the solution

Propane-1, 2, 3-triol is a viscous liquid with a high boiling point of 563 K (290 °C). Both of these properties are due to the large degree of hydrogen bonding possible with three hydroxyl groups (—OH) in the molecule.

Higher members of the alcohol series are not miscible with water because the long hydrocarbon chain masks the polar nature of the hydroxyl group. Although the hydroxyl group in the alcohols is polar, ionization does not take place. Hence the alcohols are poor conductors of electricity and are neutral to indicators.

Ethanol like its fellow alcohols is flammable. The products of combustion are carbon dioxide and water.

$$C_2H_5OH(l) + 3O_2(g) \rightarrow 2CO_2(g) + 3H_2O(g)$$

Ethanol can easily be oxidized to ethanoic acid using copper(II) oxide as the oxidizing agent. A suitable set up is shown in Figure 18.1.

Figure 18.1 Oxidation of ethanol

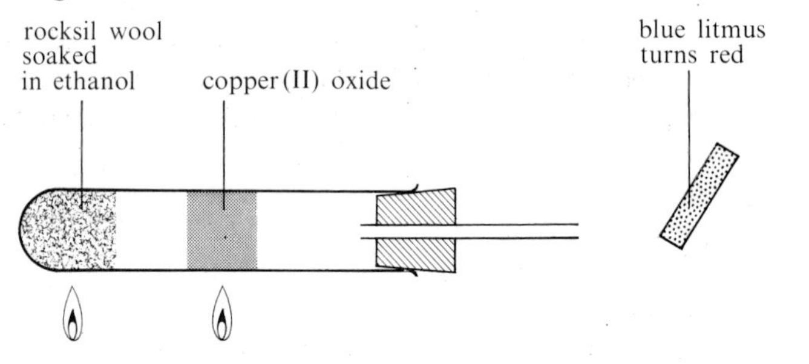

$$CH_3CH_2OH(g) + 2CuO(s) \rightarrow CH_3.COOH(l) + H_2O(l) + 2Cu(s)$$

18.3 Acids

When wine is allowed to stand open to the air, it turns sour and tastes of vinegar which means 'sour wine'. Vinegar is a dilute solution of ethanoic acid, being about 1M. Wine vinegar is made from poor quality wine by allowing it to oxidize in the air with the bacterium, *mycoderma aceti.*

The large-scale manufacture of ethanoic acid starts with ethyne gas (acetylene) which is passed into dilute sulphuric acid containing mercury(II) sulphate as a catalyst. The ethanal formed in this process is oxidized by air to ethanoic acid.

$$\underset{\text{ethyne}}{C_2H_2} \xrightarrow{\text{water}} \underset{\text{ethanal}}{CH_3.CHO} \xrightarrow{\text{oxygen}} \underset{\text{ethanoic acid}}{CH_3.COOH}$$

Ethanoic acid is a weak acid.

$$CH_3.COOH(aq) \rightleftharpoons CH_3.COO^-(aq) + H^+(aq)$$

The pure liquid boils at 391 K (118 °C) and it has a surprisingly high melting point of 289 K (16 °C). This explains why it is a solid on cold days, and is sometimes called 'glacial ethanoic acid'. These properties can be explained in terms of hydrogen bonding. The fact that the experimentally determined molecular weight is 120 and not 60 indicates that two molecules of ethanoic acid are linked together to form a **dimer.**

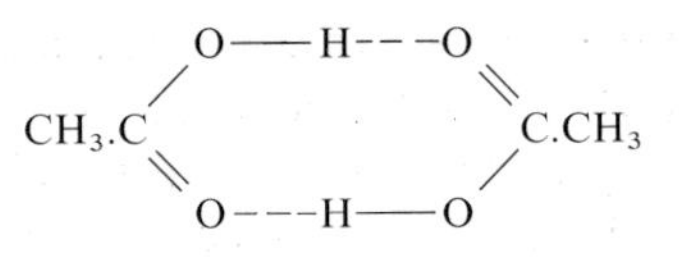

Ethanoic acid is the second member of the homologous series of acids called the **alkanoic** acids. More examples are shown below:

$H.COOH$	methanoic acid (formic acid)
$CH_3.COOH$	ethanoic acid (acetic acid)
$CH_3.CH_2.COOH$	propanoic acid

18.4 Esters

When a mixture of ethanoic acid and ethanol is heated with a few drops of concentrated sulphuric acid in a test-tube, a sweet smelling vapour is produced. This compound is the **ester,** ethyl ethanoate, which has been formed by the elimination of water. Esterification is a special case of a condensation reaction.

$$CH_3.COOH(l)+C_2H_5OH(l) \rightarrow CH_3.COOC_2H_5(l)+H_2O(l)$$

Writing the structural formula for an ester sometimes causes difficulty, especially with respect to the C—O bonds, so it is worth while considering in more detail the formula for ethyl ethanoate.

```
   H           H   H
   |           |   |
H—C—C—O—C—C—H
   |   ||      |   |
   H   O       H   H
```

Compare the formulae for ethyl propanoate $CH_3.CH_2.COOC_2H_5$, and propyl ethanoate $CH_3.COOC_3H_7$, and be sure to appreciate that they are different compounds. Many esters occur naturally, and most of them have pleasant characteristic smells, so that they are used as perfumes and flavourings. Methyl ethanoate and ethyl ethanoate are used as solvents, and they have the characteristic smell of the glue used in model construction kits. Fats and oils are esters of propane-1, 2, 3-triol (glycerol) and fatty acids such as stearic acid $C_{17}H_{35}.COOH$.

In the preparation of an ester, we usually add some concentrated sulphuric acid. When we look at the equation for the reaction, it seems as if its function is to absorb the water which is eliminated, and to encourage the reaction to go in the direction of the ester.

$$CH_3.COOH(l)+CH_3OH(l) \rightleftharpoons CH_3.COOCH_3(l)+H_2O(l)$$

If we accept this reasoning, we may not describe the sulphuric acid as a catalyst since we are using it to alter the equilibrium mixture. Chemists who want to study the concentrations at equilibrium add dilute hydrochloric acid to the reactants instead, and the $H^+(aq)$ ion does act as a catalyst, bringing the system to equilibrium more quickly. If an ester is boiled with sodium hydroxide-solution, it can be broken down into the original acid and alcohol.

$$CH_3.COOCH_3(l)+H_2O(l) \rightarrow CH_3.COOH(l)+CH_3OH(l)$$

Since this process involves the addition of water, it is called **hydrolysis.**

$$CH_3.COOH(l)+CH_3OH(l) \underset{\text{hydrolysis}}{\overset{\text{esterfication}}{\rightleftharpoons}} CH_3.COOCH_3(l)+H_2O(l)$$

Summary

From this chapter you should know:

1 Fermentation is an incomplete respiration process.

2 Enzymes are organic catalysts.

3 Alcohols can be oxidized to acids.

4 Ethanoic acid is a typical alkanoic acid.

5 Esters are formed by reaction between acids and alcohols.

6 The structure of an ester.

The experiments for this chapter are on page 288.

Questions

1 Complete the table.

Acid	*Alcohol*	*Ester*
Ethanoic acid	Methanol	
C_2H_5COOH		$C_2H_5COOCH_3$
		Ethylpropanoate

2 Write equations for the reactions between:
1 Ethanoic acid and sodium hydroxide.
2 Ethanoic acid and ethanol.
Explain why reaction **1** proceeds more readily than reaction **2.** What steps can be taken to make reaction **2** go more readily?

3 When ethanoic acid is warmed with butanol, and a few drops of concentrated sulphuric acid are added, a sweet-smelling compound is formed. Give the name and formula of this compound.

4

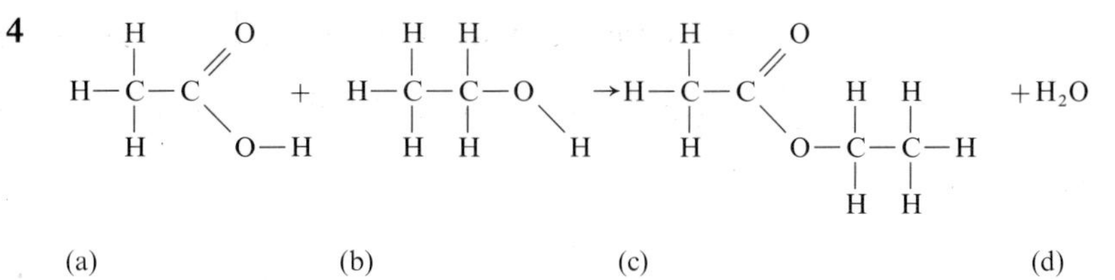

1 Name the organic compounds represented by (a), (b), and (c).
2 What type of compound is (c)?
3 If four bottles contained respectively pure samples of (a), (b), (c), and (d), how would you identify them? *P & W*

5 1 How would you distinguish between a colloidal solution and a true solution?
2 Sugar can be converted into ethanol by the process of fermentation. What chemicals are necessary to bring about this conversion?
3 Ethanol can be oxidized to ethanoic acid. Write the equation and give the experimental conditions required for the reaction.
4 When ethanol is reacted with ethanoic acid in the presence of concentrated suphuric acid, a sweet smelling substance is formed.
4.1 To what class of compound does the sweet smelling substance belong?
4.2 What is the function of the concentrated sulphuric acid.
4.3 How might the sweet smelling substance be converted back to ethanol and ethanoic acid? *P & W*

6 How would you make some of the ester ethyl ethanoate (ethyl acetate)? It is not necessary to isolate the ester.
Write the structural formula of ethyl ethanoate (ethyl acetate). *SCEEB*

7 1 The production of ethanol from sucrose can be represented by:

$$\underset{\text{sucrose}}{C_{12}H_{22}O_{11}} \xrightarrow{\text{hydrolysis}} \underset{\text{glucose}}{C_6H_{12}O_6} + \underset{\text{fructose}}{\boxed{}} \xrightarrow{\text{fermentation}} \underset{\text{ethanol}}{\boxed{}}$$

1.1 If glucose and fructose are isomers, what is the molecular formula of fructose?
1.2 Glucose and fructose are produced from sucrose by hydrolysis. Explain what is meant by hydrolysis.
2 Describe an experiment by which you could convert ethanol to ethanoic acid. (It is not necessary to isolate the acid.)
3 Ethanol reacts with propanoic acid to give the ester $C_2H_5.COOC_2H_5$.
3.1 Name the ester.
3.2 Draw the extended structural formulae for ethanol and for propanoic acid. *SCEEB*

19 Food chemistry

19.1 Photosynthesis

The green leaves of plants use the energy of the sun to convert the carbon dioxide of the air and the water from the soil into glucose, which then condenses to form starch. Chlorophyll in the leaf is a catalyst which helps this reaction to take place.

$$\left.\begin{array}{l} 6CO_2 + 6H_2O \xrightarrow[\text{chlorophyll}]{\text{sun}} \underset{\text{glucose}}{C_6H_{12}O_6} + 6O_2 \\ nC_6H_{12}O_6 \longrightarrow \underset{\text{starch}}{(C_6H_{10}O_5)_n} + nH_2O \end{array}\right\} \text{photosynthesis}$$

This is a simplified illustration of **photosynthesis,** since the process also includes the formation of vegetable proteins and vegetable oils. Oxygen is produced in this process, and it is balanced by the process of **respiration** so that the composition of the air remains constant. Photosynthesis is the reverse of respiration, which is essential to all living organisms.

$$C_6H_{12}O_6 + 6O_2 \rightarrow 6CO_2 + 6H_2O + \text{energy} \qquad \text{respiration}$$

Photosynthesis is more connected with living things than you might have suspected, since all food chains find their way back to photosynthesis. Consider the breakfast of an average greedy boy.

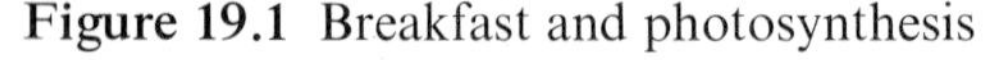

Figure 19.1 Breakfast and photosynthesis

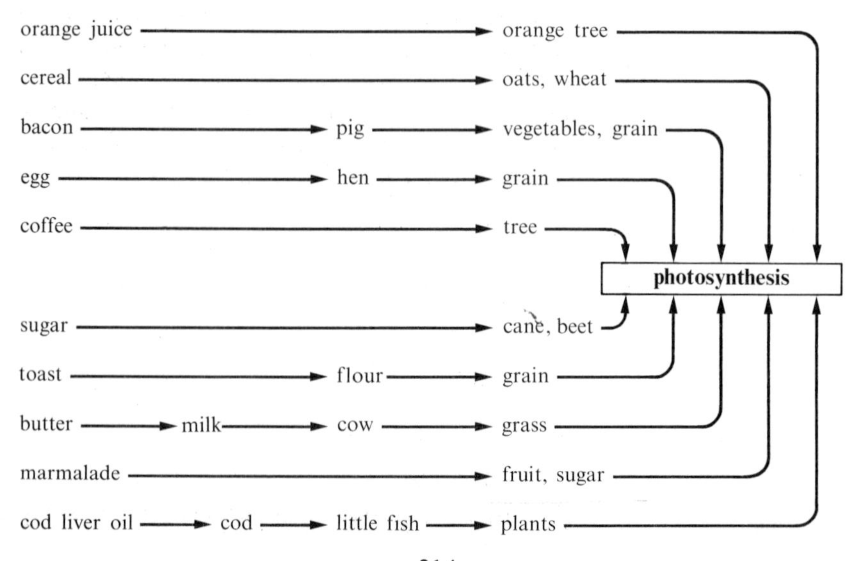

To have healthy growth, the human body requires a balanced diet, which consists of several essential ingredients. By eating a variety of different foods we ensure the intake of all these ingredients. A complete diet is made up of several types of foodstuffs: carbohydrates, proteins, fats and oils, salts, vitamins, roughage, and water. Table 19.1 gives an indication of the amounts of these ingredients contained in some foods.

Table 19.1 Composition of food

Food	*Carbohydrate (%)*	*Protein (%)*	*Fat (%)*	*Water (%)*
Orange	11	1	0.2	87
Dates	75	2	0.6	20
Potato (raw)	19	2	0.1	78
Potato (chips)	49	7	37	3
Bread	52	9	3	35
Rice (cooked)	23	2.2	0.1	74
Chocolate	54	6	34	1
Butter	0.4	0.6	81	16
Cheese	2	25	32	37
Eggs	0.7	13	12	74
Milk	5	3	4	87
Beef	0	22	30	47
Chicken	0	20	11	68
Cod	0	17	0.4	83

19.2 Carbohydrates

Carbohydrates, in the form of sugars, can be regarded as the 'instant energy' foods, since they are easily digested, and their chemical energy converted into muscular energy. This explains why those people involved in physical sports can quickly recover their strength by eating glucose sweets. The name carbohydrate suggests that these compounds are hydrates of carbon, and indeed the general formula $C_x(H_2O)_y$ would seem to bear this out. If we look at the formula for a simple sugar like glucose, $C_6H_{12}O_6$, we can see why chemists were tempted to call it a carbohydrate. However, the structural formula below illustrates that there are no water molecules present:

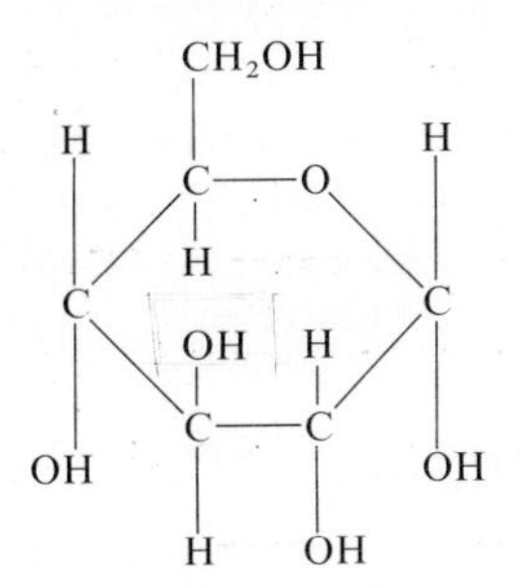

The ring is not planar. The carbon atoms have typical tetrahedral bonding.

Simple sugars with six carbon atoms are called **monosaccharides**; those with twelve carbon atoms are called **disaccharides**; and carbohydrates with a large number of carbon atoms are called **polysaccharides.**

Table 19.2

Monosaccharides ($C_6H_{12}O_6$)	*Disaccharides* ($C_{12}H_{22}O_{11}$)	*Polysaccharides* ($(C_6H_{10}O_5)_n$)
Glucose	Sucrose	Starch
Fructose	Maltose	Cellulose
	Lactose	

Test for starch

When each of the carbohydrates listed in Table 19.2 is tested with an iodine solution, only the starch produces an intense blue colour. This test is specific for starch, and it can be used to test foodstuffs to see if they contain starch.

Test for glucose

When each of the carbohydrates in Table 19.2 is tested with Fehling's solution, glucose, maltose, and lactose all reduce the copper(II) sulphate to an orange precipitate of copper(I) oxide. Sugars which do this are reducing sugars. Although this test is not specific for glucose, it is often used in schools as if it were.

Hydrolysis of starch

When a dilute solution of starch is warmed with saliva at about 310 K (40 °C) for fifteen minutes and then tested with Fehling's solution, the orange precipitate appears, indicating the presence of a reducing sugar. A solution of sucrose treated in the same way also reduces Fehling's solution, although the sucrose itself is not a reducing sugar. It would seem that when starch and sucrose are hydrolysed, they yield glucose, but Fehling's test does not prove this conclusively. Even if glucose is produced, it does not prove that glucose is the sole product of the hydrolysis. To identify the products of hydrolysis we use the technique of **paper chromatography.** Spots of known solutions are put on the base line and the sugars travel at different rates up the filter paper with the solvent. The solution under investigation is allowed to run simultaneously. When the solvent front is near the top of the paper, the spots are found by drying the paper and spraying it with a developing agent.

Figure 19.2 illustrates the results of a typical chromatogram. From this chromatogram we see that starch yields only glucose molecules on hydrolysis, and that starch is, therefore, a polysaccharide made up of glucose units. Hydrolysis of the starch is the reverse of one of the processes taking place in photosynthesis.

$$(C_6H_{10}O_5)_n + nH_2O \rightarrow nC_6H_{12}O_6$$

Maltose is a disaccharide made up of two glucose units, whereas sucrose is an isomeric disaccharide made up of one glucose unit and one fructose unit.

$$C_{12}H_{22}O_{11} + H_2O \rightarrow C_6H_{12}O_6 + C_6H_{12}O_6$$
maltose glucose glucose

$$C_{12}H_{22}O_{11} + H_2O \rightarrow C_6H_{12}O_6 + C_6H_{12}O_6$$
sucrose glucose fructose

Figure 19.2 Result of typical chromatogram

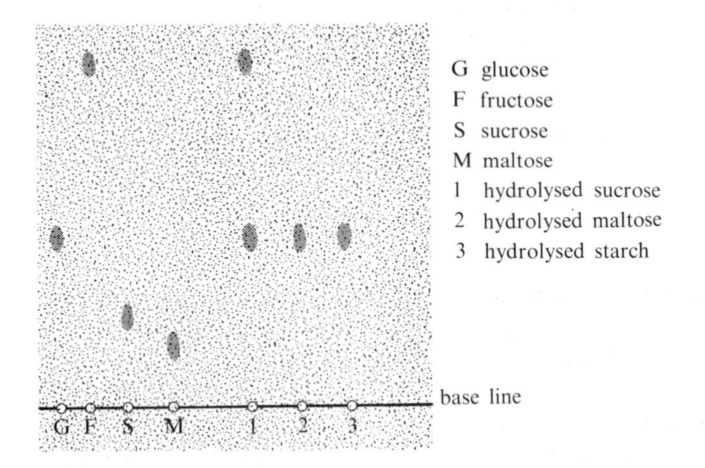

The hydrolysis of carbohydrates in our food is brought about by an organic catalyst, an enzyme called salivary amylase. The hydrolysis is carried out at body temperature, 310 K (37° C), since higher temperatures reduce the effectiveness of the enzyme. You should be careful to note that the enzyme is not living and that high temperatures do not kill it. The enzyme has the chemical structure of a protein which is denatured on heating—we all know that a boiled egg cannot be unboiled.

In the laboratory, carbohydrates are usually hydrolysed using dilute hydrochloric acid at 373 K (100 °C), or specific enzymes supplied in powder forms. An experiment carried out as routine quality control in the manufacture of biscuits consists of hydrolysing the biscuit with an enzyme called bacterase, filtering the resulting solutions, and examining the residue for solid impurities such as rat hairs.

19.3 Proteins

Proteins are large complex molecules made up of many α-amino acid units joined together. The Greek letter α in the compound indicates that the amino group $—NH_2$ must be on the carbon atom next to the carboxyl group —COOH. The simplest α-amino acid, aminoethanoic acid (glycine), can undergo a process of condensation polymerization as shown in the sequence on the following page.

When proteins are eaten, they are hydrolysed in the stomach to give a large variety of amino acids, which are then carried by the blood stream to all parts of the body. Some are used to build cell proteins in the growing body or to repair damaged cells. Most of them, however, eventually make their way to the liver where they are converted to glycogen, a polymer of glucose, and urea. Glycogen is stored, and urea is excreted. Although the body can store food as glycogen it cannot store the proteins themselves. You might like to compare the structure of the protein formed from glycine with that of nylon (page 202), and see the significance of the peptide link.

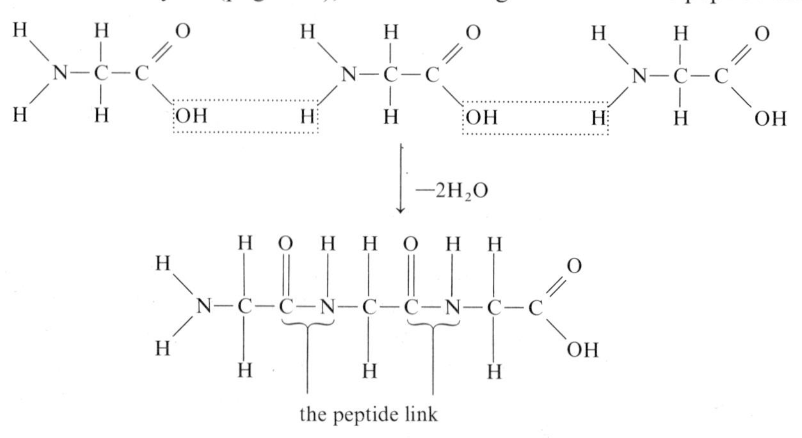

Why then is nylon not a synthetic protein? The answer lies in the products of hydrolysis, since nylon cannot be hydrolysed to an α-amino acid.

Test for proteins

Biuret Reaction. If copper(II) sulphate is added to a solution of a protein, and the resulting solution made alkaline with sodium hydroxide solution, a violet colour develops.

Xanthoproteic reaction. When a solution of protein is boiled with concentrated nitric acid and neutralized with concentrated aqueous ammonia, an orange colour is produced.

Identification of proteins

Chromatography can be used to identify the amino acids in a protein, in much the same way as we identified the sugars in a carbohydrate. Hair and nail clippings can be hydrolysed to their constituent amino acids by boiling them with sodium hydroxide solution for some time. The resulting solution can then be used to give a chromatogram with some known samples. Since the number of amino acids produced is large and separation is not very good, it is necessary to turn the chromatogram through 90° and run it again with another elutant. The spots are developed by spraying the paper with ninhydrin solution. Identification of the spots requires a lot of experience and only the principle of the method is relevant at this stage.

Proteins have recently been made from oil (page 182), and although they are unpalatable to humans, they can be used for feeding pigs and poultry which in turn provide food for humans. This process has obvious attractions in terms of world food supply, but the factors which govern its introduction are economic and political rather than technical.

19.4 Fats and oils

Naturally occurring fats and oils do not have sharp melting points. This indicates that they are mixtures and not single compounds. Lard is the name given to the fat obtained from pigs. Tallow or suet is the fat obtained from cattle and sheep. Olive oil, palm oil, castor oil, and linseed oil are obtained from plants. Fats and oils liberate much heat energy when digested, and they can be stored in the body and used as required. Fats are esters formed from polyhydric alcohols and fatty acids. Mutton fat on hydrolysis yields propane-1, 2, 3-triol (glycerol) and octadecanoic acid (stearic acid):

$$\begin{array}{l} C_{17}H_{35}.COO.CH_2 \\ \quad\quad\quad\quad\quad | \\ C_{17}H_{35}.COO.CH \\ \quad\quad\quad\quad\quad | \\ C_{17}H_{35}.COO.CH_2 \end{array} \xrightarrow{3H_2O} \begin{array}{l} CH_2OH \\ | \\ CHOH + 3C_{17}H_{35}.COOH \\ | \\ CH_2OH \end{array}$$

Oils have a similar composition but the acids obtained on hydrolysis are unsaturated, and it is the presence of the double bonds which give the oils a lower melting point. Since oils are unpalatable, as anyone who has taken castor oil well knows, they can be hardened by hydrogenation to form edible fats. Whale oil and sunflower oil are hardened and mixed with milk to produce margarine.

Test for fats If the food being tested is pressed on to a filter paper and allowed to dry, the presence of a 'grease spot' when the paper is held up to the light indicates fat or oil in the food.

19.5 Mineral salts

Plants take in a variety of minerals through the roots and supply them to our food chain. Iron is contained in the haemoglobin of the blood. Calcium, phosphorus, and magnesium are required for healthy bones and teeth. Iodine is required for the functioning of the thyroid gland.

19.6 Vitamins

Small quantities of vitamins are required by the body for the regulation of body functions. They are important for growth, good vision, and digestion. They cannot be stored in the body and have to be taken daily. Scurvy and beri-beri are deficiency diseases caused by lack of vitamin C and vitamin B respectively.

19.7 Water

Water is the solvent for all the salts in the body and it is the medium in which all the chemical reactions take place. The survival time without water is very short. The body consists of about 70 per cent water.

19.8 Roughage

The cellulose from plant foods gives the food bulk, which stimulates the wall of the alimentary canal to contract and push the food through.

We must understand that a balanced diet should contain all of the components mentioned in this chapter, since a deficiency of any category, or an excess for that matter, will lead to health problems.

Summary

From this chapter you should know:

1. Photosynthesis is the beginning of all food chains.
2. A balanced diet consists of carbohydrates, proteins, fats and oils, mineral salts, vitamins, roughage, and water.
3. Carbohydrates can be hydrolysed to simple sugars.
4. Proteins can be hydrolysed to α-amino acids.
5. Fats and oils are esters of polyhydric alcohols and fatty acids.
6. The products of hydrolysis may be identified by chromatography.
7. Lack of vitamins causes 'deficiency diseases'.

The experiments for this chapter are on page 289.

Questions

1 1 Explain the following statements:
1.1 Mountaineering clubs sometimes advise their members to take jam sandwiches rather than meat sandwiches on short expeditions.
1.2 Vegetarians tend to eat a lot of peas, beans, and nuts.
1.3 Gelatine, although a protein, has a low food value.
1.4 Fresh milk appears to turn sour when a few cm^3 of hydrochloric acid are added to it.
2 Read the following paragraph, which is part of a description written by a pupil. It contains several scientific errors. Rewrite the paragraph correcting the pupil's errors.
'Rayon, whose chemical name is nitro-cellulose, is prepared from wood or paper. The raw material is shredded and dissolved in copper sulphate solution. This solution is then forced through jets into a bath of sodium hydroxide solution. This forms a thread which can be spun. Rayon has the same chemical elements in it as silk and can be used as a substitute for silk.'
P & W

2 Name a compound which has the formula $C_{12}H_{22}O_{11}$. To what class of compounds does it belong? What would you see happen if you added some warm concentrated sulphuric acid to a few grams of this compound? Explain the reaction.
Can this compound be oxidized by Fehling's solution? *P & W*

3 1 Name the products obtained in an experiment in which sugar is burned in oxygen, and describe one test for each of the products.
2 In addition to the chemical products, what else is produced in this experiment?
3 Draw a clearly labelled diagram of the apparatus with which you could carry out the experiment and tests.
4 If you were given a sample of sucrose, glucose, and starch, describe one test by which you could identify the starch, and one test by which you could identify the glucose.
5 Describe how you would treat the sucrose and starch in order that they would then react positively to the test for glucose. What word describes the treatment carried out? *P & W*

4 Consider the following equation representing the formation of starch from glucose (G):

$$G+G+G+\cdots \rightarrow G—G—G—\cdots G$$

1.1 What other compound could be included in the equation?
1.2 On what side of the equation would it appear?
2 What kind of polymerization is this?
3.1 Describe what you would do to reverse the above reaction completely.
3.2 Name the type of reaction involved.
4 Describe fully how you would convince a non-scientist that the reaction in 3 had, in fact, taken place. *P & W*

5 Proteins are broken down in our bodies as follows:

$$\text{protein} + \text{water} \xrightarrow{\text{enzyme}} X + Y + Z + \cdots$$

1 What is an enzyme? At what temperature does the above reaction normally take place.
2 What type of reaction is this?
3 To what class of compounds do X, Y, and Z belong?
4 Are proteins condensation or addition polymers?
5 Give one other example of each type of polymer named in **4**. *P & W*

6 1 What is the difference between a carbohydrate and a hydrocarbon?
2 What are the products of combustion when glucose is completely burned in oxygen? Write a balanced equation for the reaction. How can the products be identified? *P & W*

7 1 Write the fomulae of the substances X and Y which are formed when the following compound is hydrolysed:

$$\begin{array}{c} \qquad\qquad\qquad\qquad\quad CH_3 \\ \qquad\qquad\qquad\qquad\quad | \\ H_2N.CH_2.CO.NH.CH.COOH \end{array}$$

To what class of compounds do X and Y belong?
2 How could you show that X and Y contain nitrogen? *P & W*

8 Proteins and starches are both large molecules containing thousands of atoms. They are important constituents of a balanced diet.
Chemically speaking, what is the main difference between proteins and starches and what do these substances give on hydrolysis?
How would you show that hair is a protein and not a carbohydrate? *SCEEB*

9 An experimenter suspected that a white powder was a carbohydrate. In boiling water it gave a colloidal solution. Addition of concentrated sulphuric acid to the powder charred it. After hydrolysing the powder, a test for a reducing sugar proved positive. He concluded that the powder was starch.
1 What further test could he have carried out to confirm that the substance was starch?
2 What is meant by a colloidal solution?
3 Assuming that the powder was starch, explain the action of concentrated sulphuric acid on it.
4 What is meant by saying that the carbohydrate was hydrolysed?
5 How would you carry out the hydrolysis of starch in the laboratory?
6 Name a simple reducing sugar formed by hydrolysing starch. *SCEEB*

20 Soaps and detergents

Trying to wash greasy hands or dishes with water alone is an almost impossible task. Add soap, and the problem is solved.

20.1 What is soap?

A soap is the sodium salt of a long-chain alkanoic acid, sodium stearate $C_{17}H_{35}.CO.O^{-}Na^{+}$ for example. Long-chain alkanoic acids are very often referred to as 'fatty' acids because their chief source is from esters in animal fats and vegetable oils. Mutton fat contains the ester of propane-1, 2, 3-triol (glycerol) and octadecanoic acid (stearic acid).

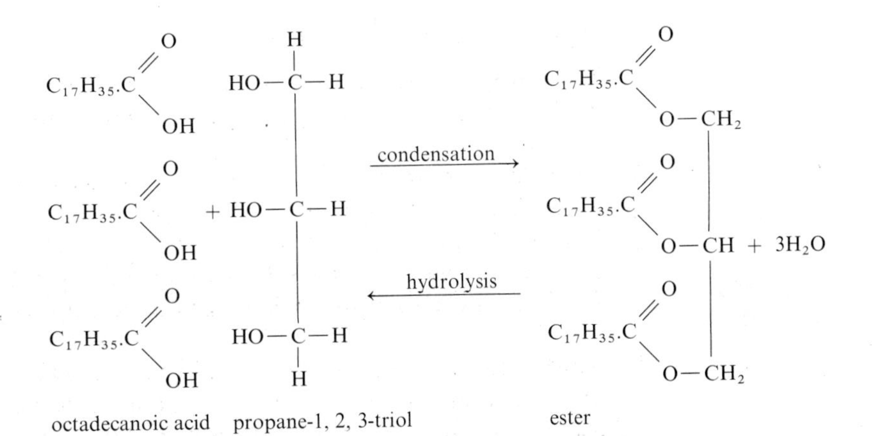

In chapter 18 we saw that esters can be hydrolysed to give the acid and alcohol of which they are composed. Hydrolysis of the ester with sodium hydroxide yields the sodium salt of the acid, that is the soap, and the alcohol. This process is called **saponification.**

$$\begin{array}{l} C_{17}H_{35}CO.O.CH_2 \\ C_{17}H_{35}CO.O.CH \\ C_{17}H_{35}CO.O.CH_2 \end{array} + 3NaOH \xrightarrow{\text{saponification}} 3C_{17}H_{35}COO^{-}Na^{+} + \begin{array}{l} CH_2OH \\ CH.OH \\ CH_2OH \end{array}$$

ester — sodium octadecanoate (sodium stearate) — propane-1,2,3-triol

In the manufacture of soap, various fats and oils are saponified: beef and mutton fat, palm oil, olive oil, cotton-seed oil, and coconut oil. When the saponification process is complete, it is necessary to separate the newly formed soap and the propane-1, 2, 3-triol from the solution. This is achieved by adding brine to 'salt out' the soap. The theory of this is that the sodium chloride saturates the solution with respect to sodium ions, and the soap, a sodium salt, can no longer remain in solution. The insoluble soap forms a crust on the surface of the solution. It is removed and dried.

20.2 How does soap work?

If we look at the structure of a soap molecule we see that it is made up of a long hydrocarbon portion and a short ionic portion.

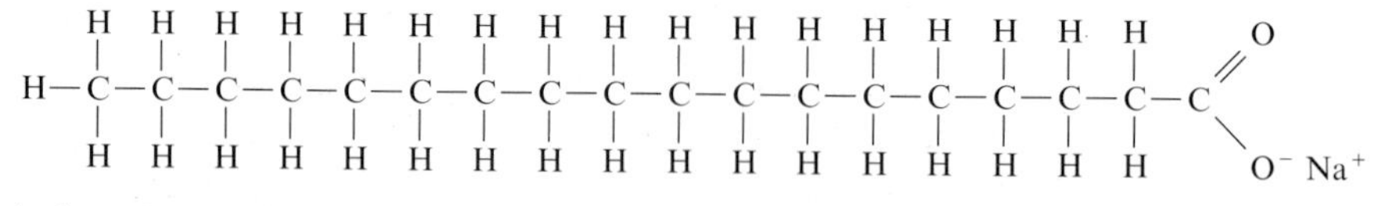

hydrocarbon portion   ionic portion

The molecule is often represented like this: ∿∿∿ O^- Na^+.

The hydrocarbon portion is soluble in oils and grease but insoluble in water. The ionic portion is soluble in water but insoluble in oils and grease.

When a soap solution is added to water it forms a colloidal suspension, soap molecules clustering together to form **micelles** (Figure 20.1). The micelles remain suspended because the like charges at the end of each soap molecule repel each other.

Figure 20.1 Soap micelles

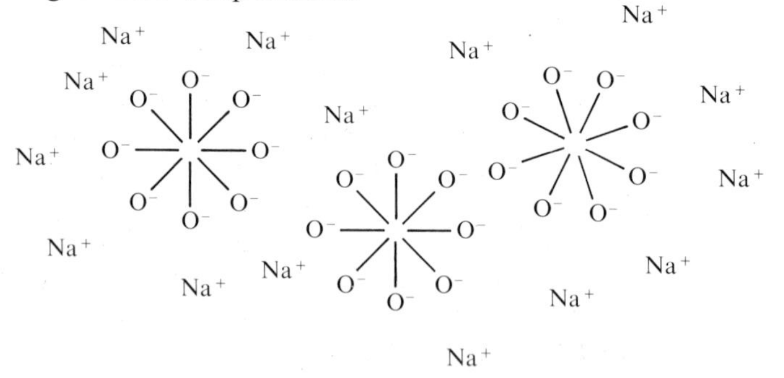

When a soap solution is added to water containing grease or oil, the micelles break up, and the hydrocarbon ends of the soap molecules are attracted to the grease or oil (Figure 20.2a). If the solution is agitated, the grease can be

Figure 20.2

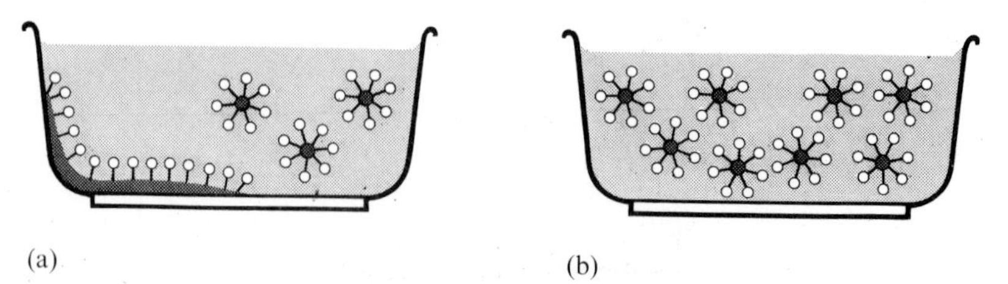

(a)   (b)

broken up into droplets which become stabilized by the soap molecules as a colloidal suspension of grease in water (Figure 20.2b). The grease or oil can then be easily floated away, and the vessel rinsed out.

20.3 Hard water

We noticed in chapter 14 (page 170) that hard water is water which contains dissolved calcium or magnesium ions. Apart from the scaling of boilers and furring of kettles, hard water is a problem because it reacts with soap to form a scum. If we accept the formula for sodium stearate as $Na^{+}St^{-}$, the formation of scum can be represented thus:

$$Ca^{2+}(aq) + 2Na^{+}(aq) + 2St^{-}(aq) \rightarrow (Ca^{2+} + 2St^{-})(s) + 2Na^{+}(aq)$$

in hard water — in soap solution — calcium stearate scum

The precipitation of scum removes the active part of the soap molecule from the solution, so the cleaning action cannot take place.

Hardness of water can be dealt with in a number of ways.

1 The offending calcium and magnesium ions can be removed from the water by using washing soda before the soap is added. Washing soda is sodium carbonate, so the reaction is a simple precipitation process.

$$Ca^{2+}(aq) + 2Na^{+}(aq) + CO_3^{2-}(aq) \rightarrow (Ca^{2+} + CO_3^{2-})(s) + 2Na^{+}(aq)$$

in hard water — washing soda

There is still an unpleasant residue of calcium carbonate which has to be carefully rinsed when clothes are being washed.

2 The calcium and magnesium ions can be removed by ion-exchange resins. Commercial 'water-softeners' such as Permutit are cannisters containing a cation exchange resin (Figure 20.3). As water containing calcium ions is passed down the column, the resin exchanges the calcium ions for some other cation, usually sodium, and the water emerges 'softened'. This is quite an expensive way of softening water because the cannisters need to be re-charged from time to time.

Figure 20.3

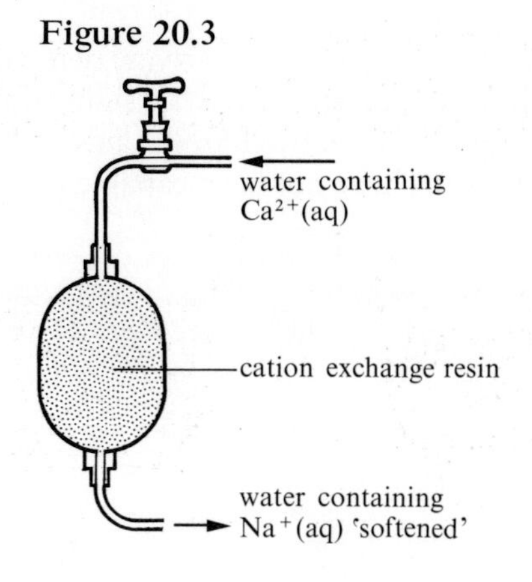

20.4 Detergents

An alternative way of dealing with hard water is to produce a suitable cleansing agent which does not form a scum with hard water as soap does. This is called a soapless detergent. Most of the detergents which are in use today are products of the oil industry. The kerosene fraction from the fractional distillation of crude oil is made to combine with an aromatic hydrocarbon to form the molecule

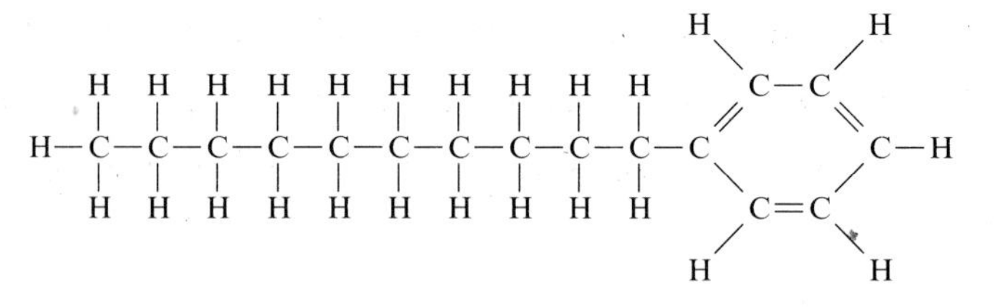

which we shall represent as: 〰⌬

This molecule is treated with sulphuric acid, followed by sodium hydroxide:

$$\text{〰⌬} + H_2SO_4 \rightarrow \text{〰⌬}\ SO_3^-H^+ + H_2O$$

$$\text{〰⌬}\ SO_3^-H^+ + NaOH \rightarrow \text{〰⌬}\ SO_3^-Na^+ + H_2O$$

The product, sodium decylbenzene sulphonate, has a very similar structure to a soap molecule, a long hydrocarbon portion and a short ionic portion, and it has similar cleansing properties. It also has the advantage over soap in that it does not form a scum with hard water.

When first introduced on the large scale, the soapless detergents created a problem which particularly affected highly populated countries. It became evident that naturally occurring bacteria were unable to digest the detergent molecules and so, due to the ease with which the soapless detergents produce a lather, large volumes of foam collected in drains, on the settling ponds in sewage plants, and on the rivers into which industrial effluent was released. Recently, however, products have been developed with a simpler structure, which can be more easily broken down by the bacteria in the sewage plant. Such detergents are said to be **biodegradable.** Some countries have passed legislation forbidding the manufacture of detergents which are not biodegradable.

The newest type of detergent is the enzyme detergent, which contains a special enzyme for acting on and removing stains which are proteins. Such detergents are able to remove blood stains and sweat stains which other types of detergents have not been capable of tackling except by bleaching.

Summary

From this chapter you should know:

1 Soap is the sodium salt of a fatty acid.

2 The cleansing action of soap.

3 Hard water forms a scum with soap.

4 Hard water can be softened with sodium carbonate or by ion exchange.

5 Detergents work in the same way as soap, but are unaffected by hard water.

The experiments for this chapter are on page 290.

Questions

1 A boy melted a mixture of fat and sodium hydroxide solution. He added this mixture to salt water, and a soft white solid formed.
1 What was the soft white solid?
2 What is the name of the process the boy carried out?
3 Explain why the boy added his mixture to salt water.

2 Hard water can be softened by adding washing soda to it.
1 What is hard water?
2 What is the chemical name for washing soda?
3 How does washing soda soften hard water?

3 When the oil tanker *Torrey Canyon* ran aground and the cargo was spilled, attempts were made to destroy the cargo by bombing it. Explain why this was only partially successful. The next step involved spraying the cargo with detergent solution. This method was more successful. Explain why.

4 What are the differences between soaps and soapless detergents?
Name two industries which are the sources of the materials required to manufacture soapless detergents, and outline the manufacture of soapless detergents from these sources.

5 Explain the following observation. 'When clothes are washed in hard water with soap a scum is formed and rinsing is difficult, whereas in using a soapless detergent, no scum is formed and rinsing is easy.' *P & W*

6 **1** Olive oil is composed mainly of an **ester** of an **unsaturated** organic acid. Explain the meaning of the terms in heavy type.
2 One of the largest users of vegetable oils is the soap industry. State briefly how soap is produced from vegetable oils.
3 Explain how soap acts in removing grease from dishes.
4 Explain why the efficiency of soap is reduced if the tap water contains Ca^{2+} or Mg^{2+} ions. *SCEEB*

21 Experimental techniques

Chemistry is largely an experimental subject. It is important, therefore, to appreciate some of the experimental techniques which are used in the laboratory.

21.1 Collection of gases

Gases, which are insoluble, or sparingly soluble in water, are generally collected in gas jars 'over water'.

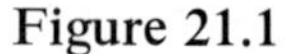

Figure 21.1

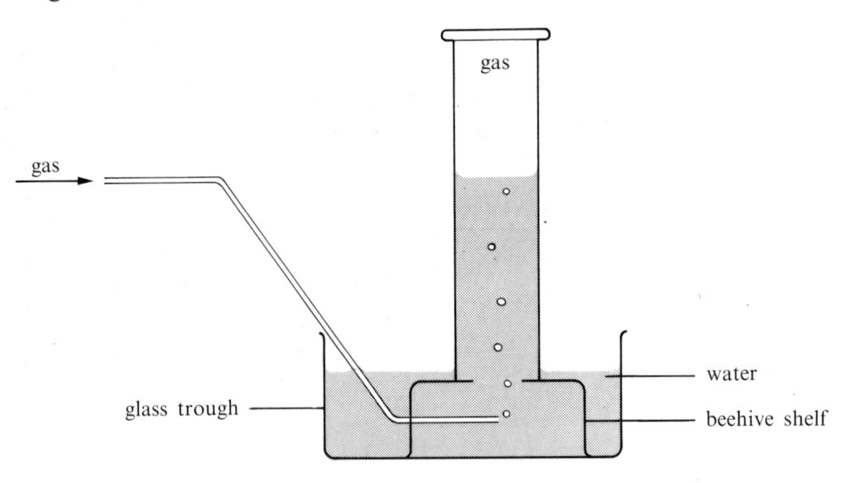

The gas jar is filled with water in the trough, inverted, and the mouth of the gas jar placed over the beehive shelf. The gas displaces the water from the jar, and, when full, the gas jar is sealed with a greased lid.

Gases which are soluble in water may be collected by air displacement. Figure 21.2a shows the method for collecting gases which are denser than air, such as carbon dioxide, sulphur dioxide, nitrogen dioxide, and chlorine. Figure 21.2b shows the method for collecting gases which are less dense than air, such as ammonia.

This method is convenient and simple, but it is not easy to tell when the gas jars are full. By using the appropriate test papers at the mouth of the jar, some indication is given, but in practice there will always be some air present.

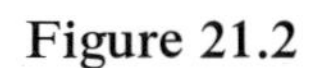
Figure 21.2

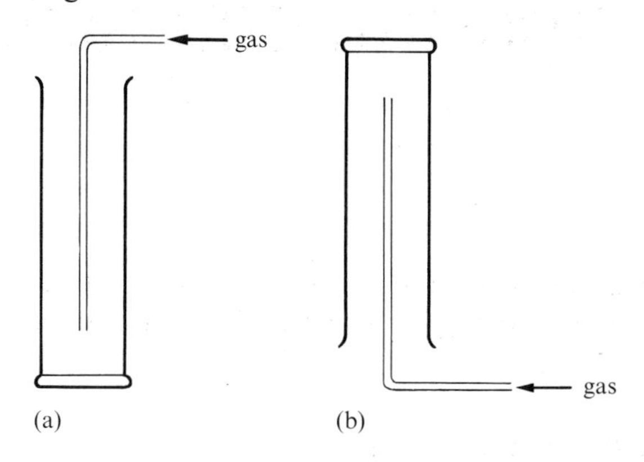

21.2 Drying gases

It is often necessary to prepare dry samples of gases. They must be dried before collection and various methods are shown in Figure 21.3.

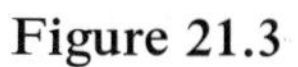
Figure 21.3

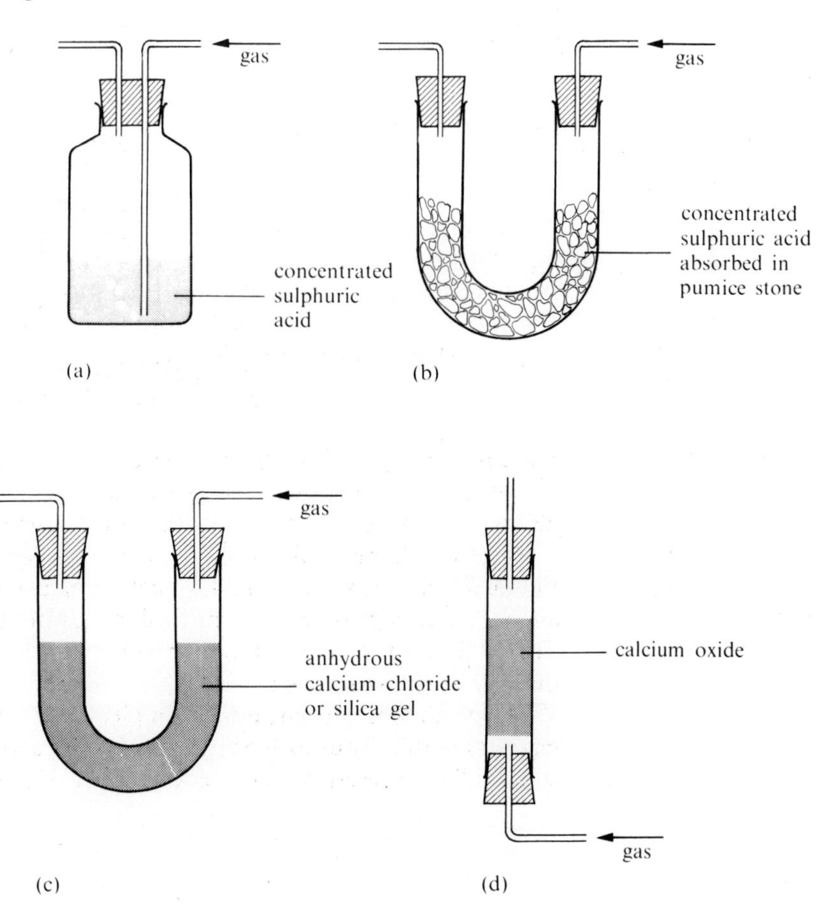

Methods (a) and (b), using concentrated sulphuric acid, are suitable for most gases except ammonia. Method (c) is also suitable for most gases except ammonia. Method (d) is used almost exclusively for drying ammonia. Remember that dried gases should not be collected 'over water'.

21.3 Identification of gases

It is possible to identify various gases as they each have characteristic tests. Those gases which can be identified by smell are dangerous so great care must be taken when testing for them.

1 Oxygen relights a glowing wooden splint.
2 Carbon dioxide turns calcium hydroxide solution (limewater) cloudy.
3 Hydrogen burns with a 'pop'.
4 Sulphur dioxide has characteristic choking smell. It gives an acid reaction with moist indicator paper.
5 Ammonia has characteristic pungent smell. It gives an alkaline reaction with moist indicator paper.
6 Hydrogen sulphide has characteristic, unpleasant smell.
7 Carbon monoxide burns with a blue flame and the product turns calcium hydroxide solution cloudy.
8 Nitrogen: if tests 1 to 7 give negative results, the gas will probably be nitrogen.

21.4 Drying liquids and solids

The only liquids which require drying are non-aqueous liquids. It would be rather pointless to attempt to dry water. Most liquids are dried by shaking them, in a flask, with anhydrous calcium chloride, and then removing the calcium chloride by filtration (Figure 21.6b).

Solids are dried by placing them in a desiccator (Figure 21.4) containing a drying agent. The drying agents which may be used are:

1 Concentrated sulphuric acid.
2 Anhydrous calcium chloride.
3 Silica gel.

Figure 21.4

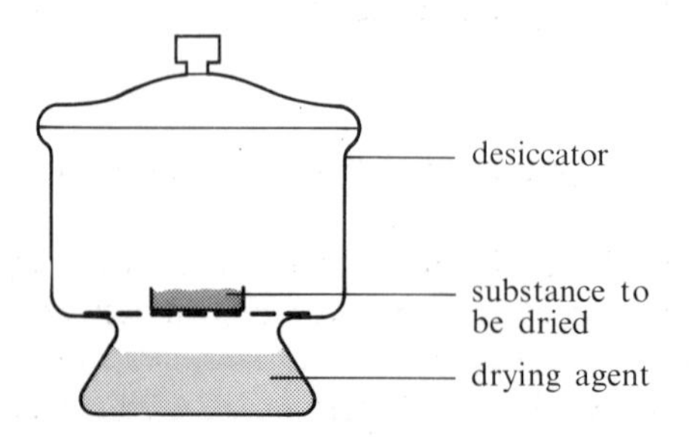

21.5 Crystallization

Crystals can be formed in several ways: cooling molten metals or non-metals; cooling water; subliming solids; seeding supersaturated solutions; cooling saturated solutions; allowing saturated solutions to evaporate. Any of these processes, which result in crystal formation, can be termed **crystallization.** Crystals have definite, regular shapes (Figure 21.5). It is often possible to identify a substance by its shape and colour.

Figure 21.5 Geological crystals: (a) Sodium chloride; (b) Halite; (c) Sulphur on celestine; (d) copper(II) sulphate

(a)

(b)

(c)

(d)

The two most common methods of crystallization are described below.

Cooling saturated solutions

A saturated solution is one in which no more solute will dissolve. As the solubility of most substances increases with an increase in temperature, so it follows that a hot saturated solution will contain more dissolved solute than a cold saturated solution. Therefore, as a hot saturated solution cools, it is unable to 'hold' all its dissolved solute, and crystallization occurs. Crystals formed in this way are usually small and very often poorly formed.

Evaporating saturated solutions

As a cold saturated solution evaporates, so all the dissolved solute cannot be held in solution, and crystallization takes place. Crystals formed in this way are normally better shaped as crystallization takes place comparatively slowly. This method also produces bigger crystals because, as the solvent gradually evaporates, the solute is deposited on the first-formed crystals making them 'grow'.

21.6 Separation and purification

The ability to separate mixtures and purify substances is an extremely important experimental technique. The method used depends entirely on the constituents of the mixture and particular properties of the substances.

Insoluble solid from a liquid

If the solid settles out of the solution, the liquid can be poured off or decanted (Figure 21.6a). If the solid is suspended in the solution the best method is **filtration** (Figure 21.6b).

Figure 21.6

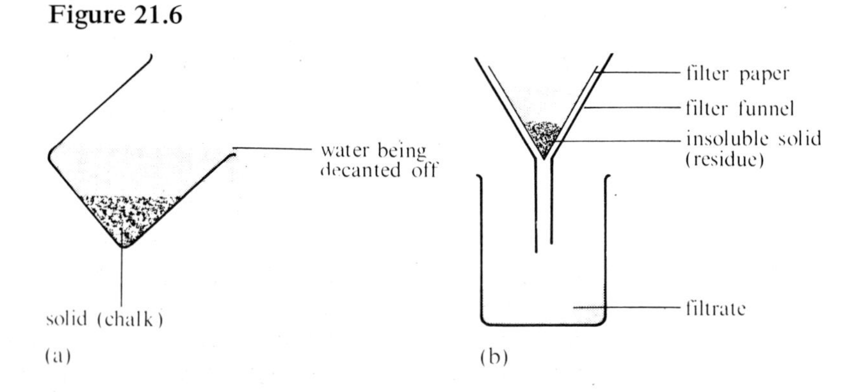

In water purification plants, impure water is filtered through gravel filter beds, which remove all the suspended solids in the water, before the water is chlorinated. Chlorination kills any bacteria present in the water, and so makes it safe to drink.

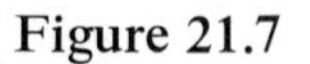

Figure 21.7

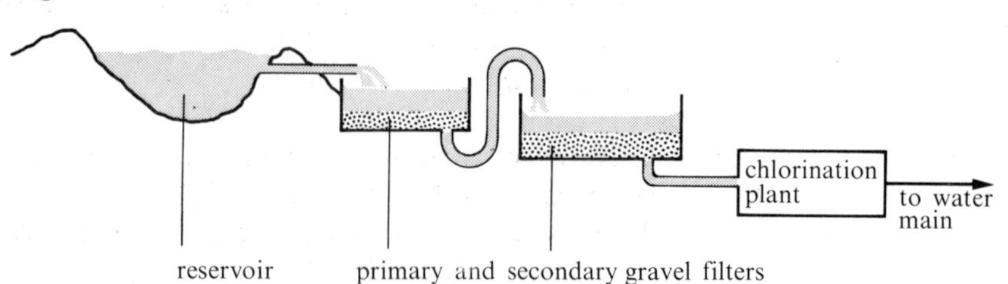

Soluble solid from a liquid

The simplest method of separation for this type of mixture is to evaporate the liquid by heating the mixture. The solid remains behind, and the liquid is removed as a vapour, which can be recovered by condensing it (Figure 21.8). This method is called **distillation.**

Figure 21.8

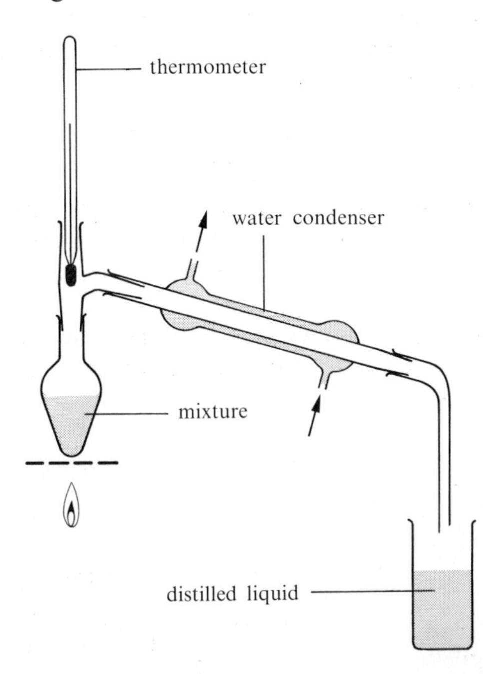

However, if crystals of the solid are required, this method is not satisfactory, as direct heating will remove any water of crystallization associated with the solid. The solution should be partially evaporated until it is saturated, and the saturated solution left to crystallize slowly. To test whether the solution is saturated, a cold glass rod should be placed in it from time to time and removed. If crystals are formed on the rod, then the solution is saturated.

Two solids, one water-soluble

The mixture is shaken with water and the water-soluble solid will dissolve. The solution is then filtered (Figure 21.6b). The insoluble solid will remain in the filter paper and the filtrate will contain the soluble solid. This can be recovered by evaporation of the filtrate. A sand/sodium chloride mixture may be separated in this way.

Two water-soluble solids

A mixture of two water-soluble substances may be separated by fractional crystallization, which depends on the solubility of the substances.

Suppose we consider a mixture of two substances X and Y, in which X has a lower solubility than Y. An aqueous solution of the mixture is slowly evaporated. The first crystals to appear will contain a high proportion of the less soluble substance (X), and a very small amount of the more soluble substance (Y). These crystals are removed and represent the 'first fraction'.

Further evaporation will produce more crystals, which will contain a higher proportion of Y and a lower proportion of X compared with the first fraction. This batch of crystals constitutes the 'second fraction'. The process is continued until a range of fractions, the first comprised mainly of X and the last comprised mainly of Y, is obtained.

Each of the fractions obtained is then dissolved in more water and each is again subjected to fractional crystallization. The process is repeated many times until pure samples of X and Y are obtained. The process takes a considerable amount of time and should only be used if every other method has failed to achieve a separation.

Two solids, one magnetic Many metal ores containing magnetic impurities are partially refined in this way. The crushed ore is placed on a conveyor belt, which has a magnetic roller at the other end (Figure 21.9). As the ore passes over the magnetic roller, it is separated into two parts, one containing the partially refined ore, the other containing all the magnetic impurities.

Figure 21.9 Magnetic rollers to separate out magnetic substances

Palabora Mining Company

Two immiscible liquids Immiscible liquids are ones which do not mix with each other. Ethanol and water are miscible—they do mix—but ether and water do not mix—they are immiscible. The separation of immiscible liquids requires the use of a separating funnel (Figure 21.10). The mixture is placed in the funnel, shaken vigorously, and allowed to settle. The liquids will separate according to their density—the less dense at the top, and the more dense at the bottom. The stopper is removed, the tap opened, and the two liquids may be collected in separate containers.

Figure 21.10

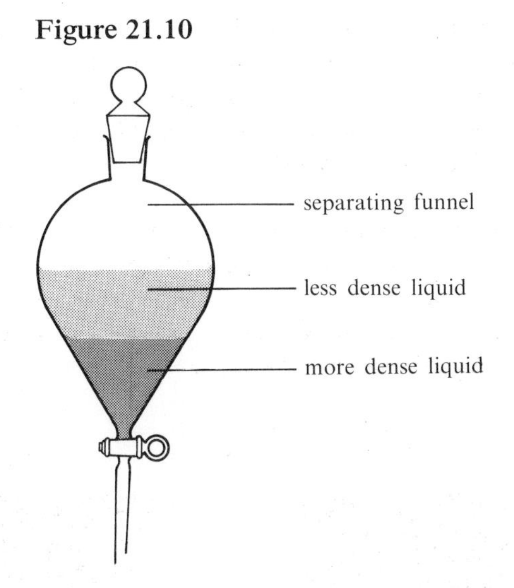

'Ether-extraction' is a technique, widely used in laboratories, to separate an ether-soluble compound from a water-soluble compound. A mixture of the two compounds is shaken with an ether/water mixture in a separating funnel. The ether-soluble compound dissolves in the ether layer, and the water-soluble compound dissolves in the water layer. When the two layers have been separated, the two compounds can be recovered by evaporation of the two solvents.

Two miscible liquids A typical example of such a mixture is ethanol and water. The separation makes use of the differing boiling points of the liquids. The process is **fractional distillation.** The apparatus used is shown in Figure 21.11.

The boiling point of ethanol is 353 K (80 °C) and that of water is 373 K (100 °C). As the mixture is heated, both liquids vaporize as their boiling points approach. As vapour rises up the fractionating column, a temperature differential is created, the temperature at the top of the column being much less than that at the bottom of the column. When the temperature at the top reaches 353 K (80 °C), the ethanol will distil over and can be collected as the first fraction. Before the water vapour reaches the top of the column it condenses and drops into the flask. The longer the fractionating column, the more efficient the separation. The oil industry uses this process to separate crude oil into its many constituents (chapter 15.4).

These techniques are used to separate the constituents of mixtures but they may also be used as methods of purification. Liquids containing very small, solid impurities can be purified by filtering them through very fine grades of filter paper. Crystals can be purified by dissolving them in a suitable solvent, and recrystallizing them. Liquids can be purified by redistillation.

Figure 21.11

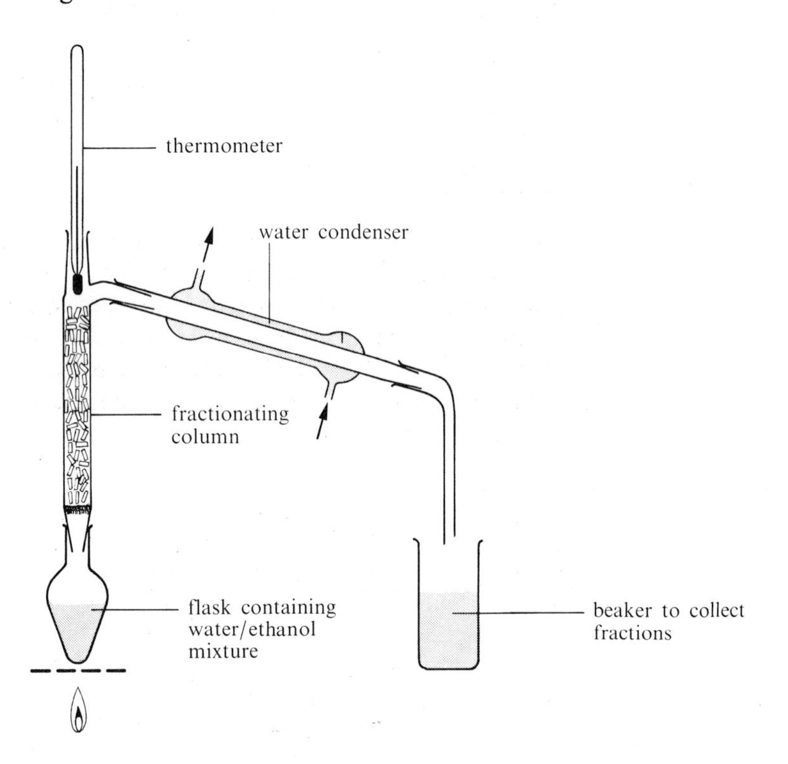

21.7 Chromatography

The separation technique of chromatography is perhaps one of the most important aspects of modern chemical analysis, as it copes with the separation and identification of extremely complex mixtures. There are various types of chromatography, but the basic principle of each method is the same.

Consider a mixture containing the components A, B, C, and D. The mixture is introduced into a continually flowing, carrying medium. Because of differences in the solubilities, particle size, and absorption power of A, B, C, and D, each component will be carried at a different speed by the carrying medium. By comparing the distances travelled by A, B, C, and D with known standards, the identities of the components can be found. The fact that these components are carried different distances also means that they can be separated and recovered. The different types of chromatography involve different carrying mediums.

Paper chromatography

Figure 21.12 A typical set up for paper chromatography

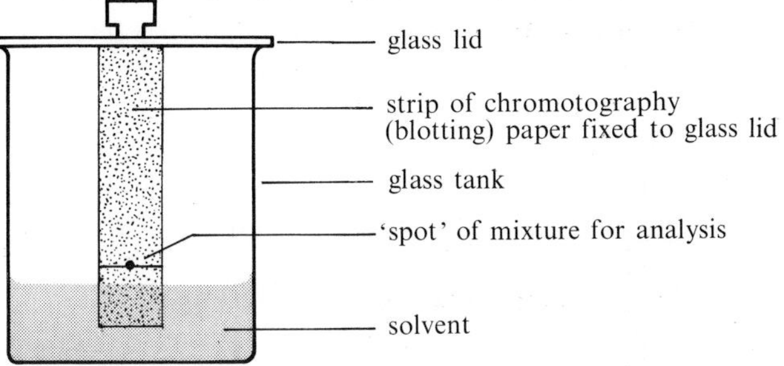

As the solvent travels up the paper, it carries the components of the mixture with it. The final chromatogram will be similar to Figure 21.13, showing that the mixture was composed of three components. The identity of the components can be discovered by measuring their R_F values. The R_F value is the distance travelled by the component divided by the distance travelled by the solvent front. The values obtained can be compared with standard tables of R_F values.

Figure 21.13

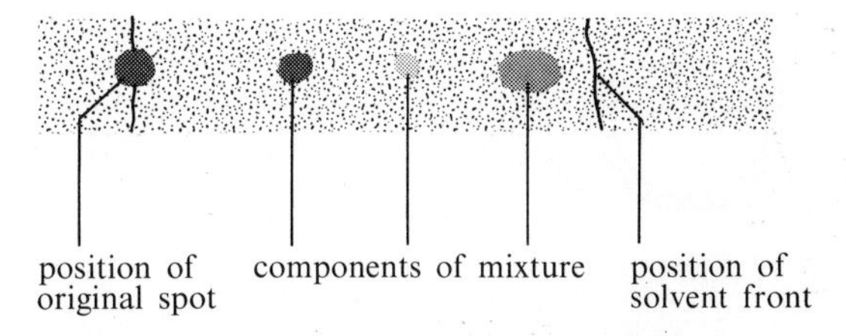

Column chromatography

A typical column is shown in Figure 21.14a. As the solvent (or elutant) is poured down the column, the components of the mixture are carried down with it. At the end of the run, the column might be as shown in Figure 21.14b. The two bands indicate that the mixture consists of two components.

Figure 21.14

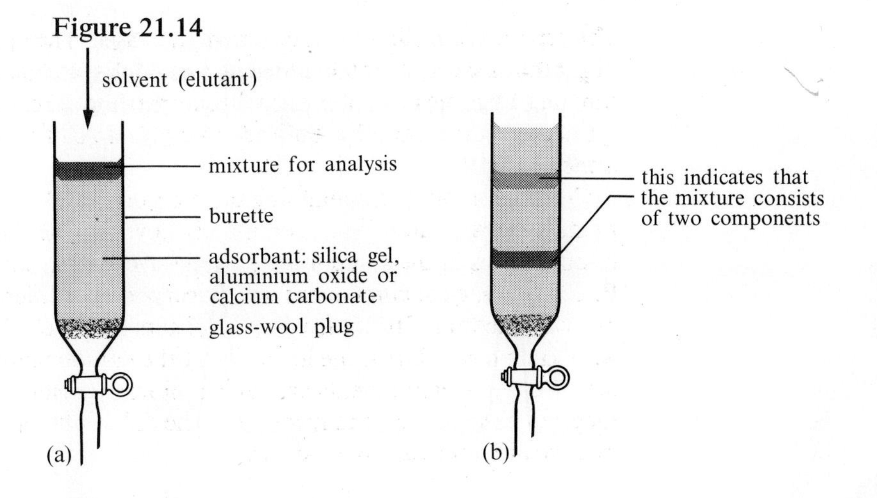

Thin-layer chromatography This method is similar to paper chromatography. It differs in that the solvent ascends a thin layer of a suitable adsorbant substance (aluminium oxide or silica gel) supported on a glass plate, instead of ascending a paper strip.

Gas chromatography This method is used to separate the components of volatile liquids or gaseous mixtures, and employs a gas as the carrying medium. A simple gas chromatograph is shown in Figure 21.15.

Figure 21.15 A gas chromatograph

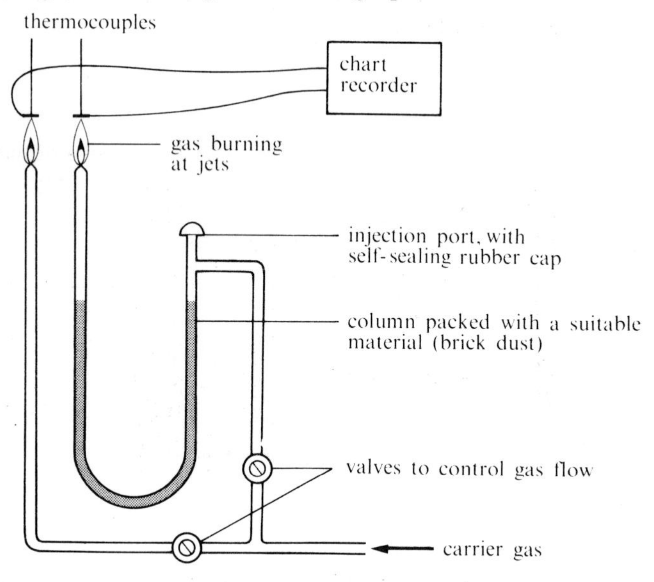

Initially the valves are adjusted so that the carrier gas is flowing through the tubes to the two jets at the same rate. This is done so that the temperatures of the two flames are the same, and there is only one line showing on the chart. The sample is introduced by means of a hypodermic syringe through the injection port seal. The components of the sample are carried through the column at different rates, and they arrive at the jet at different times. As they burn, the temperature increases. The change is detected by the thermocouples, and recorded as a peak on the chart. Figure 21.16 shows the type of chart obtained when a hydrocarbon mixture is analysed.

Figure 21.16

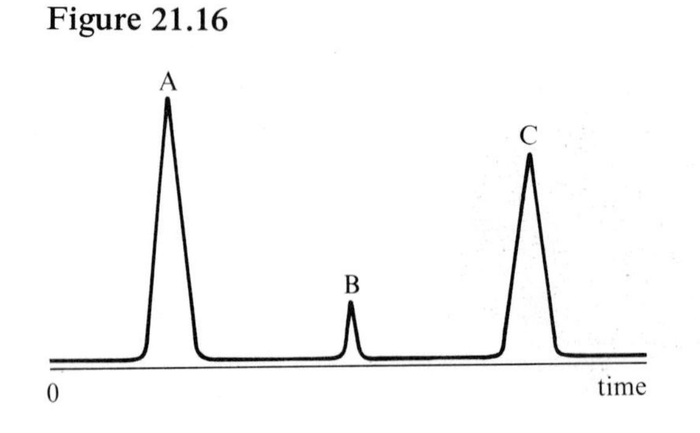

The chart shows that the mixture contains high proportions of A and C and a trace of B. By noting the position of the peaks it is possible to identify A, B, and C.

21.8 Measurement of melting points and boiling points

When the components of a mixture have been separated, it is often necessary to check if they are pure. One way in which this can be done for a solid is to measure its melting point, as even trace quantities of an impurity can make a significant difference to the melting point. The apparatus used is shown in Figure 21.17.

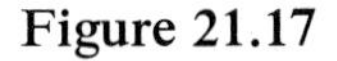

Figure 21.17

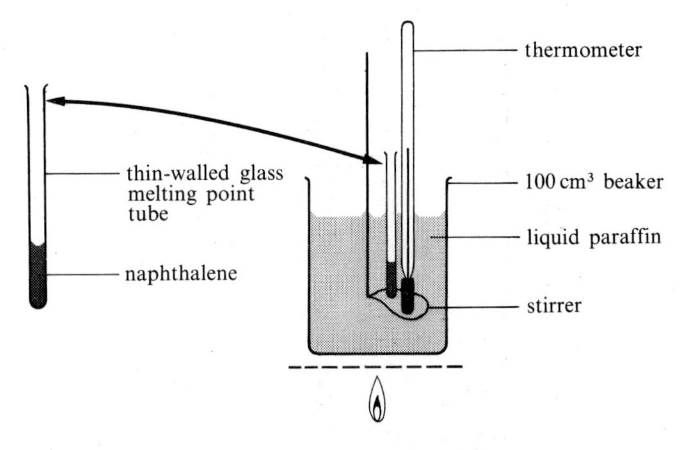

The beaker is heated slowly, and an even temperature in the bath is ensured by means of constant stirring. When the solid melts the temperature is recorded. Provided that the solid sample is contained in a narrow tube and the heating is very gradual, an accurate melting point can be obtained. In sophisticated apparatus, electrical heating and finely calibrated thermometers are used (Figure 21.18).

Figure 21.18 Electrical melting point apparatus

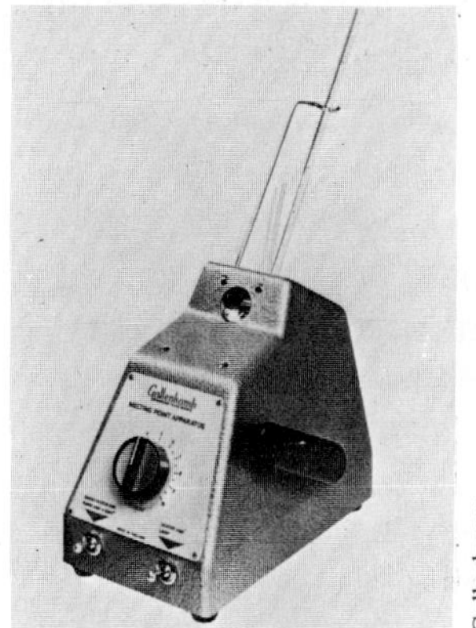

Gallenkamp

The most satisfactory method of checking the purity of a liquid is to measure its boiling point by using simple distillation. The temperature is raised slowly and the temperature at which the liquid distils over is its boiling point.

21.9 Identification of ions

If we look at a selection of copper(II) compounds, we can see that most of them are blue-green in colour. We can conclude that copper(II) ions are blue-green in colour. Many other ions have characteristic colours (Table 21.1).

Table 21.1

Ion	*Colour*
Chromate(VI)	Yellow
Dichromate(VI)	Orange
Nickel(II)	Green
Cobalt(II)	Red
Manganate(VII)	Purple

There are, however, many compounds which are colourless, and it therefore follows that the ions in these compounds are also colourless. Identification of these ions is a more complicated process. We shall consider two of the tests which can be used.

Flame tests Certain metal ions give characteristic colours in the bunsen flame (Table 21.2). It should be noted that the sodium flame tends to mask those of other metals, particularly that of potassium. It is advisable to view the flame through a cobalt-blue glass. Under these conditions the potassium flame appears crimson.

Table 21.2

Ion	*Flame colour*
Lithium Li^+	Scarlet
Sodium Na^+	Intense yellow
Potassium K^+	Lilac
Calcium Ca^{2+}	Brick-red
Barium Ba^{2+}	Yellow-green
Strontium Sr^{2+}	Crimson
Copper(II) Cu^{2+}	Blue-green
Lead(II) Pb^{2+}	Blue

Chemical tests There are many chemical tests for ions. A list of the more common ions and the corresponding tests are given in Table 21.3.

Table 21.3

Ion	*Test*	*Result*
Sulphate SO_4^{2-}	Add barium chloride solution	White precipitate, insoluble in dilute hydrochloric acid
Sulphite SO_3^{2-}	Add barium chloride solution	White precipitate, soluble in dilute hydrochloric acid
Iron(II) Fe^{2+}	Add potassium hexacyanoferrate(III) solution	Prussian-blue precipitate
Iron(III) Fe^{3+}	(a) Add potassium hexacyanoferrate(II) solution	Prussian-blue precipitate
	(b) Add ammonium thiocyanate solution	Dark red colour
Chloride Cl^-	Add silver(I) nitrate solution	White precipitate
Bromide Br^-	Add silver(I) nitrate solution	Pale yellow precipitate
Iodide I^-	Add silver(I) nitrate solution	Yellow precipitate
Ammonium NH_4^+	Add sodium hydroxide solution and warm	Ammonia gas evolved
Sulphide S^{2-}	Add lead(II) ethanoate solution	Black precipitate
Carbonate CO_3^{2-}	Add dilute hydrochloric acid	Carbon dioxide gas evolved
Nitrate NO_3^-	Add iron(II) sulphate solution, followed by careful addition of concentrated sulphuric acid	Brown ring formed at the junction of the two liquids

21.10 Removal of ions

It is possible to remove ions from aqueous solutions by using substances called *ion-exchange resins* (see also page 225), which fall into two types:

1. Those which remove positively charged ions.
2. Those which remove negatively charged ions.

Two such resins are Zeo-Karb 225 and De-Acidite FF. The former removes positively charged ions, the latter removes negatively charged ions.

Example 1 If some copper(II) dichromate(VI) solution, which is green in colour, is shaken with some Zeo-Karb 225, the colour changes from green to orange. This shows that the copper(II) ion has been removed. If the remaining orange solution is shaken with De-Acidite FF, the orange colour disappears. This shows that the copper(II) ion is positively charged and that the dichromate(VI) ion is negatively charged.

Example 2 If some dilute sodium sulphate solution is shaken with some De-Acidite FF, and the resultant solution tested with barium chloride solution, no white precipitate is formed. The resin has removed the sulphate ion showing that the ion is negatively charged.

Summary

From this chapter you should know:

1. Gases, which are insoluble in water, are collected by displacement of water. Gases, which are soluble in water, are collected by displacement of air.
2. How gases, liquids, and solids may be dried.
3. A saturated solution is one in which no more solute will dissolve.
4. How crystals may be formed.
5. There are several different methods for separating mixtures.
6. The importance of chromatographic separation.
7. How the purity of a substance may be checked using the melting point or boiling point of the substance.
8. How to identify certain ions using flame tests, chemical tests, and the colour of substances.
9. How to remove ions from aqueous solution.

The experiments for this chapter are on pages 248–51.

Questions

1

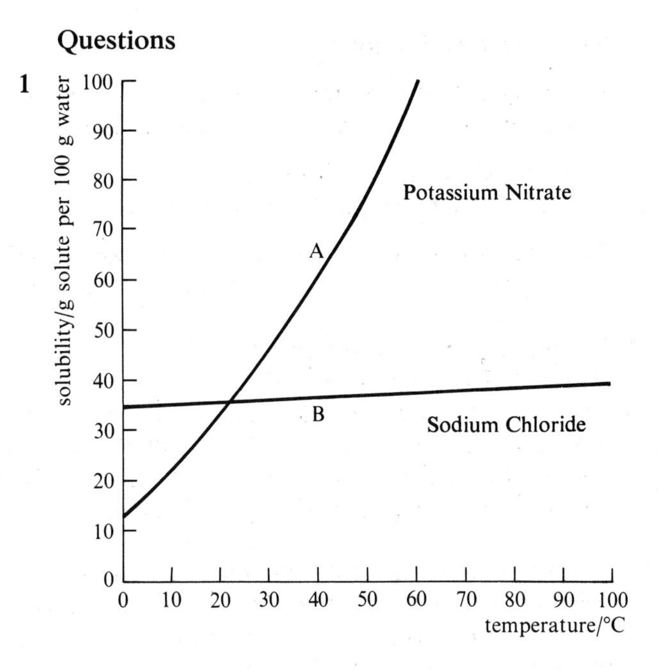

1 At what temperature are the two salts equally soluble?
2 What will happen if a saturated solution of potassium nitrate at 50 °C is cooled to 0 °C?
3 How can you get an almost pure sample of potassium nitrate from a mixture of 70 g potassium nitrate and 30 g sodium chloride? *P & W*

2 1 Describe briefly how you would determine, to the nearest gram, the solubility of sodium chloride at 20 °C.
2 The table below gives the solubilities (in g kg^{-1}) of two salts in water at various temperatures.

Temperature (°C)	0	10	20	30	40	50	60	70	80	90	100
Potassium chloride	280	310	345	375	500	430	455	485	510	540	565
Potassium nitrate	135	210	315	455	625	845	1080	1370	1680	2030	2450

2.1 Using the figures given in the above table, plot solubility curves for potassium chloride and potassium nitrate.
2.2 At what temperature are the solubilities of potassium chloride and potassium nitrate the same?
2.3 Which of the following would give a saturated solution when thoroughly mixed with 100 g of water at 80 °C:
100 g of KNO_3 or 100 g of KCl? *P & W*

3

solvent water

solvent front

black ink blue ink red ink orange ink brown ink X

Consider the chromatogram above.
1 What does the chromatogram indicate about the brown ink?
2 Which pairs of inks have common pigments?
3 X is a mixture of inks. From which inks is it made?
4 What two classes of compounds can be identified using the technique of chromatography? *P & W*

4 Criticize the statement: 'If a liquid turns anhydrous copper sulphate(II) blue, it must be pure water'. Suggest more reliable tests. *SCEEB*

5

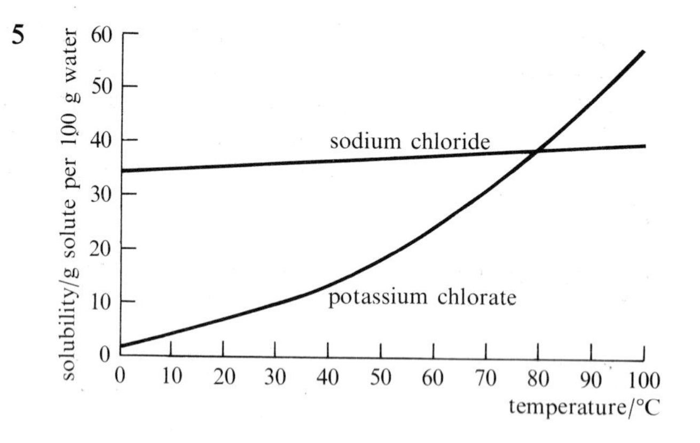

Look at the graph, then answer the following questions.
1 Which compound is the more soluble in boiling water?
2 At what temperature are sodium chloride and potassium chlorate equally soluble in water?
3 A mixture of 30 g of sodium chloride, 30 g of potassium chlorate, and 100 g of water is stirred for a long time at 100 °C. Will all the solid dissolve? If the mixture is now cooled to 20 °C, what will happen? *SCEEB*

6 Name, in each case, one pair of substances which may be separated by:
1 The use of water.
2 The use of a separating funnel.
3 Sublimation.
4 Fractional distillation.

7 Describe how you would prepare well-shaped crystals of copper(II) sulphate, starting from a finely powdered sample of copper(II) sulphate.

8 How could you remove glass splinters from a sample of salt (sodium chloride) so that the salt will be fit for use again?

9 Describe a method by which sea water can be made suitable for drinking.

10 Here are some facts about three gases, A, B, and C.

Gas	*Boiling point* (°C)	*Melting point* (°C)	*Solubility in water* (cm^3 per 100 cm^3)
A	−196	−210	2
B	5	−11	soluble, but reacts
C	−88	−90	106

With the equipment in a school laboratory, how would you go about separating a mixture of these substances and recovering a sample of each? *SCEEB*

11 A pupil shakes a powdered solid with water in a test-tube and finds that there seems to be just as much of it remaining at the bottom of the tube as when he started. He concludes that it is insoluble in water.
Explain whether he is justified in drawing this conclusion.
If not, what further experiment will he need to carry out to settle the point. *SCEEB*

12 A mixture contains three substances A, B, and C, about which the following facts are known:

Substance	*Water*	*Alcohol*	*Ether*
A	Soluble	Insoluble	Insoluble
B	Insoluble	Soluble	Insoluble
C	Soluble	Insoluble	Soluble

How would you separate the mixture? *SCEEB*

13 From the following list of separation techniques: distillation; chromatography; evaporation; separating funnel; crystallization; fractional distillation, select a method which will help you obtain:
1 Water from a mixture of water and trichloromethane.
2 Sodium chloride from a sample of sea water.
3 Alcohol from a mixture of alcohol and water.
4 Water from ink.

14 Give an example of each of the following:
1 A metal which can form blue ions.
2 An insoluble chloride.
3 An ion which gives a yellow flame test.

15 How could you demonstrate that chalk contains calcium ions?

16 Describe two tests you would use to distinguish between powdered sodium dichromate(VI) and orange poster paint.

17 How would you chemically distinguish between the following pairs of compounds?
1 Iron(II) sulphate and iron(III) sulphate.
2 Sodium sulphate and sodium sulphite.
3 Potassium chloride and potassium iodide.
4 Iron(II) chloride and ammonium chloride.
5 Sodium nitrate and sodium carbonate.

18 Some dilute sodium sulphate is poured through a column containing 'de-acidite ion-exchange resin'.
1 What do you understand by the term 'de-acidite ion-exchange resin'?
2 What do you think will have happened to the solution which was poured through the column?
3 How could you test to see if this was so?

19 Rain water which has filtered through chalky ground on its way to the reservoir, contains dissolved calcium ions. We call it 'hard water'. Hard water can be softened (i.e. the calcium ions removed) by passing it through a water softener. Give a possible explanation of how a water softener works.

20 On what two factors does the conductivity of an aqueous ionic solution depend?
Explain why the conductivity of molar hydrogen bromide solution is greater than the conductivity of molar sodium bromide solution.

Experiments

Introduction

The experiments are numbered to correspond with the relevant section in text. For example, the number **7.5** by the side of an experiment means that the experiment covers material in section 7.5 of chapter 7. The experiments for chapter 21 come first as they make use of the experimental techniques discussed in that chapter. They are followed by experiments for chapters 1–20.

Chapter 21

21.1 1 Collection of hydrogen gas

Place 5 g of granulated zinc in a 250 cm^3 flask and fit a stopper containing a thistle funnel and a delivery tube as shown in the diagram.

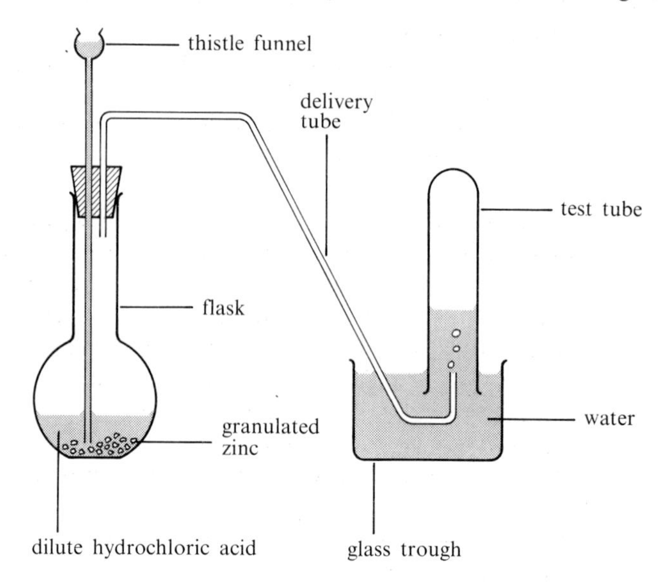

Add dilute hydrochloric acid down the thistle funnel. Allow the hydrogen gas produced to pass for about ten seconds before filling a test-tube with water and inverting it over the end of the delivery tube.
Collect several test-tubes of the gas.
Test the gas as follows:

1 Action of a lighted taper.
2 Place some calcium hydroxide solution (limewater) in a test-tube of the gas and shake the tube.
3 Is the gas more dense than air?

Record your results for each of the tests.
How would you adapt the apparatus you have used to prepare a dry sample of hydrogen gas?

21.1 2 Collection of carbon dioxide gas

The apparatus used in this experiment is the same as that used in Experiment **21.1**.1. The method is essentially the same but the zinc is replaced by calcium carbonate. Collect several test-tubes of the gas and carry out the following tests.

1 Place a lighted taper at the mouth of a test-tube of carbon dioxide gas.
2 Place some calcium hydroxide solution (limewater) in a test-tube of the gas and shake the tube.
3 Take two test-tubes of the gas. Invert one and leave both the tubes for a few minutes. Test each tube with a lighted taper. This should give some indication of the density of carbon dioxide.

Record and explain your results for each of the tests.

Draw a diagram of the apparatus you would use to prepare a dry sample of carbon dioxide gas.

21.6 1 Filtration

Weigh out 5 g of calcium carbonate and shake it up with 100 cm^3 of water. Using the apparatus shown in Figure 21.6b on page 232, separate the mixture. When you have achieved a separation, dry the filter paper plus the residue in an oven at 313 K (40 °C).
How could you determine the efficiency of your separation?
Verify your answer.

21.6 2 Separation by distillation

Make up a solution containing 5 drops of ink in 50 cm^3 of water. Place the solution in a flask and set up the apparatus shown in Figure 21.8 on page 233. Turn on the water to the condenser. Heat the flask until the solution is boiling. Continue heating until all the liquid has boiled off.
What colour was the solution when you started?
What colour was the distillate you obtained?
What has happened to the ink?
Explain your experimental results.
How could this process be used to obtain drinking water from sea water?

21.6 3 Separation of an oil/water mixture

Add equal volumes of vegetable oil and water to a separating funnel and shake the funnel vigorously.
What happens when you allow the mixture to stand?
How can this fact be used to separate the mixture?

21.6 4 Separation of a methanol/water mixture

Add 50 cm^3 of methanol to 50 cm^3 of water. You will notice that the liquids mix—they are miscible with each other. Place the mixture in a flask and set up the apparatus shown in Figure 21.11 on page 236.
The boiling point of methanol is 338 K (65 °C).
The boiling point of water 373 K (100 °C).
Allow the temperature of the flask to rise slowly by heating carefully.
Collect the liquid which distils over in the range 338–41 K (63–7 °C), and that which distils in the range 370–73 K (98–100 °C).
Measure the volume of each of these fractions.
Calculate the percentage of methanol and water recovered. Comment on the efficiency of the process.

21.7 1 Separation of the dyes in black ink

Prepare a strip of chromatography paper (blotting paper) as shown in the diagram. Use black ink as your sample.

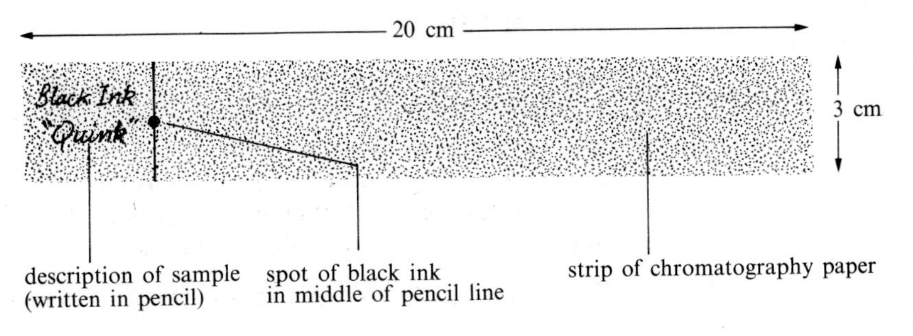

Place the prepared strip in a 100 cm^3 measuring cylinder containing 5 cm^3 of water. You must ensure that the water level is below the spot of ink. Allow the chromatogram to run for thirty minutes, then remove it, and dry it.
How many different colours appear on the chromatogram?
Why should this happen?
Give an explanation for this.

21.7 2 Separation of lead and silver ions from a mixture

Solution A: dissolve a few crystals of lead(II) nitrate in 2 cm^3 of water.
Solution B: dissolve a few crystals of silver(I) nitrate in 2 cm^3 of water.
Solution C: prepare a mixture of lead(II) nitrate and silver(I) nitrate by dissolving a few crystals of each in 4 cm^3 of water.
Prepare three chromatograms as shown in the diagram.

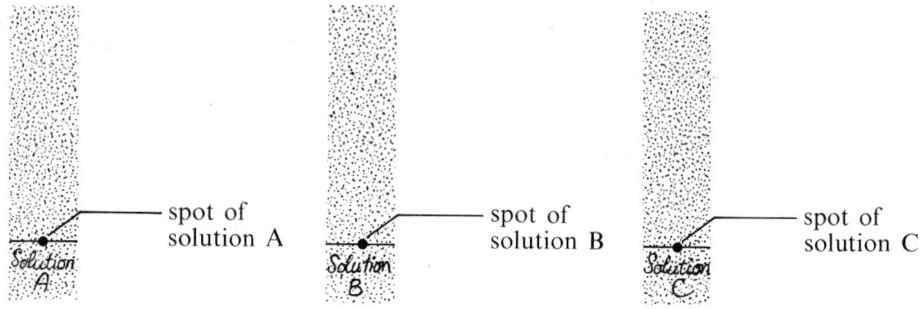

spot of solution A
Solution A
spot of solution B
Solution B
spot of solution C
Solution C

Run chromatograms A, B, and C as described in Experiment **21.7.** 1. As lead and silver are colourless in solution, it is necessary to show their presence by means of a developer, in this case sodium chromate(VI) solution. Run each chromatogram for thirty minutes, dry them and pass them through a dilute solution of sodium chromate(VI). The metals will be indicated by the appearance of a yellow spot for Pb^{2+}(aq) and a red spot for Ag^{+}(aq).
By using chromatograms A and B as reference, you will be able to identify the components of the mixture in chromatogram C.

21.7 3 Separation of the chlorophyll pigments in nettles

Obtain a sample of nettle leaves. Dry the leaves in an oven and grind up the leaves in a mortar. Add the powdered leaves to a mixture of 10 cm^3 of propanone and 120 cm^3 of petroleum ether. Shake the mixture and filter. Add some anhydrous sodium sulphate to the filtrate to remove any traces of water present. Concentrate the filtrate by evaporation on a water bath. Prepare a chromatography column as shown in Figure 21.14 on page 237.
Saturate the aluminium oxide column with a 12:1 v/v mixture of petroleum ether:propanone.
When the column is saturated, pour the concentrated extract into the top and then allow a slow flow of the petroleum ether/propanone mixture to enter the top of the column.
Leave the column for several hours with the mixture (elutant) flowing through.
How many pigments are present in the mixture?
How could you identify these pigments?

21.8 1 Determination of the melting point of naphthalene

Set up the apparatus shown in Figure 21.17 on page 239.
Place a small amount of naphthalene in the melting point tube. Attach the tube to the side of the thermometer (the liquid paraffin will hold the tube in position). Heat the beaker slowly. When the naphthalene melts, record the reading on the thermometer.
Check your result by referring to standard melting point values.
Determine the melting points of: benzoic acid; salicylic acid; tartaric acid.

21.8 2 Relationship between melting point and purity

The apparatus used in this experiment is the same as that in **21.7** 1.
To a sample of naphthalene add a small amount of sodium chloride. Grind the two substances together in a mortar.
Place some of the mixture in a melting point tube and determine the melting point.
How does this value compare with the value you obtained for pure naphthalene?
What does this indicate about the melting points of substances?
How can the melting point relate to the purity of a substance?

21.9 Flame tests

Place a few drops of concentrated hydrochloric acid on a watch-glass.
Place a small amount of potassium carbonate on the side of the watch-glass.
Dip a silica rod in the concentrated acid and then in the potassium salt.
Hold the rod in the bunsen flame.
Record the colour which you see.
Roast the rod in the bunsen flame until all traces of the colour disappear.
Wash the watch-glass and repeat the procedure for the other salts shown in the table.

Metal salt	*Colour in flame*
Potassium carbonate	
Sodium carbonate	
Calcium carbonate	
Copper(II) carbonate	
Barium carbonate	
Strontium carbonate	

Draw the table in your books and complete it.

Chapter 1

1.2 Changes in physical state

Place some crushed ice in a boiling tube and heat the tube slowly. Record the temperature of melting ice.
Continue heating until the water boils. Record the temperatures of the boiling water and the steam which is formed.
Complete the table.

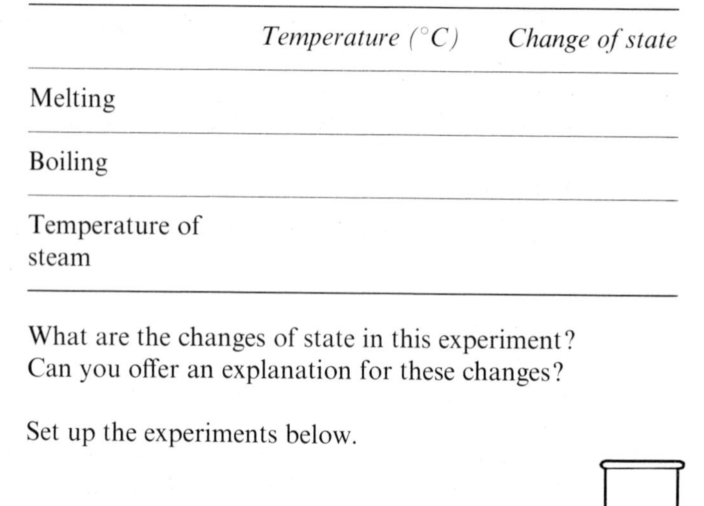

	Temperature (°C)	*Change of state*
Melting		
Boiling		
Temperature of steam		

What are the changes of state in this experiment?
Can you offer an explanation for these changes?

1.3 1 Diffusion of solids, liquids, and gases

Set up the experiments below.

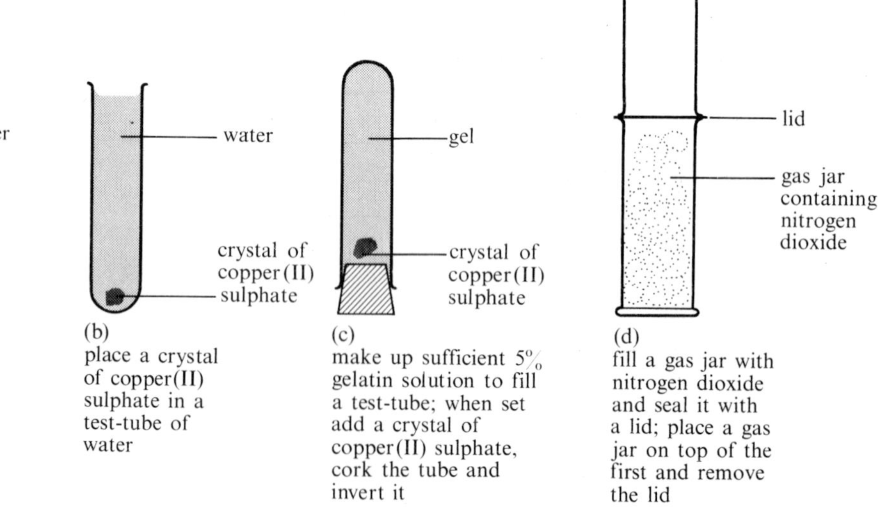

(a)
half fill a test-tube with water, add some ink so that it forms a lower layer

(b)
place a crystal of copper(II) sulphate in a test-tube of water

(c)
make up sufficient 5% gelatin solution to fill a test-tube; when set add a crystal of copper(II) sulphate, cork the tube and invert it

(d)
fill a gas jar with nitrogen dioxide and seal it with a lid; place a gas jar on top of the first and remove the lid

Leave the experiments for several hours.
Describe what happens in (a), (b), (c), and (d).
Attempt to explain your observations.

1.3 2 Brownian movement

Put some smoke in a smoke cell and seal it with the cover slip.
Place the whole unit on the stage of a microscope and focus on the smoke.
If you look carefully you will see moving specks of light.
What are these specks?
Why do they show up as specks of light?
On the assumption that the air is composed of particles, account for the movement you observe.

1.4 Elements and compounds

1 Mix 2 g of iron filings with 2 g of powdered sulphur. Bring up a magnet to the mixture.
What do you observe happening?
2 Heat a mixture of iron filings and powdered sulphur in a hard glass test-tube. When cool bring up a magnet.
What do you observe happening?

Considering the results of 1 and 2, offer an explanation for your experimental observations.

1.7 Aqueous and non-aqueous solvents

Place a crystal of iodine in a test-tube, and add a few cm^3 of propanone.
Does the crystal dissolve?
Record your result in the table as (a) soluble, or (b) partially soluble, or (c) insoluble.
Repeat this procedure using the other solvents in the table, and do exactly the same with sodium chloride, naphthalene, sodium sulphate and nail varnish. (Paint the nail varnish on cover slips, and when dry, test the solubility of the nail varnish as above).

Solvent	*Crystal of iodine*	*Naphthalene*	*Sodium chloride*	*Sodium sulphate*	*Nail varnish*
Propanone					
Methylated spirit					
Pentyl ethanoate (Amyl acetate)					
Water					
Tetrachloromethane					

Do all the substances in the table dissolve in water?
Do all the substances in the table dissolve in the other solvents used?
What conclusion can you come to about the solubility of substances and the solvents used?

1.7 2 Colloidal solutions

It is relatively simple to show whether a solution is colloidal or not.
A beam of light from a slide projector is shone through the solution.
If the solution is colloidal, the beam of light will show up as a cloudy area, similar to the projection beam in a cinema.
Make up very dilute solutions of sodium chloride and starch. Sodium chloride forms a true solution. Starch forms a colloidal solution.
Can you tell the difference by simply looking at them?
Shine a beam of light through each solution.
Now can you tell the difference?

Determine which of the following very dilute solutions are colloidal:

1 A solution of tea.
2 Potassium manganate(VII) solution.
3 Potassium chloride solution.
4 A solution of coffee.
5 Potassium dichromate(VI) solution.
6 A solution of ink.

1.7 3 Emulsions

Set up two test-tubes (a) and (b) as shown in the diagram.

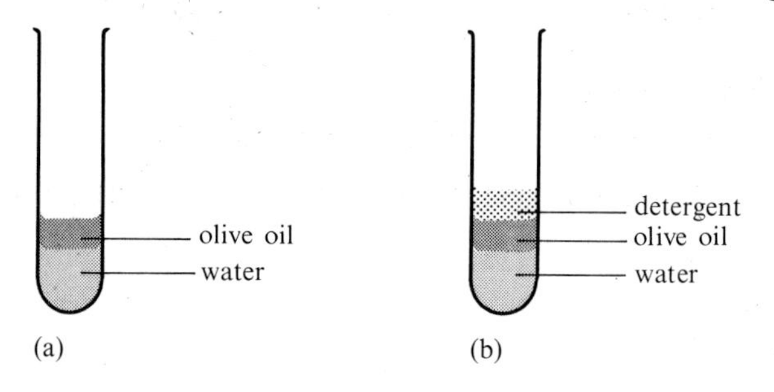

Shake the test-tubes vigorously and then allow them to stand for several minutes.
Account for the differences which you observe.
The detergent has acted as an emulsifying agent. Why is this process important when you consider the increase in oil pollution of the seas?

Chapter 3

3.5 Polarity of molecules

Set up a burette in a burette stand. Fill the burette with water. Allow a fine jet to come from the burette.
Bring a charged poly(ethene) rod up to the jet. Is the jet deflected?
Draw the table in your book and record your results.
Repeat the procedure with the other substances in the table.
Clean and dry your burette in each case.

Substance	*Is the jet deflected?*
Water	
Tetrachloromethane	
Trichloromethane	
Methanol	
Ethanol	
Propanone	

Account for each of your results by considering the shape and structure of each molecule.

Chapter 4

4.1 1 Conduction of electricity by solids

Set up the apparatus shown in the diagram.

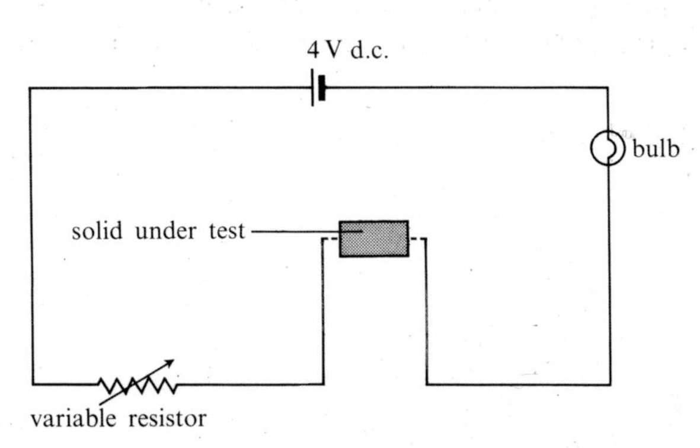

Connect the substances, shown over the page, into the circuit above one at a time, and find out if they are conductors or non-conductors of electricity. Draw the table in your book and complete it.

Substance	*Conductor or non-conductor*	*Substance*	*Conductor or non-conductor*
Copper		Sodium carbonate	
Sulphur		Lead	
Copper(II) chloride		Rubber	
Zinc		Silver	
Sodium chloride		Glass	
Aluminium		Carbon	
Iodine			

With the exception of carbon, what do all the conductors have in common?

4.1 2 Conduction of electricity by solutions and liquids

Set up the apparatus shown in the diagram.

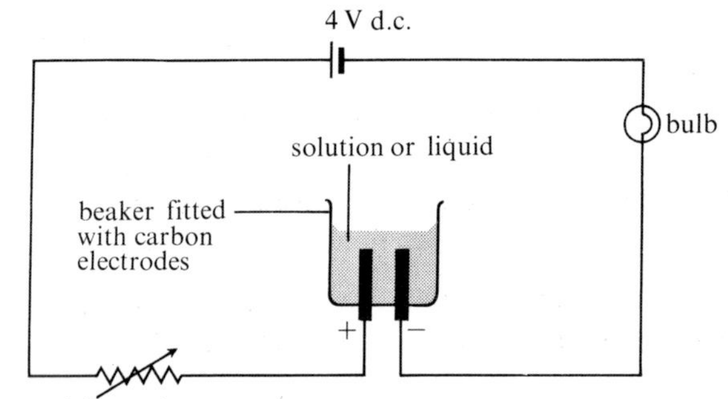

Place the solutions (or liquids) given in the table opposite in the beaker and find out if they will conduct an electric current.
If any gases are evolved at the electrodes, collect them and try to identify them.
Draw the table in your book and complete it.
Make a list of the conductors and non-conductors.
Can you draw any conclusions from your lists?

Solution or liquid	Does it conduct electricity?	Gases evolved	
		Positive electrode	Negative electrode
Copper(II) chloride			
Glucose			
Potassium iodide			
Tetrachloromethane			
Sodium carbonate			
Sodium chloride			
Methanol			
Potassium bromide			
Ethanol			
Trichloromethane			

4.1 3 Conduction of electricity by melts

Warning This experiment should be carried out in a fume-cupboard as some of the vapours are toxic.

A melt is obtained by heating a substance until it becomes molten. Set up the apparatus shown in the diagram.

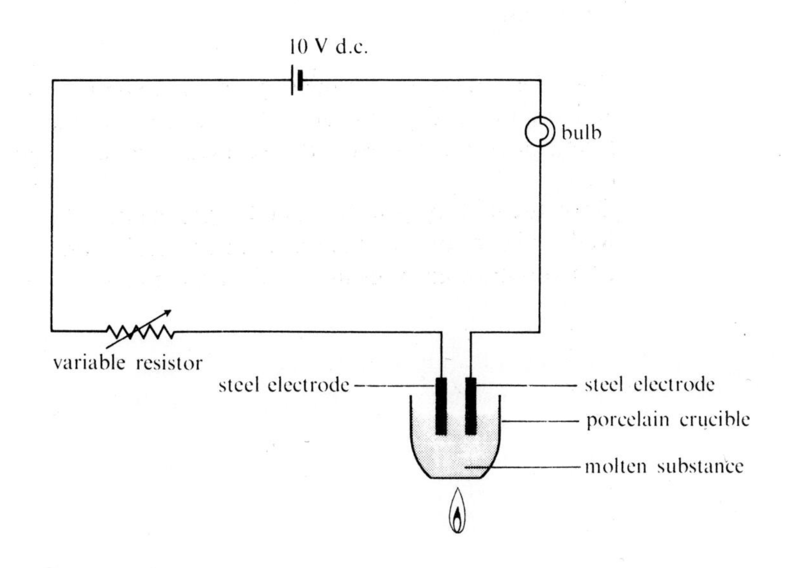

Place the substances shown in the table in the crucible, one at a time, and find out if they will conduct an electric current (a) when solid, and (b) when molten.
If any gases are evolved at the electrodes, or any new materials formed at the electrodes, attempt to identify them.

	Does it conduct electricity?		*Gases or materials*	
Substance	*When solid*	*When molten*	*Positive electrode*	*Negative electrode*
Lead(II) bromide				
Cadmium(II) iodide				
Zinc(II) chloride				
Potassium iodide				
Sulphur				
Glucose				
Sucrose				
Paraffin wax				

Draw the table in your book and complete it.
Can you draw any conclusions from your results?

4.4 1 Colour of compounds

Look at the following groups of compounds:

1 Lead(II) chromate(VI) and potassium chromate(VI).
2 Copper(II) sulphate; copper(II) chloride; copper(II) carbonate; copper(II) nitrate.
3 Potassium dichromate(VI); ammonium dichromate(VI); sodium dichromate(VI).
4 Nickel(II) sulphate; nickel(II) carbonate; nickel(II) chloride.
5 Cobalt(II) nitrate and cobalt(II) chloride.

Which colours occur in 1, 2, 3, 4, and 5?
Which ions would appear to be responsible for each of these colours?

4.4 2 Migration of ions

Half-fill a W-tube with a concentrated solution of potassium nitrate.
Prepare a solution of copper(II) manganate(VII) by mixing equal volumes of solutions of copper(II) sulphate and potassium manganate(VII).
Weight this solution with urea, and pour it down the centre limb of the W-tube to form a lower layer. Place carbon electrodes in the W-tube and apply 20 V from a direct current source for one hour.

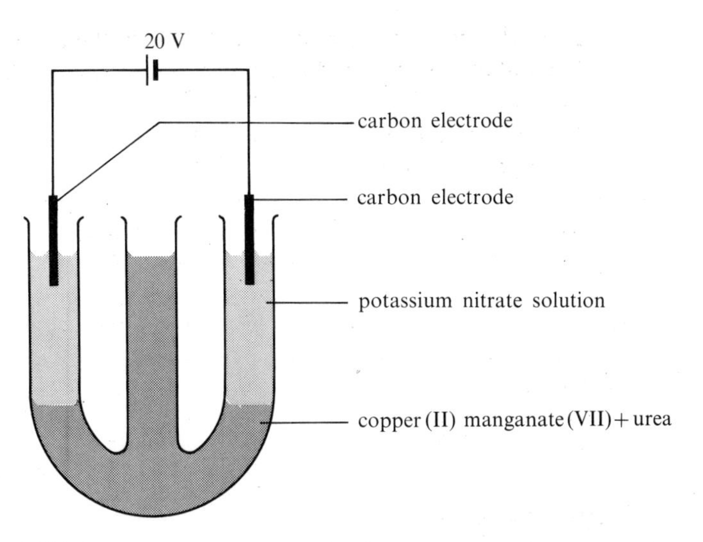

Which colours move towards the positive and negative electrodes?
Which ions are these colours due to?
What does the movement of these colours tell you about the charge on these ions?

4.4 3 Migration of ions

Prepare a 5 per cent solution of gelatin, by adding 10 g of gelatin to 200 cm^3 of boiling water. When the gel is still hot add 5 g of copper(II) sulphate and stir until all the solid has dissolved. Half-fill a U-tube with this solution. When the gel has set add a concentrated solution of potassium nitrate to each limb of the U-tube.
Place carbon electrodes in each limb of the U-tube and apply 20V from a direct current source for one hour.

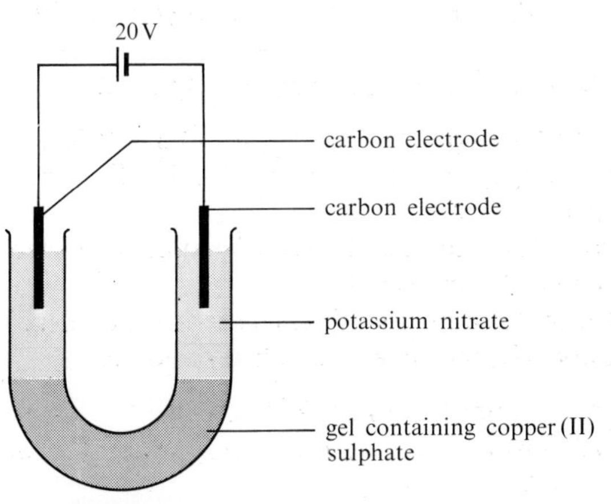

Which colour moves towards the negative electrode?
Which ion is this colour due to?
What does the movement of the colour tell you about the charge on the ion?

4.4 4 Migration of ions

Prepare a 5 per cent solution of gelatin by adding 5 g of gelatin to 100 cm^3 of boiling water. Add to this solution a few drops of phenolphthalein indicator. Stopper one end of an open tube and fill it with the gelatin solution. Allow the gel to set. Remove the stopper, and place the tube in a crystallizing dish containing sodium hydroxide solution. Place carbon electrodes as shown, and apply 20V from a direct current source for one hour.

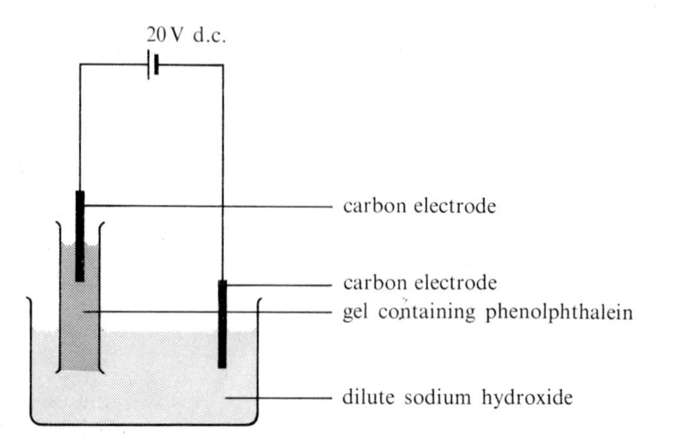

Which colour moves towards the positive electrode?
What causes this colour?
What does this movement of colour indicate?

4.4 5 Migration of ions

Half-fill a W-tube with dilute nitric acid.
Heat 100 cm^3 of dilute hydrochloric acid in a beaker and add copper(II) chromate(VI) until a hot saturated solution is obtained. Weight this solution with 20 g of urea. Allow the solution to cool. Then pour the copper(II) chromate(VI) solution down the centre limb of the W-tube to form a lower layer. Using carbon electrodes, apply 20V from a direct current source for thirty minutes.

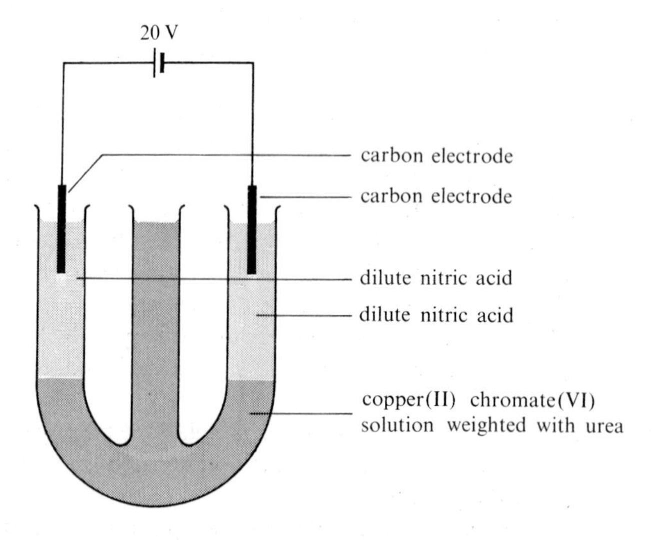

Which colours move towards the positive and negative electrodes?
Which ions are these colours due to?

What does the movement of these colours tell you about the charge on these ions?

4.5 1 Conductivity: concentration of ions

Set up the apparatus shown in the diagram.

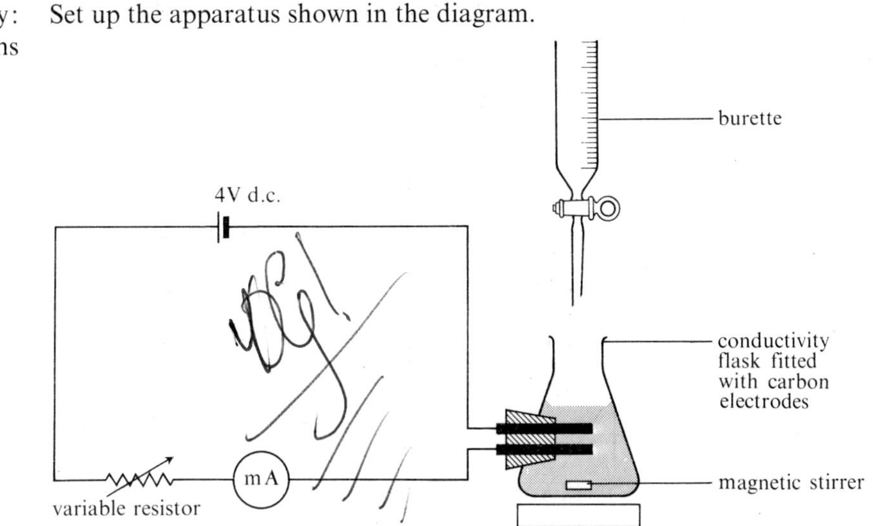

Cover the carbon electrodes with distilled water, close the switch and take the reading on the milliammeter. Add 0.1M hydrochloric acid, $1.0\,cm^3$ at a time, from the burette. Take the reading on the meter after each addition. Stop when you have added $10\,cm^3$. Draw a table in your books, and record your results.
Repeat the procedure using 0.1M sodium hydroxide and 0.1M sodium chloride.
How does the conductivity of the hydrochloric acid vary with the concentration of the hydrcohloric acid?
Is this true for all the solutions used?

4.5 2 Conductivity: mobility of ions

Use the apparatus described in the last experiment.
Place $50\,cm^3$ of 0.1M hydrochloric acid in the conductivity flask and adjust the variable resistor to give a full-scale deflection. Record the reading on the milliammeter. Do not alter the setting of the variable resistor.
Repeat this procedure with (a) $50\,cm^3$ of 0.1M sodium hydroxide and (b) $50\,cm^3$ of 0.1M sodium chloride. Record your results.
Which variables have you kept constant?
What must cause the conductivity to vary? (Explain this in terms of ionic mobility and try to determine an order of mobility for the ions present.)

4.5 3 Ion size

Make up a 5 per cent solution of gelatin in boiling water and pour an equal volume of the hot gel into each of six test-tubes (a), (b), (c), (d), (e), and (f). Allow the gel to set.
Place $10\,cm^3$ of copper(II) nitrate solution in test-tube (a).
Place $10\,cm^3$ of potassium dichromate(VI) solution in test-tube (b).
Place $10\,cm^3$ of potassium manganate(VII) solution in test-tube (c).

Place 10 cm^3 of nickel(II) nitrate solution in test-tube (d).
Place 10 cm^3 of potassium chromate(VI) solution in test-tube (e).
Place 10 cm^3 of cobalt(II) nitrate solution in test-tube (f).
Allow the tubes to stand for twenty-four hours.
Are the distances travelled the same in each case?
Explain your answer in terms of ion size.

4.5 4 Ions and mobility

Prepare a 5 per cent solution of gelatin by adding 5 g of gelatin to 100 cm^3 of boiling water. To this add some sodium chloride and some Universal Indicator.
Add the hot solution to an extended U-tube, and allow the gel to set.
Add 0.1M hydrochloric acid at one end and 0.1M sodium hydroxide at the other. Connect the carbon wire electrodes as shown. Apply a direct current of 20V from a direct current source for one hour.

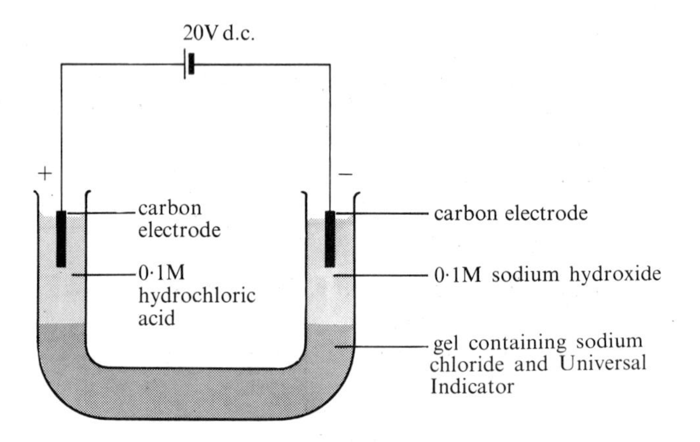

Which colours move towards the positive and negative electrodes?
Which ions are these colours due to?
What does the movement of these colours tell you about the charge on the ions present?
Compare the distances travelled by each ion. How can you relate this to ion size and ion mobility?

Chapter 5

5.2 1 Empirical formulae

The oxides of copper, lead, and iron are suitable for this experiment. Note: natural gas can only be used for copper. Calor gas can be used for copper, lead, and iron.

metal oxide + gas → metal + water

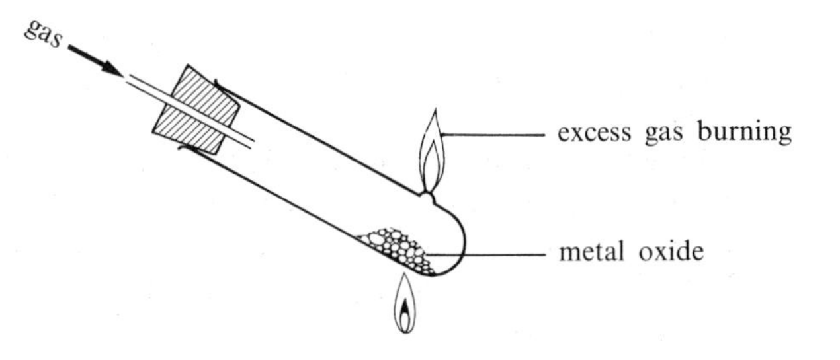

Weigh the tube empty. Place some metal oxide in the tube and weigh again. Allow the gas to pass for a few seconds, to remove all the air, before lighting the excess gas.
Heat the tube strongly for ten minutes.
Allow the tube to cool to room temperature, and reweigh it.
Complete the table of results.

Weight of tube + metal oxide = g
Weight of tube = g
Weight of metal oxide = g

Weight of tube + metal = g
Weight of tube = g
Weight of metal = g
Weight of oxygen = Weight of metal oxide − Weight of metal
= g

1 Calculate the combining ratio of the metal and oxygen in the metal oxide.
2 Does this ratio agree with the formula obtained from theoretical considerations?
3 Why was it necessary to ensure that all air was removed from the combustion tube?

5.2 2 Empirical formulae

Weigh a clean, dry porcelain crucible and lid.
Take approximately 25 cm of magnesium ribbon, fold it up, and place it in the crucible.
Reweigh the crucible, lid and magnesium.
Set up the apparatus as shown on the next page.

Heat the crucible with a bunsen flame until all the magnesium has reacted. The magnesium reacts with the oxygen of the air to form magnesium oxide:

$2Mg(s) + O_2(g) \rightarrow 2MgO(s)$

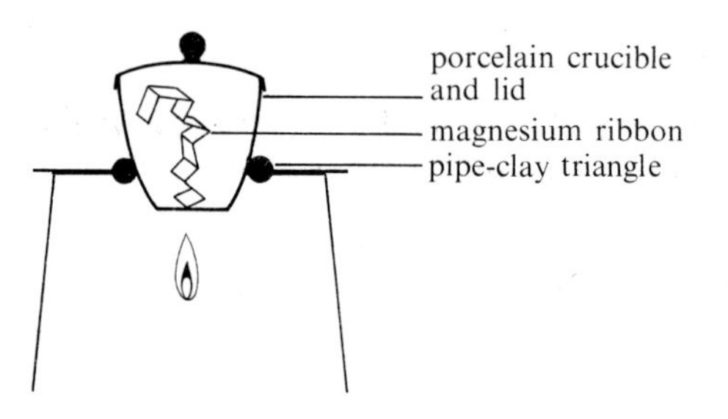

Copy and complete the table of results.

Weight of crucible + lid + magnesium = g
Weight of crucible + lid = g
Weight of magnesium = g

Weight of crucible + lid + magnesium oxide = g
Weight of crucible + lid = g
Weight of magnesium oxide = g
Weight of oxygen = Weight of magnesium oxide − Weight of magnesium
= g

1 Calculate the combining ratio of magnesium and oxygen in magnesium oxide.
2 Does your formula agree with that obtained from theoretical considerations?

5.2 3 Empirical formulae

Weigh a **small** piece of lead foil. Place the foil in a 250 cm³ beaker, and add 20 cm³ of 50 per cent nitric acid. (**Care** The acid is corrosive.)
The remainder of the experiment must be done in the fume cupboard.
Allow the lead to react with the nitric acid. Heat the solution if necessary.

lead + nitric acid → lead nitrate + water

When the lead has reacted, dilute the solution with distilled water to 100 cm³.
Add potassium iodide until all the lead has been precipitated as lead iodide.

lead nitrate + potassium iodide → lead iodide + potassium nitrate

Filter off the lead iodide, transfer the filter paper + lead iodide to an oven and allow it to dry. Weigh the filter paper + lead iodide.
Copy and complete the table of results.

Weight of lead foil = g
Weight of filter paper + lead iodide = g
Weight of filter paper = g
Weight of lead iodide = g
Weight of lead foil = g

1 Calculate the combining ratio of lead and iodine in lead iodide.
2 Does it agree with the formula obtained from theoretical considerations?
3 How would you know that all the lead had been precipitated as lead iodide?

Chapter 7

7.2 1 Using indicators

Use pH paper or Universal Indicator to determine the pH of a selection of common solutions, and list your results in three groups in a table.

pH of solution		
pH<7	*pH = 7*	*pH>7*

Explain your results.

7.2 2 Using indicators

Familiarize yourself with a number of different indicators by finding out their colours in acid conditions and in alkaline conditions.
Tabulate your results.

Indicator	*Colour in acid conditions*	*Colour in alkaline conditions*

7.2 3 Effect of concentration of H^+ ion on pH

Make an approximately 0.1M solution of hydrochloric acid by diluting 1 cm^3 of a 1M solution (measured with a syringe) up to 10 cm^3 in a measuring cylinder. Make sure the solution is well mixed and reserve a small portion for testing the pH.
Make up a 0.01M solution by diluting 1 cm^3 of the 0.1M solution up to 10 cm^3.
Mix and reserve a portion as before.
Make up solutions of $\frac{M}{1000}$, $\frac{M}{10\,000}$, $\frac{M}{100\,000}$, $\frac{M}{1\,000\,000}$, and $\frac{M}{10\,000\,000}$
by a similar method, setting aside a portion of each.
Test the pH of each sample and record the results in a table.
What is the effect of the concentration of the hydrogen ion on the pH of the solution?
Is there any relationship between the two?

7.5 Comparison of properties of weak and strong acids

Carry out the following tests on 1M ethanoic acid and 1M hydrochloric acid and compare the results: pH, conductivity, reaction with magnesium, reaction with sodium carbonate, and reaction with sodium hydroxide solution.
Record your observations in a table.
Can you account for the observed differences?

7.6 Properties of dilute acids

Carry out the following tests on dilute hydrochloric acid and dilute sulphuric acid: pH, reaction with magnesium, reaction with sodium carbonate, reaction with copper(II) oxide (the unreacted copper oxide will have to be filtered off to see if a reaction has taken place), and reaction with sodium hydroxide solution (in the presence of indicator paper).
Record your observations in a table.
Try to write an equation for each reaction.

7.7 1 Comparison of strong and weak alkalis

Carry out the following tests on 1M sodium hydroxide and 1M aqueous ammonia: pH, conductivity, and reaction with dilute hydrochloric acid (in the presence of an indicator).
Record your observations in a table.
Compare the results you obtain for each test.
Can you account for the observed differences?

7.7 2 Hydroxide precipitation

Add a few drops of sodium hydroxide solution to solutions of the following salts:

1 Copper(II) sulphate
2 Magnesium chloride
3 Iron(III) chloride
4 Aluminium sulphate
5 Potassium chloride
6 Silver nitrate
7 Aluminium chloride

Filter off the insoluble hydroxides and describe their nature.
Record the results in a table. From this compile a list of soluble hydroxides and insoluble hydroxides.

7.8 pH of salt solutions

Measure the pH of the following salt solutions:

1 Copper(II) sulphate
2 Ammonium chloride
3 Sodium sulphate
4 Sodium ethanoate
5 Potassium chloride
6 Sodium carbonate
7 Ammonium sulphate
8 Sodium nitrite
9 Iron(III) chloride
10 Nickel sulphate

List your results in the table.

pH of solutions		
pH<7	*pH = 7*	*pH>7*

Explain what is common about the members of each group. Write an equation for each group to show why the pH has the value that you found.

Chapter 8

8.1 1 Preparation of NaCl by neutralization

Using a pipette, add 20 cm^3 of 0.1M sodium hydroxide solution to a 250cm^3 conical flask. Add two drops of phenolphthalein indicator to the flask.
Fill a burette with 0.1M hydrchloric acid.
Carefully add the acid from the burette, 1 cm^3 at a time, to the alkali in the flask. The contents of the flask should be well mixed after each addition.
As the end-point approaches, the pink colour of the indicator gets fainter. When this happens the acid should be added drop by drop, until the pink colour just disappears.
To remove the indicator from this neutral solution add some activated charcoal, shake the flask, and filter the solution.
Evaporate the filtrate to a small volume in an evaporating basin and then pour the concentrated filtrate into a crystallizing dish.

Set the dish aside and allow the remaining liquid to evaporate off at room temperature. Crystals of sodium chloride will be formed.

8.1 2 Preparation of $(NH_4)_2SO_4$ by neutralization

Using a pipette, add 20 cm^3 of 0.1M sulphuric acid to a 250 cm^3 conical flask. Add two drops of screened methyl orange indicator.
Fill a burette with 0.1M aqueous ammonia. (**Note** It is normal practice to put the alkali in the flask. However, we have reversed this here as aqueous ammonia is an unpleasant liquid to draw up into a pipette.)
Add carefully the alkali from the burette, 1 cm^3 at a time, to the acid in the flask.
The contents of the flask should be well mixed after each addition.
The end-point is reached when the indicator turns from magenta to green.
As the end-point approaches the alkali should be added drop by drop.
Remove the indicator as described in Experiment **8.1**.1.
Evaporate the filtrate to a small volume in an evaporating basin and then pour the concentrated filtrate into a crystallizing dish.
Set the dish aside and allow the remaining liquid to evaporate off at room temperature. Crystals of ammonium sulphate will be formed.

8.3 1 Neutralization using conductivity measurements

The apparatus required for this experiment is described in Experiment **4.5**.1 (page 261).
1 Strong acid/strong base (0.1M HCl/0.1M NaOH).
Cover the electrodes with distilled water and add 5 drops of 0.1M NaOH.
Switch on the circuit. Adjust the variable resistor to obtain a mid-scale reading on the milliammeter.
Record this reading and switch off the circuit. Do not alter the resistor setting.
Add 0.1M hydrochloric acid drop by drop.
After each addition, mix well, and record the meter reading.
You must switch off between additions to avoid electrolysing the solution.
Continue this procedure until you have added 10 drops of the 0.1M hydrochloric acid.
Plot a graph of meter reading against drops of acid added.
Repeat this procedure for each of the following:

2 Weak acid/strong base (0.1M CH_3COOH/0.1M NaOH).
3 Strong acid/weak base (0.1M H_2SO_4/0.1M $Ba(OH)_2$).
4 Weak acid/weak base (0.1M CH_3COOH/0.1M NH_4OH).

Write balanced equations for the reactions occurring in 1, 2, 3, and 4.
Interpret the shape of each of the graphs by considering the reactions taking place and the ionic species present.
Account for the position of the end-point in each graph.

8.3 2 Neutralization of an acid by a solid

The apparatus required for this experiment is described in Experiment **4.5**.1 (page 261).
Place 50 cm^3 of 1M sulphuric acid in the flask and adjust the variable resistor to obtain a full-scale deflection on the milliammeter. Record the reading on the meter.
Weigh out ten 1 g portions of calcium carbonate.

Add 1 g of calcium carbonate to the acid in the flask. When the reaction has ceased record the meter reading.
Repeat this procedure until 10 g of calcium carbonate have been added.
Plot a graph of current against time.
Write the equation for the reaction.
Account for the shape of the graph.

8.3 3 Neutralization of an acid by a metal

The apparatus required for this experiment is described in Experiment **4.5**.1 (page 261).
1 Use 1M H_2SO_4/Zinc
Place 50 cm^3 of 1M sulphuric acid in the flask, and adjust the variable resistor to obtain a full-scale deflection on the milliammeter. Record the reading on the meter.
Weigh out ten 0.5 g portions of zinc powder.
Add 0.5 g of zinc powder to the acid in the flask. When the reaction has ceased, record the meter reading.
Repeat this procedure until 5 g of zinc powder has been added.
Plot a graph of current against mass of zinc added.
2 Use 1M HCl/Zinc
Repeat the procedure in (1), but use 1M hydrochloric acid instead of 1M sulphuric acid.
Plot a graph of current against mass of zinc added.

Account for the shape of each of the graphs.
Are the graphs identical? If not explain the differences.

8.4 Reaction between $Ca(OH)_2$ and CO_2

The apparatus required for this experiment is described in Experiment **4.5**.1 (page 261).
Place calcium hydroxide solution (limewater) in the conductivity flask so that it covers the electrodes.
Use the variable resistor to obtain a mid-scale deflection on the milliammeter. Record the reading on the meter.
Using a drinking straw, blow into the calcium hydroxide solution. Record the meter reading every two minutes, for twenty minutes.
Plot a graph of current against time.
Account for the shape of the graph.
Write equations for the reactions occurring before and after the end-point.

8.5 Heat of neutralization

Measure out 50 cm^3 of 2M hydrochloric acid and put it in a polystyrene cup.
Record the temperature (t_1) of the acid.
Measure out 50 cm^3 of 2M sodium hydroxide, and put in a polystyrene cup.
Record the temperature (t_2) of the alkali.

Calculate the average initial temperature $\frac{t_1+t_2}{2}$

Put the acid and alkali into a third polystyrene cup and record the highest temperature (t_3) of the mixture.
Calculate the rise in temperature (Δt).
Repeat the procedure using (a) 2M nitric acid, and (b) 1M sulphuric acid.
Draw the table below in your books and fill in your results.

Acid	*Alkali*	*Initial temp.* $\frac{t_1+t_2}{2}$	*Final temp.* t_3	*Rise in temp.* Δt
2M HCl	2M NaOH			
2M HNO_3	2M NaOH			
1M H_2SO_4	2M NaOH			

Why was 1M sulphuric acid used instead of 2M, as in the other examples?
Can you make a general conclusion from your table of results?
If so, can you explain this conclusion.
Repeat the experiment using 2M ethanoic acid and 2M sodium hydroxide and account for any differences you observe.

8.8 1 Preparation of a standard Na_2CO_3 solution

Weigh out **approximately** 2.5 g of anhydrous sodium carbonate.
Weigh (watch glass + Na_2CO_3) **accurately** and record the reading.
Transfer the sodium carbonate to a beaker.
Weigh (watch glass—Na_2CO_3) **accurately** and record the reading.
From the two readings you have recorded, calculate the **accurate weight** of sodium carbonate which was transferred to the beaker.
Dissolve the sodium carbonate in the minimum volume of de-ionized water that you can. Transfer the solution to a 250 cm^3 standard flask.
Rinse the beaker several times with de-ionized water adding the rinsings to the flask. Make the level of the solution in the standard flask up to the mark, stopper and mix. Retain this solution.
Calculate the molarity of the solution.

8.8 2 Standardization of H_2SO_4 using standard Na_2CO_3 solution

Titrate 25 cm^3 portions of the standard sodium carbonate solution prepared in the previous experiment with the sulphuric acid of unknown molarity.
A suitable indicator for this titration is screened methyl orange, which changes from yellow/green to pink at the end-point.
The titrations should be repeated until two titres are obtained within ± 0.05 cm^3 of each other.
Record your results as shown below:

2nd burette reading:
1st burette reading:
Titre in cm^3:

Calculate the molarity of the sulphuric acid.

Chapter 9

9.1 Reactivity of metals

Warning Wear your safety glasses.

Metals: zinc; calcium; aluminium; silver; magnesium; tin; copper; iron; lead.
Do not use sodium or mercury. If you wish to see the reactions of these metals with oxygen, water and acid, ask a teacher to demonstrate them for you.

1 Reaction of a metal with oxygen.
Fill 10 boiling-tubes with oxygen gas (O_2) from a cylinder. Place a small amount of a metal in a combustion spoon. Warm the spoon in a bunsen flame and place it in a tube of oxygen. Note your observations in the table. Repeat this procedure with the other metals given in the list above.
2 Reaction of a metal with water.
Place a small amount of a metal in a test-tube of cold water and note your observations in the table. If a gas is evolved, try to identify it. Repeat this procedure with the other metals given in the list.
3 Reaction of a metal with acid.
Place a small amount of a metal in a test-tube containing dilute hydrochloric acid and note your observations in the table. If a gas is evolved, try to identify it. Repeat this procedure with the other metals given in the list.
Take care when you use calcium and magnesium. Do these reactions in a fume-cupboard.

Metal	*Reaction with oxygen*	*Reaction with water*	*Reaction with dilute hydrochloric acid*
Potassium	Burns with a lilac coloured flame	Melts and $H_2(g)$ burns	Decomposes acid explosively
Sodium	Burns with a bright yellow flame	Melts and $H_2(g)$ evolved	Decomposes acid explosively
Gold	No reaction	No reaction	No reaction
Mercury	Forms a red oxide	No reaction	No reaction

Use your results to construct a reactivity series for metals.

9.2 1 Reactions of oxides

Warning Wear your safety glasses.

Place a **small** amount of a metal oxide in a dry, hard-glass test-tube.

Hold the tube in a test-tube holder, and heat the tube in a bunsen flame (gently to begin with).
Record your results for each metal oxide as you test it.
Metal oxides: silver(I) oxide; copper(II) oxide; lead oxide; tin(II) oxide; iron(III) oxide; aluminium oxide; magnesium oxide; calcium oxide.

Oxide	*Formula*	*Action of heat on oxide. Does the metal form?*	*Action on glowing wooden splint on any gases evolved*

9.2 2 Reactions of oxides

Warning Wear your safety glasses

Mix equal amounts of zinc powder and solid calcium hydroxide. Place this mixture in a test-tube. On heating, this mixture will generate hydrogen gas. Set up the test-tube as shown in the diagram.

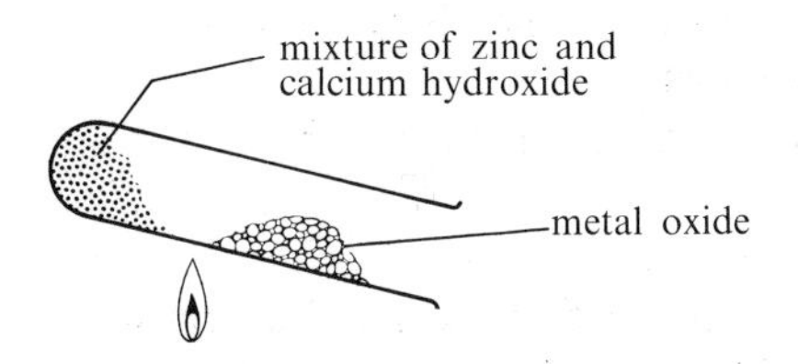

Heat a small amount of the oxide for a few minutes and then adjust the bunsen so that both the oxide and the mixture are heated at the same time. This allows hydrogen gas to pass over the heated tube.
Heat the tube in this way for about ten minutes, and then allow it to cool.
Examine the tube and record your results in the table.
Repeat the procedure for all the oxides given in the list.
Metal oxides: silver(I) oxide; copper(II) oxide; lead oxide; tin(II) oxide; iron(III) oxide; aluminium oxide; magnesium oxide; calcium oxide.

Oxide	*Formula*	*Action of hydrogen on metal oxide. Does the metal form?*

9.2 3 Reactions of oxides

Warning Wear your safety glasses.

The apparatus you will use is shown in the next page.
Mix a small amount of the metal oxide with an equal amount of carbon, and place it in the combustion tube. Allow the gas to pass for a few seconds before lighting it. When the gas is burning, heat the tube with a bunsen flame for ten minutes. Turn off the bunsen **but** allow the gas to burn until the tube has cooled down.
Examine the tube, and record your results in the table.
Repeat for the other metal oxides.
Metal oxides: silver(I) oxide; copper(II) oxide; lead oxide; tin(II) oxide; iron(III) oxide; aluminium oxide; magnesium oxide; calcium oxide.

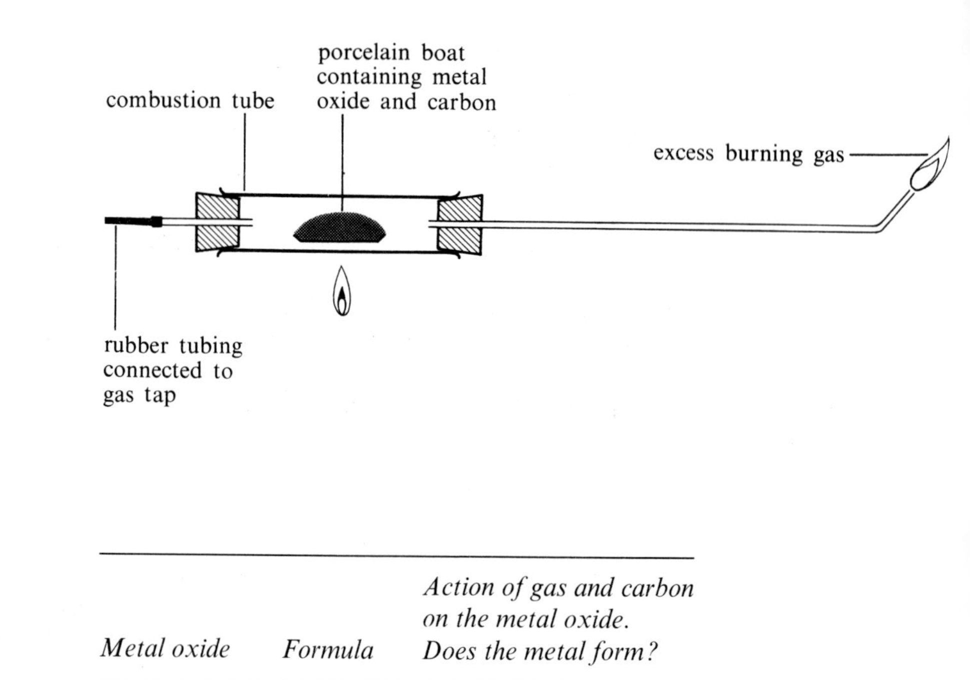

Metal oxide	*Formula*	*Action of gas and carbon on the metal oxide. Does the metal form?*

By considering the reactions of metal oxides in your table, show how these are related to the reactivity series of metals.

9.3 1 Displacement

In this experiment you have to discover which metals will displace other metals from solutions of the salts of the latter metals, and relate the displacements to the position of the metals in the reactivity series.
Place a small amount of a metal salt solution in a test-tube.
To this solution add a small amount of a metal.
If displacement occurs it should be easy to observe.
Try the example shown in the table, and then further combinations.
Fill in the rest of the table as you do each combination.

Metal	*Salt solution*	*Does displacement occur?*
Zinc	Copper(II) sulphate	Yes. Copper deposited

9.3 2 Displacement

You have carried out several displacement reactions, and now you will attempt to show that there is a definite relationship between the masses reacting and the masses produced.
Clean a small piece of zinc with emery paper.
Weigh the piece of zinc.
Add 50 cm^3 of copper(II) sulphate to a 100 cm^3 beaker.
Place the zinc in the copper(II) sulphate solution.
Weigh a filter paper.
When all the zinc has reacted, filter the solution through the filter paper, and dry the filter paper in an oven.

Record your results as shown.

Weight of zinc	=	g
Weight of filter paper + copper	=	g
Weight of filter paper	=	g
Weight of copper	=	g

You now know the mass of copper which is displaced by a certain mass of zinc.
Divide each of these masses by their respective relative atomic masses and calculate the ratio: moles of zinc reacted: moles of copper produced.

9.4 1 Electrode potential

Set up the apparatus shown in the diagram.

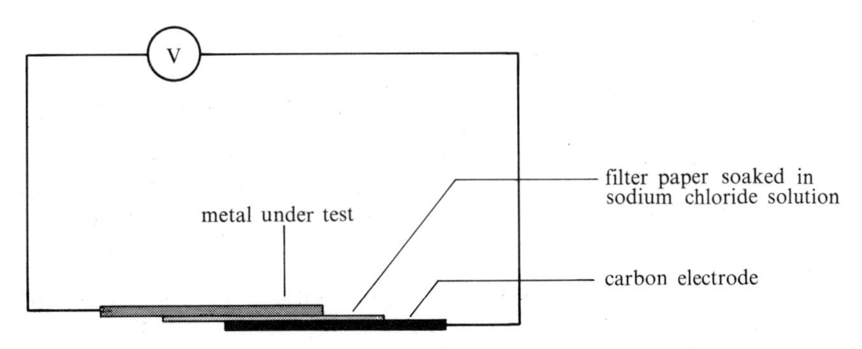

Using a strip of one of the metals listed below, complete the circuit shown above. Record the reading on the voltmeter. Repeat for the other metals
Metals: magnesium; aluminium; zinc; iron; tin; lead; copper; silver.
Give your results in a table.
How do your results compare with the order of the metals in the reactivity series?

9.4 2 Electrode potential

In this experiment you are going to use an electrode which behaves in a similar way to a hydrogen electrode.
You are going to attempt to produce a more accurate table of electrode

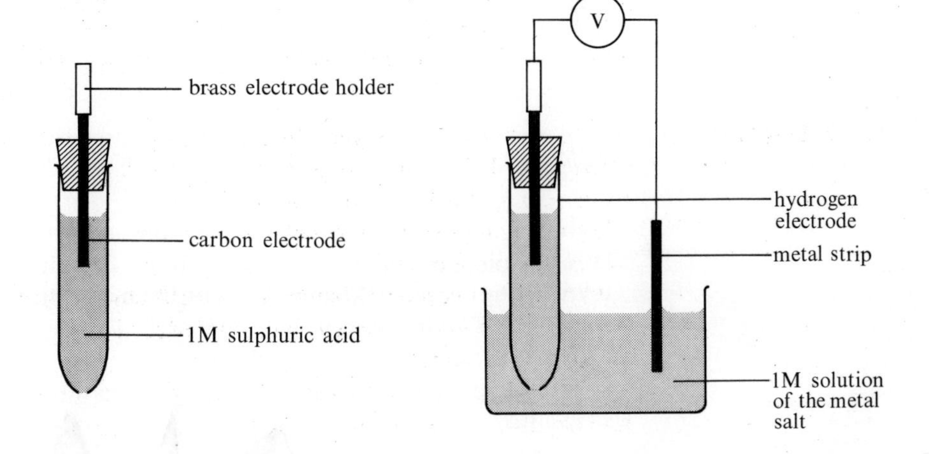

potentials than in the last experiment. Use the arrangement shown on the last page and the metals used in the previous experiment.

Give your results in a table.
How do your results compare with:

1 The values obtained in the previous experiment?
2 The standard values given in tables?

Can you explain the differences?

9.5 Electrochemical cells

1 Set up the following arrangements.

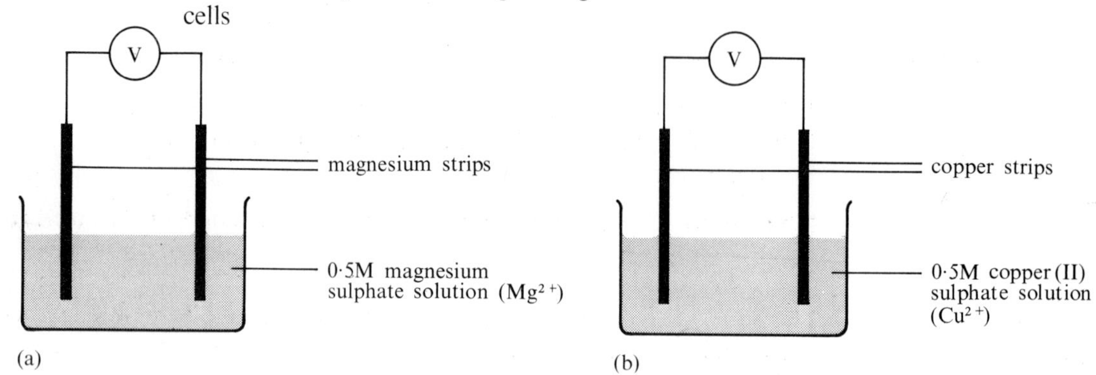

Is there any reaction in (a) or (b)?
Is there any reading on the voltmeter in (a)?
Is there any reading on the voltmeter in (b)?

2 Modify the above arrangements as shown below.

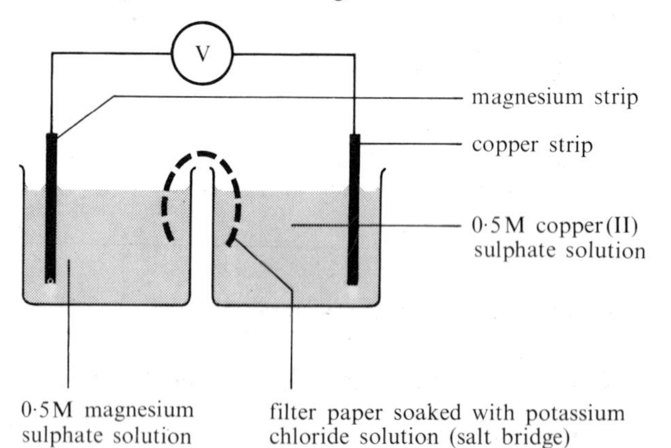

Is there a reading on the voltmeter? If so what is it?
How would you establish that electrons are flowing in the external circuit?
Is there any change in the solutions or the metal strips?
Account for your results in 1.
What is the function of the salt bridge?
Write equations to show what is happening to the magnesium and copper strips in 2.

Chapter 10

10.3 1 Oxidation and reduction

Dissolve some crystals of iron(II) ammonium sulphate in dilute sulphuric acid and add this solution to a very dilute solution of potassium manganate(VII). Observe the colour change and write electron half-equations for the oxidation and reduction reactions.

10.3 2 Oxidation and reduction

Boil a few copper turnings in 2 cm^3 of concentrated sulphuric acid **(care)** for five minutes. **Allow the test-tube to cool** and pour the contents carefully into about 50 cm^3 of water. Note the colour of the solution and explain the reaction in terms of oxidation and reduction.

10.4 Oxidizing agents

Add sodium sulphite solution to each of the following solutions:

1 Potassium manganate(VII) acidified with dilute sulphuric acid.
2 Potassium dichromate(VI) acidified with dilute sulphuric acid.
3 Bromine water.

Note the colour changes and write electron half-equations for the oxidizing agent in each case.

10.5 Voltaic cells

Place pieces of copper foil and zinc foil in a beaker of dilute sulphuric acid, as shown in the diagram, and connect them to a voltmeter. Note the reading and compare it with that obtained from tables of standard electrode potentials.

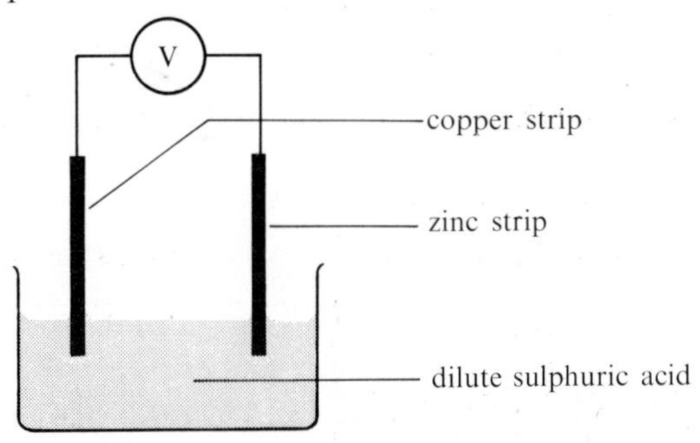

on the voltmeter drops after a time.

10.6 Electrolysis

Using the apparatus shown on the next page, electrolyse solutions of:

1 1M sulphuric acid.
2 2M sodium hydroxide.
3 2M sodium chloride.

Which gases are given off at the anode and cathode in each case? Explain your results in terms of the preferential discharge of ions. Use electron half-equations to establish that:

1 Oxidation takes place at the anode.
2 Reduction takes place at the cathode.

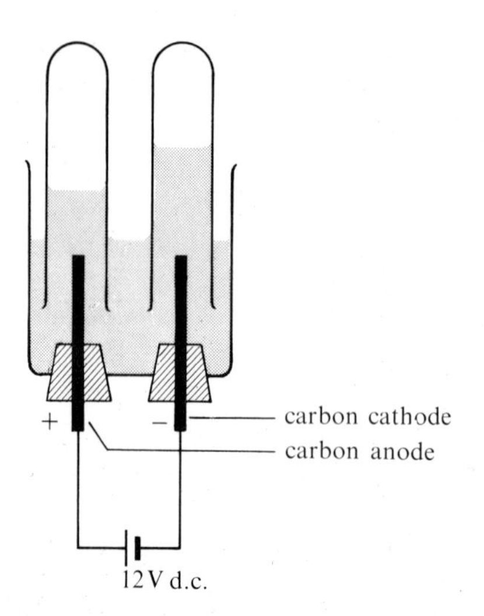

Chapter 11

11.2 2 Conditions for rusting

Set up three test-tubes as shown in the diagram and leave them for a few days.

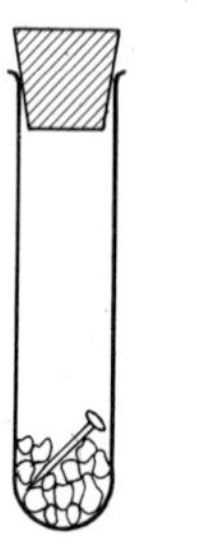

iron nail in sealed test-tube containing anhydrous calcium chloride

iron nail in boiled water with a layer of oil above the water

iron nail in water with the test-tube open to the air

State whether rusting has taken place in each case.
What conclusion can you draw from this experiment?

11.2 2 Ferroxyl indicator

Make some ferroxyl indicator by dissolving some potassium hexacyanoferrate(III) crystals in water and adding a few drops of phenolphthalein. Test each of the following solutions with the ferroxyl indicator.

1 Iron(II) sulphate
2 Iron(III) chloride
3 Sodium chloride
4 Sodium sulphate
5 Sodium hydroxide
6 Sodium carbonate
7 Potassium hydroxide
8 Steel wool in hydrochloric acid

Which solutions produce a deep blue colour?
Which solutions produce a pink colour?

11.3 1 Rate of corrosion

Set up three test-tubes with a gel containing ferroxyl indicator as shown in the diagram. Clean three nails and put them in the gel. Note the colours which develop after half an hour.

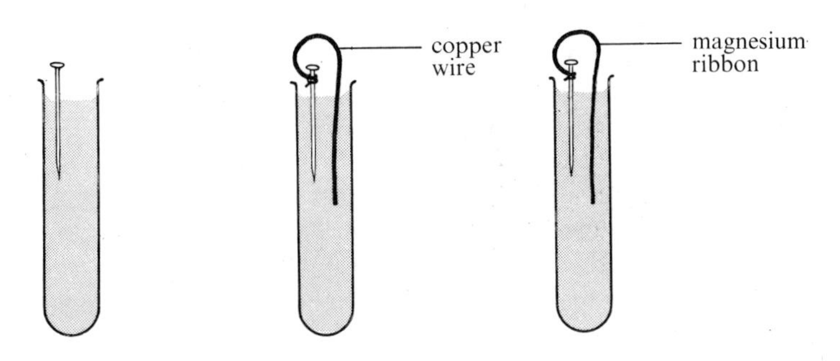

Explain your results.

11.3 2 Rate of corrosion

Dip two identical nails in a solution of ferroxyl indicator and connect them to a 12 V d.c. source as shown in the diagram.

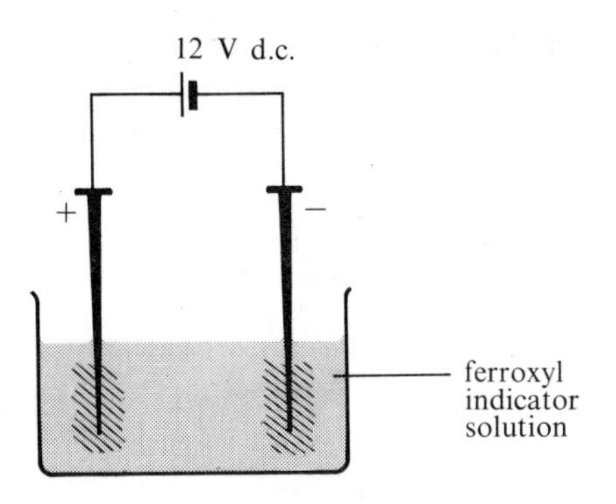

Explain the colours produced in the solution.

11.4 1 Tin plating

Set up the apparatus shown in the diagram and allow it to run for about twenty minutes.

Wash and dry the nail and dip into a test-tube of ferroxyl indicator gel. Put a control nail into a similar test-tube.
Explain your results.

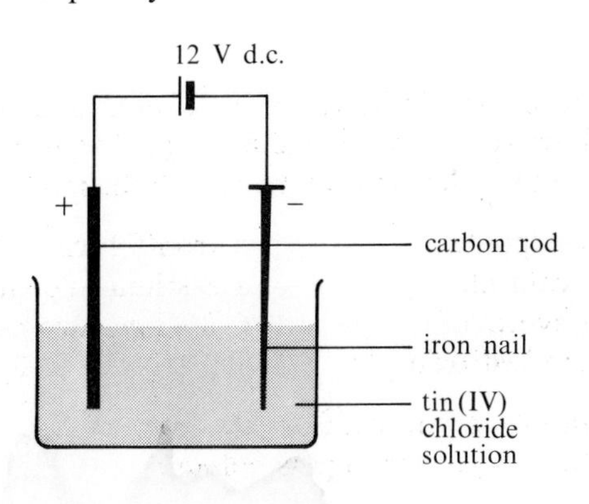

11.4 2 Galvanizing

This experiment should be carried out in a fume-cupboard.
Clean a small square of iron wire gauze by heating it for a short time in dilute hydrochloric acid. Then wash it and dry it.
Heat some granulated zinc in a crucible, and when it is hot, add a large spoonful of ammonium chloride. Dense fumes are produced, but the zinc melts. Dip the wire gauze into the melt, and you should find that, on removing it, it is coated with zinc.

11.5 Anodizing

Clean a small piece of aluminium by rubbing it with tetrachloromethane on a piece of cotton wool. Then place it in dilute sodium hydroxide until it effervesces. Wash the aluminium workpiece, taking care to handle it by the edges to avoid covering it with grease from your fingers. Set up the apparatus shown and allow the process to take place for about half an hour.

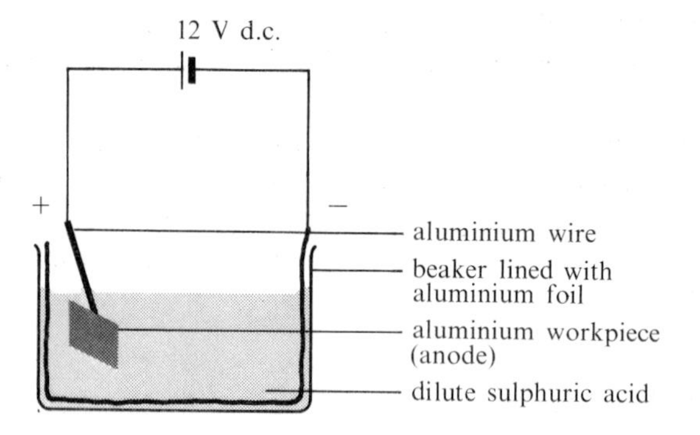

Remove the workpiece and boil it for ten minutes in a solution of alizarin. If the aluminium remains coloured when you wash it you have successfully anodized it.

Chapter 12

12.1 Polymorphs of sulphur

1 Add a little sulphur powder to a few drops of toluene in a test-tube. Warm the tube carefully. Allow the toluene to evaporate slowly in a fume cupboard. Filter off and examine the crystals of rhombic sulphur which are formed.

2 Warm a little sulphur powder in a test-tube until it just melts, and then pour it quickly into a funnel made from filter paper. As the surface begins to harden, open out the filter paper and examine the crystals of monoclinic sulphur which are formed.

3 Place about two inches of sulphur powder in a test-tube and warm gradually. You should notice that the sulphur goes through three different liquid polymorphic forms. Describe the colour and viscosity of these three forms. When the sulphur reaches its third liquid form pour it quickly into a beaker of cold water and examine the plastic sulphur which is formed.

12.3 1 Preparation of sulphur dioxide

Examine the effects of (a) heat and (b) dilute hydrochloric acid on the following sulphur-containing compounds, and determine a suitable method for preparation of sulphur dioxide in the laboratory.
Test the effect of heat by heating the material on asbestos tape.

Sulphur
Iron(III) sulphide
Sodium sulphite
Calcium sulphate

Sulphur dioxide can be identified by smell (caution), and by the decolourizing of a filter paper soaked in acidified potassium dichromate(VI) solution.

12.4 1 Properties of sulphur dioxide

As sulphur dioxide is an irritating gas in large quantities, your teacher will demonstrate the following reactions of sulphur dioxide.

1 Burning magnesium in a jar of sulphur dioxide.

2 Effect of sulphur dioxide on coloured petals.

3 Effect of sulphur dioxide on bromine water.

The following reactions you may carry out yourself, making small amounts of sulphur dioxide as required (see the previous experiment).

4 Effect of sulphur dioxide on moist pH paper.

5 Effect of sulphur dioxide on paper moistened with potassium dichromate(VI) solution.

6 Effect of sulphur dioxide on potassium manganate(VII) solution.

7 Effect of sulphur dioxide on iron(III) chloride solution.

Account for reactions 3, 5, 6, and 7 in terms of electron half equations.

12.4 2 Sulphite ion as electron donor

Place a plug of glass wool at the bend of a U-tube as shown in the diagram. Pour a sulphite solution down one limb of the tube and a dichromate(VI) solution down the other limb of the tube **at the same time** so that the levels remain the same. Place a carbon electrode in each limb, and connect up to a milliammeter as shown.

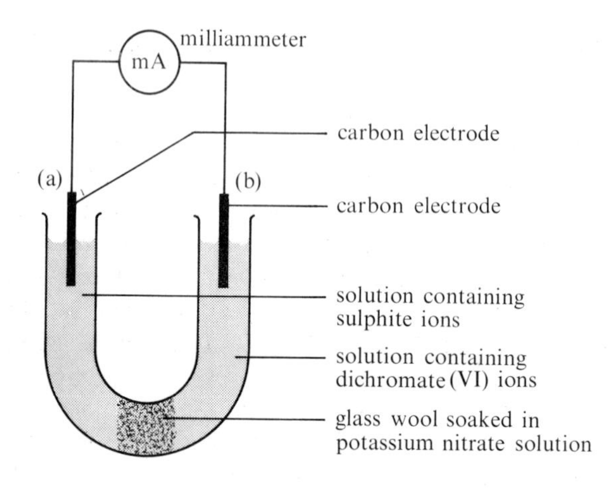

A positive reading on the milliammeter implies that electrons are travelling from (a) to (b). Is that the case? Is the sulphite solution the electron donor?

12.4 3 Sulphate/sulphite test

Add a few drops of barium chloride solution to solutions of sodium sulphate and sodium sulphite. Note the results.
Now add a little dilute hydrochloric acid to each and note the results again. How could you differentiate between a sulphate solution and a sulphite solution?
Use this information to determine which of the unknowns you have been given are sulphates and which are sulphites.

12.7 1 Dehydrating power of concentrated H_2SO_4

Warning Care is required when using concentrated sulphuric acid since it is extremely corrosive.

1 Place about 3 cm of water in a test-tube. Clasp the test-tube in the palm of your hand, and cautiously add concentrated acid drop by drop from a pipette.
Is there any evidence for a chemical reaction?

2 Heat a crystal of copper(II) sulphate-5-water on a piece of asbestos paper. Note the colour of the anhydrous copper(II) sulphate which is formed. Place a crystal of copper(II) sulphate-5-water on a watch-glass and cover it with concentrated sulphuric acid. What happens?
Pour off any remaining acid and add a little water.
What happens now?

3 Place a drop of concentrated sulphuric acid on a piece of paper. Describe what happens.

4 Add about 5 cm^3 of concentrated sulphuric acid to some sucrose in a boiling tube, and allow it to stand in a rack for a short time.
Describe what you observe. Complete the equation:

$$C_{12}H_{22}O_{11} - \square \rightarrow \underset{\text{carbon}}{\square}$$

What do these experiments lead you to conclude about concentrated sulphuric acid?

12.7 2 Involatility of concentrated H_2SO_4

Hold a glass rod which has been dipped in concentrated aqueous ammonia near the mouth of a bottle of concentrated hydrochloric acid. Describe what happens and write an equation for the reaction. Add a few drops of concentrated sulphuric acid to some sodium chloride in a test-tube, and hold a glass rod dipped in aqueous ammonia near the mouth of the test-tube. What is the product of the reaction between concentrated sulphuric acid and sodium chloride? Write an equation for this reaction.

12.7 3 Covalent nature of concentrated H_2SO_4

1 Set up the conductivity apparatus as described in Experiment **4.5**.1 (page 261), and measure the conductivity of molar sulphuric acid, using the variable resistor to make sure the reading is not off the scale. Leaving the resistance the same, measure the conductivity of concentrated sulphuric acid.

2 Take a strip of blue litmus paper and moisten half of it. Dry off the excess water, and drop the strip on to the surface of some concentrated sulphuric acid. What happens to the wet half of the strip in comparison to the dry half?

What do these experiments lead you to conclude about the degree of ionization of concentrated sulphuric acid?
Write an equation to illustrate your conclusion.

12.7 4 Comparison of the reactions of dilute and concentrated H_2SO_4 with metals and non-metals

Carry out a series of reactions which will enable you to complete the following table.

	Zinc	*Copper*	*Charcoal*	*Sulphur*
Cold dilute H_2SO_4				
Warm dilute H_2SO_4				
Cold conc. H_2SO_4				
Warm conc. H_2SO_4				

Be prepared to identify any gases which might be given off, particularly hydrogen and sulphur dioxide.
What conclusions would you draw from this experiment?

Chapter 13

13.1 Properties of nitrogen

Carry out the following tests on nitrogen gas: odour, colour, effect on moist pH paper, effect on lighted taper, effect on calcium hydroxide solution (limewater), solubility. Record your results in a table.
From your results, do you consider nitrogen to be a reactive or unreactive element?

13.3 Properties of ammonia

Prepare some ammonia gas by gently warming concentrated aqueous ammonia, and carry out the following tests: odour (**care**), colour, effect on moist pH paper, effect on HCl vapour (hold a glass rod which has been dipped in concentrated HCl near the ammonia), solubility (collect ammonia in a test-tube, add a little water, stopper and shake, invert over water and remove stopper).
Record your results in a table.
From your results suggest suitable identification tests for ammonia.

13.4 1 Tests on ammonium salts

Examine a collection of ammonium salts and comment on: colour, solubility in water, pH of resulting solutions, effect of heat, effect of warming with sodium hydroxide solution.
Be prepared to identify any gases which may be evolved in the last two tests.
Record your results in a table.

13.4 2 Heat on ammonium salts

Warm some ammonium chloride as shown. Record your observations.

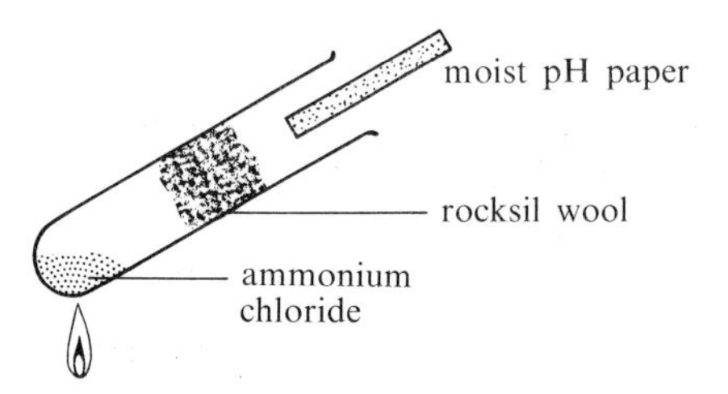

Offer an explanation for your observations and write an equation for what is happening.

13.6 Comparison of the reactions of dilute and concentrated HNO_3 with metals and non-metals

Carry out a series of reactions which will enable you to complete the following table.

	Magnesium	*Copper*	*Charcoal*	*Sulphur*
Very dilute nitric acid[1]				
2M nitric acid				
Concentrated nitric acid				

[1] To make 'very dilute' nitric acid, cover a piece of magnesium with water and add just sufficient dilute nitric acid to start the reaction going. Make solutions of similar concentration to test with other elements.

Be prepared to identify any gases which may be evolved, particularly hydrogen, nitric oxide (colourless), and nitrogen dioxide (brown).

13.7 1 Brown ring test

Add a few drops of freshly prepared iron(II) sulphate solution to a nitrate solution, and with the test-tube tilted at an angle of 45°, carefully pour in concentrated sulphuric acid to form a lower layer.
What do you observe?
Use this information to determine whether the unknowns are nitrates or not.

13.7 2 Heat on nitrates

Heat small amounts of the given nitrates in test-tubes, and observe the reactions carefully.
Be prepared to note such observations as: colour change, evolution of water vapour, evolution of gases (particularly oxygen and nitrogen dioxide), speed of reaction.
Record your results in a table.
Group the nitrates into two groups:
1 Nitrates which decompose readily evolving oxygen and nitrogen dioxide.
2 Nitrates which decompose with difficulty evolving oxygen only.
Is there any relationship between 1 and 2, and the position of the corresponding metals in the reactivity series?

Chapter 14

14.1 Polymorphs of carbon

Make models of graphite and diamond. Attempt to measure the bond angles. How do your models confirm the polymorphism of carbon?

14.4 1 Preparation of CO_2

Set up the apparatus shown in the diagram.

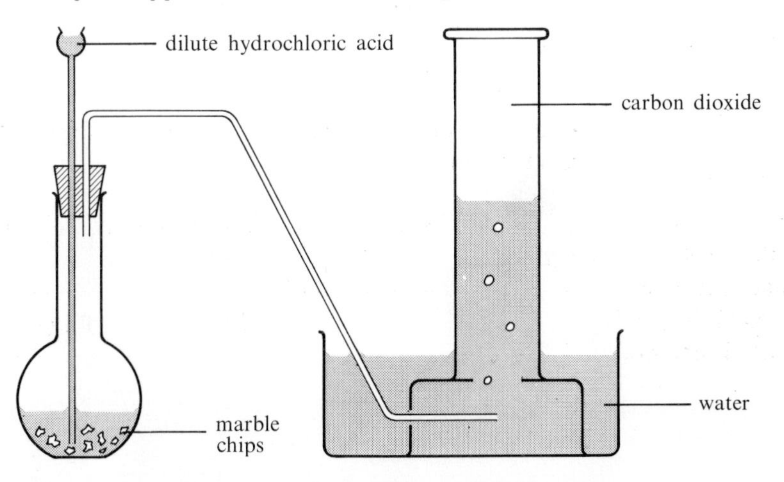

Collect several gas jars of carbon dioxide. Write the equation for the reaction between calcium carbonate and dilute hydrochloric acid.

Test your samples as follows:

1 With moist pH paper.
2 Pour the gas on to a candle flame.
3 Plunge a piece of burning magnesium ribbon into the gas.
4 Shake the gas with calcium hydroxide solution (limewater).

Account for each of your results by writing an equation.
What do your results indicate about the gas?

14.4 2 Acid and normal salts

Bubble carbon dioxide gas through a solution of calcium hydroxide in a test-tube. Note the formation of the normal salt and the acid salt. Record the pH of the normal salt and the acid salt solutions. Write equations for each of the reactions you observe.
Use the chemistry of this experiment to prepare a sample of anhydrous sodium carbonate.

14.5 Action of heat on a carbonate

Place some copper(II) carbonate in a clean, dry test-tube and weigh the tube. Clamp the test-tube in a stand and heat it until all the powder has turned black. Weigh the test-tube again. Record your results.

Weight of test-tube + copper(II) carbonate = g
Weight of test-tube + copper(II) oxide = g
Weight of carbon dioxide = g

Use your results to calculate the percentage of carbon dioxide in the sample. How does your result agree with the theoretical calculation of the percentage of carbon dioxide?

Chapter 15

15.2 Destructive distillation of coal

Set up the apparatus as shown in the diagram.

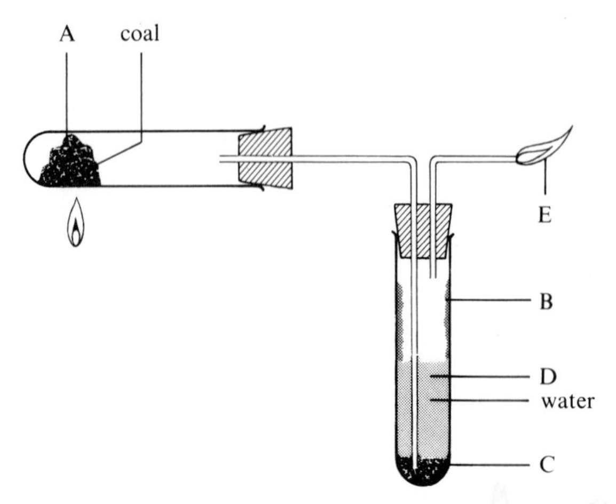

Describe the products A, B, C, D, and E.

15.4 Fractional distillation of crude oil

Set up the apparatus as shown in the diagram.

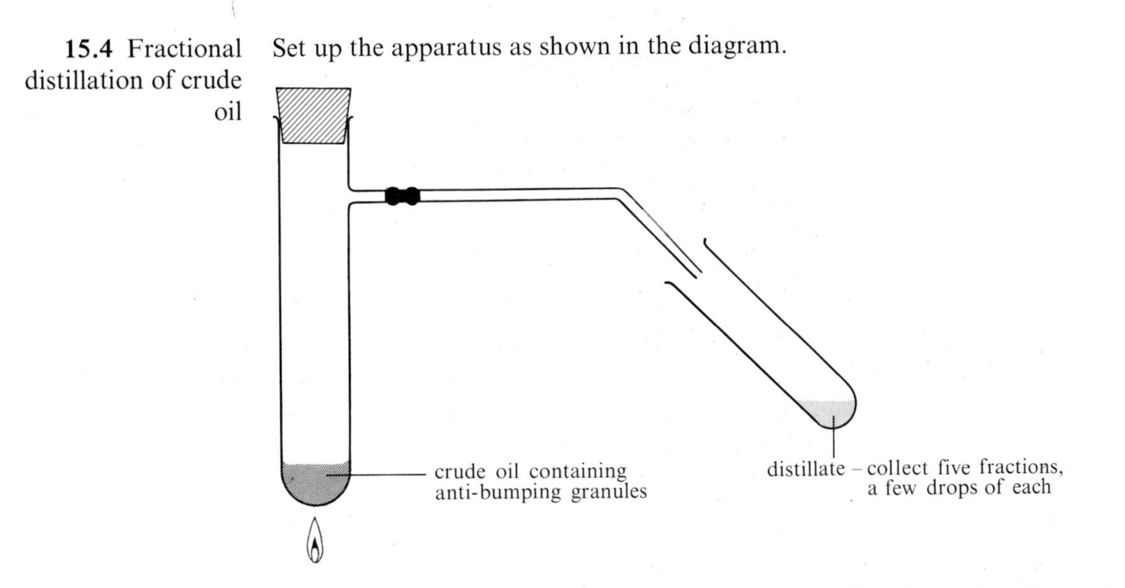

Compare the five fractions under the headings: smell, colour, viscosity, and volatility. (Volatility can be tested by leaving a drop of oil on a piece of waxed paper and recording the time taken to evaporate.)

15.8 Examination of bunsen flame

Carry out the following tests on a fairly steady bunsen flame.

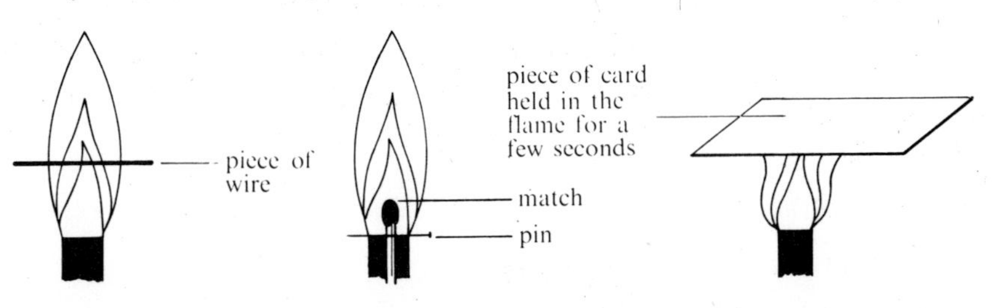

What do the three tests tell you about the zones in the bunsen flame?

Chapter 16

16.2 Preparation of methane

Set up the apparatus as shown in the diagram.

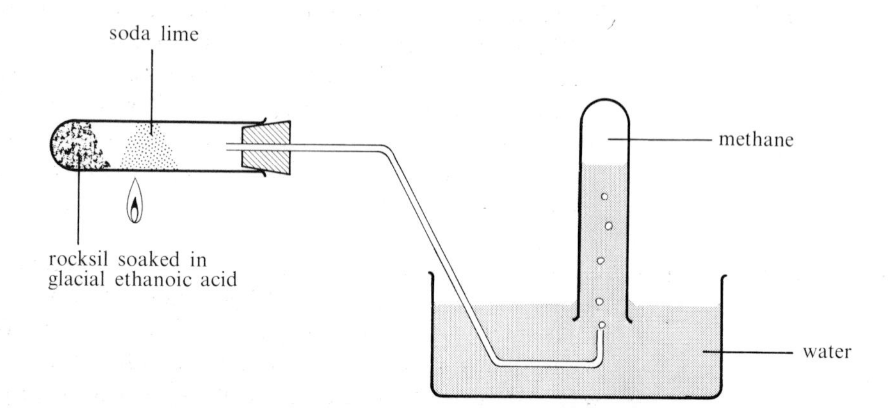

Describe the product and test its ease of combustion and reaction with bromine water.

16.5 Cracking medicinal paraffin

Set up the apparatus as shown in the diagram.

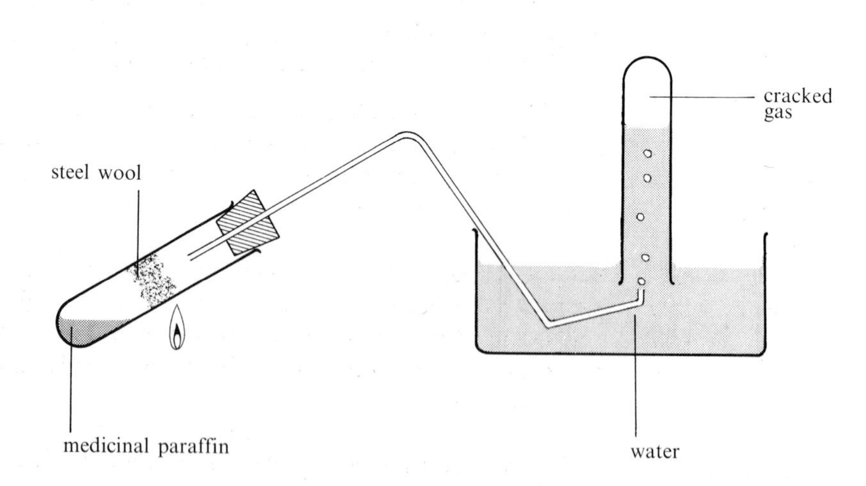

Test the product with bromine water to see if the cracking process has been successful.

16.6 Unsaturation test

Test the following substances with bromine water to see if they are unsaturated: olive oil, coal gas, medicinal paraffin, cyclohexane, cyclohexene.

Chapter 17

Warning Many of the chemicals used in this section have harmful vapours. All the experiments should be carried out in a fume-cupboard.

17.2 1 Rayon

To about 20 cm^3 of water in a small beaker, add copper(II) sulphate crystals until a saturated solution is obtained. Add sodium hydroxide solution to precipitate copper(II) hydroxide and filter off the solid. Pour a little concentrated aqueous ammonia through the filter, and collect the deep blue solution produced. Dissolve some cotton wool in this solution until it is syrupy. Inject the solution from a plastic syringe into dilute sulphuric acid in a beaker. Rayon fibre is formed.

17.3 1 Perspex

Shake 10 cm^3 of methyl 2-methylpropenoate (methyl methacrylate) with a few cm^3 of 40 per cent sodium hydroxide, allow it to settle and suck off the aqueous layer with a dropping pipette. Wash the methyl 2-methylpropenoate with water to remove the sodium hydroxide. Remove the water in the same way. Add a small quantity of di(benzoyl)peroxide or lauryl peroxide and place the tube in an oven at 343 K (70 °C) for an hour. The test-tube can be carefully broken and a piece of perspex is obtained.

17.3 2 Polystyrene

Phenylethene (styrene) monomer is cleaned with sodium hydroxide and water as in the previous experiment. The di(benzoyl)peroxide is added and the test-tube heated in an oven at 363 K (90 °C) for two to three hours. A clear solid plastic is obtained.

17.3 3 Nylon

You will be provided with two solutions:
1 1 cm^3 of hexanedioyl dichloride (adipyl chloride) in 25 cm^3 of tetrachloromethane.
2 1 g of 1,6- diaminohexane and 1 g of sodium hydroxide in 25 cm^3 of water.

Pour the aqueous solution carefully down the side of a beaker on to the tetrachloromethane solution so that the solutions do not mix. A white layer of nylon forms at the interface. Use a pair of forceps to pull the nylon, and a continuous fibre is obtained.

17.3 4 Urea-formaldehyde resin

To some methanal (formaldehyde) in a test-tube, add urea until the solution is saturated. Decant the mixture into another test-tube and add a few drops of concentrated sulphuric acid. Stir the mixture with a wooden spill, and a vigorous reaction takes place. A solid plastic called urea-formaldehyde is formed.

17.3 5 Thermosetting or thermoplastic?

Collect as many samples of plastics as you can. Heat each one in a beaker of boiling water. If the plastic softens, it is a thermoplastic. If not, it is a thermosetting plastic.

Chapter 18

18.1 Preparation of alcohol

Add a paste of yeast to a solution of glucose in a test-tube. Incubate the test-tube for twenty-four hours at a temperature of 313K (40° C). Add two glass beads to the test-tube and distil the mixture as shown.

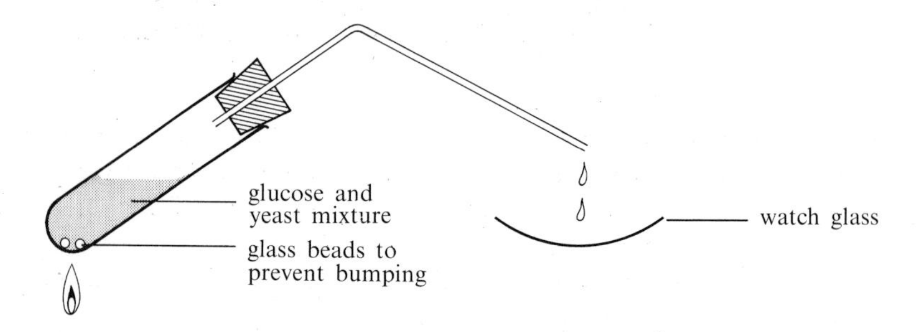

The first few drops of the distillate should produce the burning sensation of alcohol on the tongue.

18.2 1 Oxidation of ethanol

Heat some copper(II) oxide in a dry test-tube. When it is very hot, tip it quickly into a small evaporating basin containing some ethanol. Explain the colour of the solid in the basin.

18.2 2 Oxidation of ethanol

Set up the apparatus shown in the diagram.

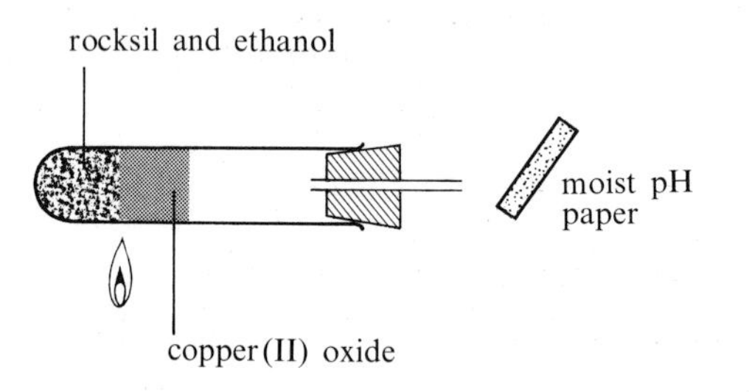

Test the pH of the vapour coming out of the tube, and explain why it is less than seven.

18.4 Esterification

From a selection of alcohols and organic acids attempt to make some esters. Name the esters, draw the formulae, and attempt to describe their smells.

Chapter 19

19.2 1 Test for starch

Make a solution of starch and add a few drops of iodine to it. Observe the colour produced. Try the effect of iodine on glucose, fructose, sucrose, maltose, lactose, and cellulose (paper).
Do you think this is a good test for starch?
Test as many foodstuffs as you can for the presence of starch and tabulate your results.

19.2 2 Test for glucose

Make a solution of glucose. Add Fehling's No. 1 solution and then Fehling's No. 2 solution until the solution in the test-tube just deepens in colour. Warm the mixture in a water bath and note the colour of the precipitate which forms.
Try this test on all the carbohydrates listed in the previous experiment and tabulate your results.
Do you consider this to be a good test for glucose?

19.2 3 Hydrolysis of carbohydrates

Attempt to hydrolyse starch, sucrose, and cellulose by:

1 Boiling with dilute hydrochloric acid.

2 Warming with saliva.

Test all the solutions with Fehling's solutions and tabulate your results. Explain why humans could not exist on a diet of grass.

19.3 1 Tests for proteins

1 To some milk in a test-tube, add a few drops of copper(II) sulphate, followed by a few drops of sodium hydroxide solution. Note the colour of the contents of the test-tube.

2 To some milk in a test-tube, add a few drops of concentrated nitric acid and warm the mixture in a water bath. When the solution is **cold,** add concentrated aqueous ammonia, and note the colour produced.

What conclusion can you draw from these tests?

19.3 2 Proteins contain nitrogen

Heat a piece of cheese in a test-tube with some soda lime.
Test the gases given off at the mouth of the test-tube with a piece of moist pH paper. Note the pH, and name the gas given off. Draw a conclusion from your results.

19.4 Tests for fats

Put a drop of olive oil on a filter paper and hold it up to the light. Press a piece of cheese on to a filter paper to see if it contains fat. Does it?

Chapter 20

20.1 Preparation of soap

Boil a mixture of 10 cm^3 olive oil and 40 cm^3 sodium hydroxide in a small beaker for about thirty minutes, adding a little water from time to time to replace the water which boils off. Stir the mixture well during this time to ensure good mixing. Add 100 cm^3 of brine to the mixture and leave it to cool. Remove the crust which forms on top of the liquid, and wash it with a little water. Press the solid between filter papers and shape it to form a small bar of soap.

20.3 1 Hardness of water

Dissolve a tablespoonful of soap flakes in 100 cm^3 of water and 50 cm^3 of ethanol. Label three conical flasks (a), (b), and (c). Put 20 cm^3 of distilled water in (a), 20 cm^3 of tap water in (b), and 20 cm^3 of calcium hydroxide solution (limewater) in (c). Titrate each flask with the soap solution until a permanent lather develops with shaking. Note the volumes of soap solution required.

20.3 2 Hardness of water

Dissolve a tablespoonful of soapless detergent in 100 cm^3 of water and 50 cm^3 of ethanol. Label three flasks (a), (b), and (c) as before. Put 20 cm^3 of distilled water in (a), tap water in (b), and calcium hydroxide solution (limewater) in (c). Titrate each flask with the soapless detergent until a permanent lather develops with shaking. Note the volumes required and compare the results of the experiment with those of the previous experiment.

Answers to numerical questions

Chapter 2

1.1 (a) 17 protons and 47 protons
1.1 (b) 20 neutrons and 61 neutrons
7.3 Relative atomic mass = 55.9
8.1 93 protons
8.2 145 neutrons

Chapter 5

2.1 166.1 g
2.2 81.4 g
2.3 132.1 g
2.4 60.1 g
2.5 279.5 g
2.6 367.0 g
2.7 179.0 g
2.8 154.0 g
2.9 170.0 g
2.10 106.8 g
3 0.25 moles
4 0.10 moles of Na^+; 0.05 moles of CO_3^{2-}
5.1 $(Na_2S_2O_3)_n$
5.2 $(Na_2CO_3.H_2O)_n$
5.3 $(K_4FeC_6N_6)_n$
6 $C_4H_{10}O$
7.1.1 204.2
7.1.2 200.3
7.2 0.05 moles
8.1 Na = 57.5 per cent
O = 40 per cent
H = 2.5 per cent
8.2 $(Mn_2O_7)_n$
9.1 310.3 g
9.2 $(BaCl_2.H_2O)_n$
10.2 PbI_2
11.2 6.5 g
11.3 $(PbCl)_n$
11.4 White lead contains 26.7 per cent lead
Chrome yellow contains 64.2 per cent lead
12.1 1M
12.2 0.2M
12.3 0.1M
13.1 1.12 g

	13.2	69 g
	13.3	74.5 g
Chapter 6	2	4 g oxygen
	3	0.1 moles sodium hydroxide
	4	28 g nitrogen
	5	0.4 moles sodium
		0.4 g hydrogen
	6.2	$(Cu_2O)_n$
	7.1	(a) 40.1 g; (b) 23 g
	7.3	0.2 g hydrogen
	8.1	Cu_2O
	8.2	9 g of water
	9.1	2 g
	9.2	16 g
	9.3	1 mole
	9.4	0.5 mole
Chapter 7	7.1	0.01 mole
	7.2	0.005 mole; the magnesium will give more hydrogen
Chapter 12	7.8	1.25×10^6 kg
Chapter 13	2.4	14.9 g
	7.1.3	N_2O
	8.4	40 g
Chapter 16	5.3	416 g

Index

All page numbers in heavy type refer to experiments.